ISAMBARD KINGDOM BRUNEL

'The finest work in England'

THE CONSTRUCTION OF THE GREAT WESTERN RAILWAY

Great Western Railway Office.

23rd October, 1833.

Considerable progress has been made in the establishment of this Company, and in the preliminary arrangements for the Railway, since the accompanying prospectus was issued to the public in the month of August last.

The line of road has in the interval been accurately surveyed and selected by the Directors, and the result of the survey is in every respect satisfactory.

The distance between London and Bristol will be reduced to 117 miles.

The calculation of revenue has been confirmed by minute enquiries, and may be safely relied upon.

Under these circumstances, the Directors of the Great Western Railway Company have resolved to make application, in the approaching Session, for authority to construct the Sections of the main Railway extending between London and Reading, (with a Branch to Windsor) and between Bristol and Bath, thereby rendering the ultimate completion of the whole line more certain, upon a further application to Parliament in the following year.

This measure is sanctioned by the provisions of the Parliamentary Contract, and is recommended by many essential advantages to the Proprietors.

The standing Orders of the two Houses of Parliament, referable to this partial line of Railway, will be complied with by a deposit of the Plans and Book of reference, previously to 30th November.

The number of Shares required for this part of the undertaking will be 12,500, of which 2,500 will be reserved for the proprietors of land, &c. and consequently no application for shares can be entertained so soon as 10,000 shall have been subscribed; of which a very considerable proportion has been already allotted.

The estimates of cost and revenue for the sections of the line adverted to, are highly satisfactory; and this course of proceeding promises a beneficial and quicker return to the Proprietors for the capital invested.

It is intended also by the Directors, to insure to the Proprietors a preferable option of taking an equal number of new Shares upon the future extension of the subscription list to complete the line between Reading and Bath; thereby reserving to the original subscribers whatever advantage may accrue from any improved value in the Shares.

Subscribers will not be answerable beyond the amount of their respective Shares.

The Parliamentary Notices will be given in the first week in November.

Application for the Shares remaining to be allotted to complete the limited subscription list, should be immediately addressed to the Secretary in London or Bristol, from whom the Prospectus may be obtained.

1833 Prospectus

ISAMBARD KINGDOM BRUNEL

'The finest work in England'

THE CONSTRUCTION OF THE GREAT WESTERN RAILWAY

David Clifford

First produced in 2006 by FINIAL PUBLISHING

ISBN 1-900467-28-3

Produced by:
Finial Publishing
15 Abingdon Drive, Caversham,
Reading, Berks RG4 6SA England
Telephone/Fax: 01189-484103
www.finial.ndirect.co.uk
Email: mail@finial.co.uk

Jacket Image: Detail from a larger drawing by G. H. Andrews, illustrating the Hanwell Viaduct under construction. *(Alan Mott/The Institution of Civil Engineering)*

Printed and bound in Great Britain by Henry Ling Limited, at the Dorset Press, Dorchester DT1 1HD

DEDICATION

To my father - Arthur James Clifford who died at Bristol on 13 December 1992 and to my wife Valerie for her support during the many hours taken to research this book.

INTRODUCTION

T his book is based on fact and as recorded in the early records of
the Great Western Railway Company. That this has been
possible at all is only because of the diligence and
conscientiousness of an unknown number of anonymous clerks in
the Company's offices at the time, whose responsibility it was to copy
the copious and frequently lengthy correspondence and legal
documents which were required for the promotion and eventual
construction of what would become the most famous of all railway
companies.

This correspondence, all in copper-plate hand-writing and contained
in the thick, heavy leather-bound ledgers of the period, can be found
today mainly in the archives of the Public Record Office at Kew, the
ledgers containing faithful copies of letters and other correspondence
sent by Brunel and other Company servants at the time.

Thus, this volume consists of mainly previously unpublished
material, using official Great Western Railway records from the
period, together with material from many other sources. In fact,
compiling this work, has been like working on a huge jigsaw puzzle,
with literally hundreds of references having to be pieced together to
make as complete a picture as possible of the early days of the Great
Western Railway.

This book is not intended to be a record of the construction of the
whole of the original Brunellian main line. It is more a microcosm -
or case study - of one section of the railway. However, as work on the
various sections of the enterprise commenced - with a few exceptions
- very similar situations would take place, one section of the line
being very much like the others.

The illustrations used are from various sources, the majority of which
it is believed have not been used before in previous histories of the
Great Western Railway. The illustrations acknowledged 'OPC/BR'
originated from the erstwhile OPC/BR collections, which at the last
attempt to clarify the location and status of this unique collection
appeared to be unobtainable.

DAVID CLIFFORD

CONTENTS

ACKNOWLEDGEMENTS

Research first began on this record in the summer of 1984 and depending on time available, has continued right up to the present day. Although in many cases their circumstances may have changed during the intervening 20-odd years, I am very grateful to the following: Mr. Nick Lee (Archivist and Special Collections Librarian) and Mr. Michael Richardson (Special Collections Librarian) of Bristol University Library for their patience in dealing with my numerous enquiries relating to the Brunel Collection. Their knowledge greatly assisted me in my quest to discover previously unpublished material relating to the inception and construction of the Great Western Railway. I am also grateful to Mr. Geoffrey Ford M.Sc, A.L.A. (Librarian) Bristol University Library for permission to publish material from The Brunel Collection. I would also like to acknowledge the assistance given by the Royal Archives, Windsor Castle in obtaining material dealing with Queen Adelaide's early travels by train and for the gracious permission of Her Majesty The Queen in permitting publication of this material. For permission to reproduce excerpts from the Minutes of the Thames Commissioners, I am grateful to the 'County Archivist, Berkshire Record Office'. Thanks also to Andrew P. M. Wright for assistance with photography and to my friend and colleague John Villers of Finial Publishing for his moral and practical support.

Thanks also to:
>   Lyndsay Lardner, The Wellcome Institute for the History of Medicine
>   Berkshire Record Office
>   David & Charles
>   Tim Bryan, Great Western Railway Museum, Swindon
>   Ian Nulty, Regional Railways (South Wales & West), Swindon
>   Cholsey & Wallingford Railway Preservation Society
>   David and Marion Canning
>   Departmental Record Officer, British Railways Board
>   Maidenhead Reference Library.
>   Judy & Stuart Dewey, Wallingford Museum
>   Michael Vanns, Ironbridge Gorge Museum Trust
>   Mary K. Murphy, Institution of Civil Engineers
>   Gail Boyle, Roger D. Clark, David Eveleigh, P. W. Elkin, Bristol Museum & Art Gallery
>   Elizabeth Ralph, The Society of Merchant Venturers
>   Jill Greenaway, Archaeology Assistant, Reading Museum and Archive Service
>   David Payne, County Reference Library, Reading
>   Allan Mott
>   Colin Maggs
>   Staff at the Public Record Office, Kew
> To any one omitted, please accept grateful thanks.

This Book
Commemorates
the Bicentenary
of the Birth of

ISAMBARD KINGDOM BRUNEL

FRS

9th April 2006

ILLUSTRATIONS

PREFACE

During recent years, one has become aware of a reawakened interest in the life and works of that most famous of all British engineers - Isambard Kingdom Brunel.

In 1999, the then UK Culture Secretary Chris Smith introduced a 'Tentative List' of sites for possible nomination during the next 5-10 years in the United Nations Educational, Scientific and Cultural Organisation (UNESCO) list of World Heritage Sites. UNESCO were unlikely to consider any sites unless included on the 'Tentative List' and the UK's 1999 proposals sought to ensure that some of Britain's industrial archaeological sites were appropriately represented. In introducing the UK's latest 'Tentative List', Chris Smith pointed out that the process of industrialisation had changed the way in which all peoples of the world now live and that this process had started in Britain. Included on the list were parts of Isambard Kingdom Brunel's Great Western Railway, including Brunel's 220-ft train shed at Bristol's Temple Meads station, with its 72-ft single roof span.

In February 2001, a television programme was broadcast of recent excavations conducted by Channel 4 Television's 'Time Team' at the site of what would become known as 'The Inter-City Villa'. In 1838, navvies excavating Brunel's Great Western Railway found what they called 'Roman pavements' at Lower Basildon in Berkshire, paintings made at the time showing two Roman floor mosaics, possible from a villa. The mosaics were broken up shortly after their discovery and no further attempts to excavate the site were made until 'Time Team' set to work. Although the remains of two Roman walls were uncovered during these latest excavations, the consensus was that the villa must have been obliterated by the widening made to Brunel's original trackbed in the 1890s.

In the autumn of 2002, Isambard Kingdom Brunel was short-listed by the BBC in its top 10 contenders - out of a list of a 100 of the country's most significant individuals - for the title 'Greatest Briton'. Beginning on Sunday 20 October 2002, a highly popular weekly series of programmes hosted by Anne Robinson, profiled each of 10 finalists, celebrities and commentators arguing the case for their own particular favourite. Jeremy Clarkson, TV presenter and technological aficionado, presented the case for Isambard Kingdom Brunel on Tuesday 22 October 2002. Brunel was the only engineer to reach the top 10 and Clarkson said of him: 'Brunel built modern Britain, and Britain built the world, which means that Brunel built the modern world. And that makes him a pretty damned great Briton in my book'. In the end, on Sunday 24 November 2002, Isambard Kingdom Brunel was beaten to the title 'Greatest Briton' by Sir Winston Churchill, the Second World War leader attracting 447,423 votes, beating Brunel, his nearest rival, by more than 56,000 votes.

As further evidence of the iconic status of Isambard Kingdom Brunel, it was widely reported in March 2004 that for years, drivers crossing the Grand Union Canal near Paddington station, had simply assumed that they were passing over just another modern canal bridge. However, encased within the structure was a secret that had remained hidden for decades. Unrecognisable, except from below, the brick structure contained what was considered to be the earliest surviving iron bridge designed by Isambard Kingdom Brunel. Minus its railings, the bridge - the earliest of only eight Brunel iron bridges to be found in the country - was discovered days before contracts were due to be let to demolish the structure as part of a road improvement scheme. However, following the discovery, it was stated that Westminster City Council had halted its demolition plans and given instructions for the bridge to be carefully dismantled and moved to a safe location. It was hoped that the bridge would be rebuilt as a pedestrian footway further along the canal in time for the Bicentenary of the engineer's birth in 2006.

Despite various vicissitudes concerning first of all Nationalisation in 1948 and the more recent *volte-face* involving the complete privatisation (and aftermath) of the British rail network, the name 'Great Western' lives on. On 4 February 1996, Great Western Trains Co. Ltd., formerly a wholly owned subsidiary of the British Railways Board, became the first high-speed train operator to be privatised and became known as First Great Western. Ownership has since passed to FirstGroup Plc, the parent company of First Great Western and First Great Western Link.

On 24 June 2005, the final plan to improve Western rail services was published, the 'Great Western Main Line Route Utilisation Strategy' defining the changes required to reduce overcrowding and improving service patterns for passengers by making better use of existing tracks and trains on the route. The strategy, covering the Thames Valley, the Cotswolds, South Wales and the West Country for the period up to 2012, predicted that many of the changes could be introduced with the start of a new 'Greater Western' rail franchise in April 2006. The new franchise would combine the current First Great Western and First Great Western Link routes, with those operated by Wessex Trains and would run for seven years initially. At the time of going to press, no announcement had been made regarding the choice of the new franchise-holder

Finally, as a Bristolian, I have always been proud that it was the citizens of Bristol who had the vision and foresight to conceive and expedite the construction of the Great Western Railway. This project, which at the time of its inception and construction, was the longest railway yet constructed in England, would remain perhaps, the best known of Britain's early railway systems and all the signs are that this will the case for the foreseeable future.

I hope, therefore, that this volume proves of great interest to people with similar interests to my own, i.e. a deep affection for the Great Western Railway and a desire to find out as much as possible about Brunel's 'great enterprise'.

DAVID CLIFFORD
Reading, Berks 2006

PART I
PRELUDE

'I am always building castles in the air,
what time I waste.'

1

ANNO QUINTO & SEXTO

GULIELMI IV. REGIS.

****

Cap. cvii.

An Act for making a Railway from *Bristol* to join
the *London* and *Birmingham* Railway near *Lon-*
don, to be called " The Great Western Railway,"
with Branches therefrom to the Towns of *Brad-*
ford and *Trowbridge* in the County of *Wilts*.

[31st *August* 1835.]

CHAPTER 1
GENESIS

At the time of the proposals for the construction of the Great Western Railway, there were other distractions in many of the areas along the line of the proposed railway. The period was one of great political upheaval in the United Kingdom and radical proposals were afoot for the total reform of both national and local government.

As Peter G. Richards in his book 'The Reformed Local Government System' (1973) explains, the first major reform was the 1832 Reform Bill which would have an immediate impact on local administration. The reform of Parliament was clearly necessary, as the majority of the Members of the House of Commons came from southern England, which prior to the Industrial Revolution, was the most thickly populated area of Britain. The five western counties, Wiltshire, Somerset, Dorset, Devon and Cornwall elected 25% of the House of Commons. The London area, which comprised only one-tenth of the population of the country, returned 10 MPs to Parliament, while Wales was obviously inadequately represented with only 5% of the total members. The need for reform was clearly necessary if revolution in England and the dire consequences which had already been witnessed across the English Channel were to be avoided!

Distress in the country about 1815 had been accentuated by 20 years of war and also by an inherent change to the factory system, with restricted demands for goods created by unemployment. There were riots in agricultural areas and enclosures drove out smallholders. Wages were low and labourers turned to poaching. Penalties increased in severity and convicts were transported to Australia. Returning soldiers and sailors after Waterloo, added to the number of unemployed and on the Poor Rate. European competition in trade began, but impoverished Europe could not afford to buy British goods and raised tariffs to protect home industries. This situation was the background to the clear necessity for Reform.

The 1832 Reform Act was the first big reform of Parliament to take place in England. Previous to this Act, all counties returned two members, irrespective of size and there were 558 Members of Parliament. Under the 1832 Act, it was proposed that 52 boroughs would cease to return a MP, while 30 boroughs would in the future return only one member instead of the two previously elected. Most of the boroughs thus affected were in an area south of a line from the Wash to Stroud in Gloucestershire. Twenty boroughs, mostly in the north of England, would now send two members each to serve in Parliament and a further 20 boroughs would send one member each.

The Act ensured that the existing rights of freeholders were to be maintained. In every city or borough, any owner or tenant of any house which had a yearly value of £10 would be able to vote - if he was registered. No person would be registered as a voter if he had in the previous 12-months received alms or poor relief. No person would be registered as a voter unless he was in actual possession of rent or profits for six months before the registration or if he had been an owner of land for not less than 12-months. The first reformed Parliamentary election took place on 10-11 December 1832. The election was seen as a loss of status for many towns and boroughs, particularly in the south of England, although in the north of the country and in Wales, the opposite was clearly the case.

The other major change in local reform concerned the Poor Law. In 1832, a Poor Law Commission had been appointed to report on the existing arrangements. The Commission sent out investigators to examine conditions in about 300 parishes. The final report portrayed a situation of incompetence, confusion and waste. The Poor Law Amendment Act 1834, based on the Commission's recommendations, provided a new and uniform basis for poor relief. A Poor Law Commission - a central body in London - was to supervise the whole system nationwide. The central body would unite parishes into convenient areas for the administration of Poor Relief. This proposal was a new concept and ignored many traditional parochial divisions and many unions would overlap county boundaries. The Poor Law Unions would be *ad hoc* bodies i.e. they were formed to carry out a particular service. This was not a new idea in 1834, as turnpike trusts had existed successfully for many years. However, the Poor Law Unions were the first example of *ad hoc* authorities which covered the whole country.

The 1834 Act decreed that all who claimed Poor Relief should be removed to the Workhouse. It was argued that under the previous system, Poor Relief provided no incentive for a man to find employment to feed himself and his family. Under the new system, the threat of being incarcerated in an institution, being separated from wife and children and being forced to work, would provide ample enough incentive to find work!

The third drastic change in local government during this period was provided by the Municipal Corporations Act 1835. During 1833, Commissioners were appointed by His Majesty King William IV to enquire into the state of Municipal Corporations in England and Wales. The final report of the Commission was damning. Some Corporations were so decayed as to be virtually non-existent and many did nothing of value for the local inhabitants. The Municipal Corporations Act 1835 would give the boroughs a new constitution and would insist on proper financial management. Borough councillors would be elected by the ratepayers and a quarter of the council members of a borough would be aldermen, elected by the councillors. These measures were strongly resisted by many boroughs, but despite the protests, the Bill progressed through Parliament, with the newly constituted councils throughout the land meeting for the first time in January 1836.

Needless to say, the considerable changes which were taking place in the local government scene at that period appeared to have engrossed some councils more than others. The result was that the various proposals to construct a railroad between Bristol and London caused very different reactions in some locations along the proposed route of the railway.

For instance Wallingford, a small town in Berkshire situated between Reading and Oxford, some three miles from the line of the proposed Great Western Railway, had been mortally wounded by the Reform Act. The town had also been affected by the Municipal Corporations Act and the six aldermen and 18 burgesses of the old council had fought a bitter fight to hang onto their élitest status. At Wallingford, from the time of the first proposal to construct a railway between Bristol and London, right up to the time when the line was finally completed, no mention of the railway proposals or of any effects on the town, were recorded in the Town Council's Minute books. However, at Abingdon, a similar sized town, a few miles from Wallingford, the reverse was true. Such was the concern, that a petition was raised to keep the proposed railway away from the town.

THE Gentlemen deputed by the Corporation, the Society of Merchant Venturers, the Dock Company, the Chamber of Commerce, and the Bristol and Gloucestershire Rail Road Company, to take into consideration the expediency of promoting the formation of a RAIL ROAD from BRISTOL to LONDON, request you to favor them, in writing, with such information as you may be able to afford, respecting the expediency of the proposed Rail Road, addressed to the CHAIRMAN, in time to be laid before an adjourned Meeting of the said Deputies, to be held at the COUNCIL-HOUSE, on THURSDAY, the 31st Instant, at Twelve o'Clock.

I am, &c.

JOHN CAVE,

Chairman

BRISTOL, 21st Jan. 1833.

FIGURE 1. The letter illustrated is regarded as probably the earliest circular extant connected with the Great Western Railway.   *(OPC/BR)*

The idea of a railroad from the metropolis to the West Country had first been put forward as early as 1800, a Dr. James Anderson proposing a railway to run alongside the high road from London to Bath. However, this proposition was never proceeded with. The first proposal to construct a railway to be worked by locomotives between Bristol and the metropolis had been made in December 1824, but this scheme also foundered. A stronger attack took place on 19 January 1825, following a proposal from mostly shareholders in the Kennet & Avon Canal Trust, who put forward the idea of a 'Rail Road from London to Reading', later entitled the 'London & Reading Rail Road'. As history records, this proposal was also doomed to failure. However, the frustration felt by Bristol merchants continued, as the existing means of transporting goods from Bristol to the metropolis proved more and more inhibiting to trade.

During the Roman occupation of Britain, London had been linked to the west - particularly with Bath - by road. This route was later abandoned, as alternative roads came into existence serving different destinations. A main highway developed between London and Bath, as the latter was the premier Spa city of the country, a factor clearly instrumental in the development of this main highway to the west. It was in the 17th-century that the six main 'post' roads radiating from London - of which the Bristol road was one - were laid down. An atlas of the principal roads of Britain published in 1675, shows that the road from London to Bristol was one of the principal roads at that period. The turnpiking of the Bath road took 50 years to complete and it was not until the second half of the 18th-century that the road was sufficiently improved to allow the greater speed and efficiency of travel which marked the finest years of the coaching age.

The evolution of the Kennet and Avon navigation commenced with making navigable the River Avon under an Act of 1712. The next step in point of time, although undertaken quite independently, was the canalising of the tributary River Kennet, from its confluence with the River Thames at Reading to Newbury under an Act of 1715. The construction of the wholly artificial canal connecting these two river navigations - for which the original survey was made by John Rennie in 1793 - was effected under an Act of 1794.

The canal was opened in 1810 and the Kennet and Avon navigations were amalgamated in the second decade of the last century. This provided a fairly direct line between the large ports of Bristol and London, as well as between the open seas on either side of England, the navigation being expected to afford first class facilities for a large flow of merchandise.

Dissatisfied with the existing means of transporting goods to London, merchants in Bristol had first discussed in the autumn of 1824 a proposal to construct a railway between Bristol and the metropolis. Bristol at that time was the second city in the country and the merchants were seeking an improved means of transporting their merchandise to the capital. MacAdam, the famous road engineer and at that period, Surveyor to the Bristol Turnpike Trust, produced a plan for a railway worked by locomotives between Bristol and London via the Vale of White Horse, through Wallingford. From Wallingford, the line might have been constructed along either bank of the River Thames, to a terminus in London. This scheme did not come to fruition and neither did five other proposals which were made in the following year.

The railway fever in the west country lay dormant for a further seven years, but the delays in the transport of merchandise to and from Bristol to London continued. The transport of heavy or bulky goods by road was far too expensive and there was no alternative but to use the inland waterways. Up the River Avon to Bath, through the Kennet & Avon Canal to Reading and down the Thames to

London and vice versa. This route was slow and painfully dependent upon the weather, as in a dry season the water level might be so reduced that boats could be held up for several weeks. In winter, frost closed the waterways and floods could wreck the barges. Some of the worst delays occurred on the Thames between Reading and London, where conditions were sometimes so severe that goods by water had to be unloaded at Reading wharves and sent on by road at enormously increased expense.

Much impressed by the success of the Liverpool & Manchester Railway, which opened in September 1830 and of the Stockton & Darlington five years earlier, interest again stirred in Bristol. A line had already been surveyed between Liverpool and Birmingham and between Birmingham and London and concern was expressed that the Port of Bristol could lose trade to Liverpool. The matter was again raised in May 1832, when the 'Bristol & London Railway' (quickly changed to the 'London & Bristol Railway') was proposed. This scheme was still alive in January 1833, but as sufficient financial support was not forthcoming, no more was heard of this particular project. However, the topic was still being frequently discussed in commercial circles in Bristol and in local journals of the period.

FIGURE 2. The first meeting place. The idea of a railway linking Bristol, Bath and London had been discussed in business circles and in the press as early as 1800. However, it would not be until the Autumn of 1832 that the four originators of the scheme to construct the Great Western Railway - as it would be later called - met in a small office in 'Temple Back', an obscure street long since swept away, that the scheme would come to fruition.
(OPC/BR)

CHAPTER 2
THE
GREAT WESTERN RAILWAY

Trade between Bristol and the metropolis had taken place for many years and by many methods, but it was the determination of four influential businessmen in the autumn of 1832 which ensured that this trade would continue in a much improved fashion. The four merchants resolved to press the matter forward and immediately began to seek support from their fellow merchants in Bristol. Before the end of the year, they had met with enough success to form a committee of prominent merchants and others, to investigate the feasibility of a railway between Bristol and London. The first meeting of this committee took place on 21 January 1833, when favourable reports on the probable success of such a venture were received. Consequently, funds were made available for a preliminary survey and estimate of costs, a sub-committee being appointed to make all the arrangements, including the appointment of an engineer.

As history records, Isambard Kingdom Brunel was appointed engineer on 7 March 1833 and two days later he and William Townsend (a local man who had surveyed and also supervised the construction of the Bristol & Gloucestershire Railway) commenced their survey. Although Townsend had been appointed on the same day as Brunel and officially was of equal status, Brunel quickly dominated the scene. Consequently, Brunel - by his own choice - bore the brunt of the work involved, with Townsend being largely confined to work at the Bristol end of the proposed line. However, Brunel did employ a few surveyors along the rest of the route to assist him.

Brunel had been informed that the objective was to survey the country between Bristol and London, with a view to selecting the best line of communication. Brunel's instructions were to survey the country and select the best line for the 'western district'. Brunel described this as:

> 'drawing a line a little west of Oxford and the north and south. The line comprehended the country between the Bristol and English Channels, including South Wales and Gloucester. It is difficult to define what I mean; I should say Devonshire, Cornwall, and Somersetshire, Wiltshire, Gloucestershire and Berkshire'.

However, following his appointment as engineer, Brunel received instructions to examine the whole of the district between Bristol and London and suggest a line which would link Bristol, London and South Wales. Consequently, Brunel set out with his assistants to investigate the best route for the proposed railway.

Brunel later recalled that it was immediately impressed upon him by the sub-committee, the propriety of embracing Gloucester, Gloucestershire and South

Wales and the engineer was not only to consider the best line of communication between Bristol and London. Shortly after commencing the preliminary survey, Brunel reported his conclusions after he had examined two of three different routes. One of these routes passed to the south of the Marlborough Downs and the other to the north, the engineer stating that the northern line would embrace the communication between Bristol and London and also include Gloucestershire and Gloucester itself. Brunel, after taking sufficient levels to form an opinion, reported that the southern line would pass over a very much higher summit level and it was also in other respects an inferior line to the northern. The engineer recommended that unless the southern line embraced more important towns than the northern line, he must recommend the northern.

At the time, enquiries had been instigated by Brunel as to the population and traffic in the areas being investigated. The engineer had appointed persons to take a census of the traffic on important roads and observers were positioned at Oxford, Witney, Reading, Maidenhead and Newbury and all the different roads spreading to the west and north-west. Brunel concluded that the northern line's catchment area had a greater population and would also allow a communication to be established with the Port of Gloucester.

The surveys and estimates having been completed and delivered, Brunel's recommendations were duly considered. The routes to the south were via Bradford, Devizes, the Pewsey Vale and Newbury and to the north of the Marlborough Downs via Chippenham, Swindon, the Vale of White Horse and the Thames Valley. The engineer's recommendations were accepted by the committee and on 30 July 1833, these proposals were put forward at public meeting held at Bristol Guild Hall. The meeting resolved that:

> *'a Company should be formed for the establishment of Railway communication between Bristol and London, and for that purpose that a body of Directors for Bristol be appointed, who, in conjunction with a similar body to be appointed in London, shall constitute a General Board of Management for securing subscriptions and obtaining an Act of Parliament for effecting the same object'.*

The first joint meeting of the two committees took place in London on 19 August 1833 and it was at this meeting that the title 'Great Western Railway' was adopted. The prospectus for the formation of the company was issued before the end of the month and the Board of Directors was formed, consisting of two Committees of 12 members from both Bristol and London.

CHAPTER 3
REACTION TO THE RAILWAY PROPOSALS

The first report of the Provisional Committee meeting at Bristol appeared on 10 August 1833 and the prospectus giving details of the proposed railway appeared in September 1933. It was stated that the cost of the line of 120 miles was estimated at £2,805,330 and that construction would take four or five years. The advantages would be numerous as a railway would:

> *'multiply the number of travellers, improve the conveyance of goods, encourage manufactures, defuse the advantages of the vicinity of towns over the country intersected by the railway, improve the supply of provisions to the metropolis and extend the market for agricultural produce, give employment to the labouring class, both during construction and by its subsequent effects, and increase the value of property in the neighbourhood'.*

The prospectus also stated, in somewhat provocative terms, that:

> *'generally the landowners along the line were in favour of the project'.*

In Berkshire this last statement was certainly not true and caused a lot of resentment. At a meeting held on 19 September 1833 at the George Inn, Reading angry landowners through whose property the line would probably be constructed met together. They took exception to the statement by the Directors that generally landowners were in favour of the railway proposals and the meeting conclusively resolved:

> *'That we the undersigned, so far from having given any encouragement to the said Railway, are of the opinion that it will be injurious to the several interests of landed proprietors as well as others; and therefore, do hereby call upon those who may entertain similar objections to signify their concurrence either personally or by letter addressed to the Committee, George Inn, Reading'.*

It was decided that a further meeting would take place on 28 September 1833. Thus the battle began! The opposition hardened and in the county of Buckinghamshire a meeting of interested parties took place on Tuesday 19 November 1833 at the Windmill Inn, Salthill near Slough. At this meeting, over 200 people attended, including some noblemen and MPs. During the ensuing discussion only four of those present spoke in favour of the construction of the railway and by the end of the meeting even one of these had changed his mind! The conclusion of the meeting was almost total opposition to the proposed railway and it was recommended that Buckinghamshire unite with Berkshire in a united front, which it was anticipated would defeat the proposers of the scheme.

A letter published in the *Berkshire Chronicle* - the mouthpiece of the Conservative landowners and whose text was consistently anti-railway - stated:

> *'Throughout the entire counties of Berks and Bucks there is, we believe, not one landowner, through whose property the proposed road would pass, who is not decidedly and resolutely determined to oppose it in all its stages. Is the defacing and demolishing of parks and fields, the obliteration of cherished and beloved spots, the destroying of old family scenes, and the haunts of our forefathers; are these losses for which NO MONEY can be an equivalent, are such mischiefs as these to be inflicted on an unwilling and indignant gentry, without good reason?'.*

The response by the public was also hesitant towards the railway proposals and this reluctance was evidenced by the slow take-up of shares, particularly in Berkshire, Buckinghamshire and Oxfordshire. The issuing of shares was handled by direct application to Charles Alexander Saunders, Secretary to the London Committee in London or by application to brokers (normally solicitors) in each county acting on behalf of the railway company. The majority of prospectuses and shares issued in Berkshire were handled by Mr Edward Vines - a solicitor of Reading - in conjunction with smaller firms of solicitors across the county.

One such solicitor was Charles Hedges, a member of the family firm of solicitors Hedges & Son, with offices in the Market Place, Wallingford. Hedges, on his own initiative, wrote to Saunders in London on 6 September 1833 requesting that £5 worth of shares be registered in the name of John Allnatt Hedges, the head of the firm. Saunders replied immediately, but stated that the request would be considered the following day, when the shares were allotted. The Secretary with this communication, also enclosed a few copies of the prospectus stating:

> *'taking the liberty to send a few copies which the Directors will feel peculiarly obliged by your circulating in the neighbourhood to those who may feel interested in the success of the undertaking'.*

The Directors were becoming increasingly concerned at the lack of public interest shown, as barely a quarter of the necessary capital had been subscribed. At least half the capital required to construct the railway had to be promised before the Great Western Railway Bill could be presented to Parliament and it was becoming evident that the completion of the whole line of railway was not going to be feasible. Consequently, at the end of October 1833, the Directors decided on a compromise. They reluctantly decided to seek Parliamentary approval for the construction of the two extremities of the line i.e. that between Bristol and Bath and between London and Reading (with a branch to Windsor), for which capital of £1,250,000 was required. It was hoped to obtain powers to complete the rest of the line during the following year.

All this time, Brunel and his assistants continued their detailed survey of the whole line. On 23 October 1833, the Directors issued a circular, stating their intention to make an application in the approaching session of Parliament for authority to construct the two separate sections of the railway. Brunel had already been directed by the Directors on 18 October 1833 to discontinue his survey

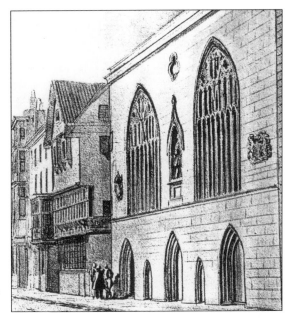

FIGURE 3. The Guild Hall of the City of Bristol in the year 1833. As the civic centre of one of the most important cities in the kingdom at that period, the building had naturally been the scene of many historic occasions. By no means the least notable of these was the public meeting of citizens which took place on 30 July 1833, to consider the report on the proposed railroad between Bristol and London. A comprehensive report by the full committee - including the results of Brunel's initial survey - being submitted to the gathering, it was decided that 'a company should be formed for the establishment of railway communication between Bristol and London . . .'.

(OPC/BR)

between Reading and Bath and to confine 'all future expenses' to the two extremities of the proposed line.

A further advertisement appeared in Berkshire journals on 7 December 1833, announcing a meeting at the Bear Inn, Reading on Monday 9 December at noon. This meeting was intended to effectively oppose the progress of the railway and the advertisement had been inserted by 22 prominent citizens of Berkshire. Over 30 owners of land likely to be affected by the railway proposals attended the meeting. Also present was the Secretary to the Thames Commissioners - Mr. William Payne - who had brought a ledger which contained the names of all the landowners between Maidenhead and Reading affected by the proposed railway. The ledger also contained full details of all the land which would be affected by the proposals.

Each landowner's name was called, each in turn denying that he had ever given his consent to any agent of the Great Western Railway. Each also denied that he was in favour of the scheme. During the meeting, individual speakers emphasised the injurious consequences to agricultural interests, the inundation of foreign labourers and the necessity for an increased 'poor rate' for each parish through which the railway would pass. This meeting was headlined by one journal as 'The Great Anti-Railway Meeting' and Robert Palmer MP for Berkshire - who lived at Holm Park, near Reading - told the assemblage that the scheme would destroy some of his best farms and divide his estate in seven different places. At the end of the meeting, the landowners were unanimous in their resolve to oppose the railway and a total of eight proposals were resolved, one of these stating:

'That the projected railway would be injurious to the interests and repugnant to the feelings, of the owners and occupiers of the land through or near to which it is proposed to be carried'

Finally, a committee was formed with clear instructions to convene a public

FIGURE 4. In 1835, the Directors of the Great Western Railway purchased a site in the heart of the City of London and erected buildings for use as their principal office in the capital. The Company Secretary's office was situated in Princes Street, Bank and the Registration of Shares and General Office was located at 449 West Strand. This reproduction shows the entrance to these premises, which was opposite the Mansion House and a short distance from St. Mary-le-Bow Church, both clearly visible in the print.
(OPC/BR)

meeting. Political support was also to be sought and county and borough MPs for Berkshire and Oxfordshire were urged to support the landowners with the following statement:

'Members for Berks and Oxon. and for all those Boroughs within these Counties, be earnestly requested to support the opposition to a measure so pregnant with injurious consequences to their Constituents'.

As reported, a representative of the Thames Commissioners had attended the meeting on 9 December 1833, to emphasise to the gathering the Commissioners total opposition to the proposed railway. The responsibilities for the maintenance, improvement and navigation of the River Thames from London Bridge to Cricklade was divided - under an Act of 1771 - into six districts, each district being administered by a committee of local commissioners.

The districts were as follows:

1. London Bridge to the City Stone
2. City Stone to Boulter's Lock
3. Boulter's Lock to Mapledurham
4. Mapledurham to Shillingford
5. Shillingford to Oxford
6. Oxford to Cricklade.

Following the new Act of 1771, the Thames Commissioners appeared to have adopted a brisk attitude to their responsibilities. They immediately commenced constructing new pound locks, establishing towing paths and improving the accommodation required by lock keepers, amongst other projects. To facilitate these improvements, large amounts of public money had been borrowed and to repay these loans and interest to the bond holders, it was essential that the tolls taken at locks on the river be maintained. It became obvious to the Commissioners that the projected railway would serious deplete their revenue and it was, therefore, not surprising to hear of the urgent and active opposition to the railway quickly instigated by the Commissioners. The opposition from the Commissioners appeared to take the form of pointing out the probable loss of facilities to towns to which the railway would not be directly adjacent. Quite justifiably, it was pointed out that these small riparian towns and their dependence on river trade would be placed in jeopardy if the proposed project was successful.

The Thames Commissioners were well aware of the power of steam and as early as 1780, a Thomas Hunt had submitted a project for the towing of barges by steam power. The Commissioners themselves had first utilised steam power in June 1828, when a stationary steam engine was purchased for draining pound locks during their construction. As early as 11 February 1829, the General Clerk to the Thames Commissioners had been instructed to arrange the purchase of:

'the best map which he can procure of the several railroads and canals throughout the Kingdom'.

As the threat of the proposed railway became apparent, a General Meeting consisting of Commissioners from all six districts took place at Windsor on 5 October 1833. The General Clerk reported to the assembly:

'A project is now on foot for making a railway from Bristol to London, under the denomination of the Great Western Railway and also another project for making a railway between London and Windsor, both and each of which may be greatly injurious to the interest of the Thames navigation'.

After discussion it was agreed that:

'the General Committee be now instructed, and invested with power to take all such steps they shall deem advisable for effectively opposing their progress'.

Consequently, it was announced in local journals on 12 October 1833, that:

'it was unanimously resolved that the General Committee be instructed and empowered to take all such steps as they shall deem advisable for effectually opposing the progress of this useless and mischevious project'.

The Commissioners were very aware of the threat posed by the proposed railway. The river's almost total monopoly of goods conveyancing was very vulnerable and the Commissioners in the past had been quick to try to stifle competition, such as in 1825 when the Commissioners had opposed the Kennet & Basingstoke Junction Canal. Despite this vociferous opposition, there were still many people in Berkshire in favour of the proposed railway and local journals carried scathing criticism of the Thames Commissioners:

'Mr. Secretary Payne is driven to his wits end to make out a case to justify his pernicious opposition to the projected railway'.

Another correspondent wrote:

'The Thames Commissioners have no right to spend public money opposing another scheme of

internal communication and the only effective opposition would be the improvement of the Thames Navigation by shortening it with canals'.

This latter statement was a reference to the almost innumerable projects for canals proposed in the closing third of the 18th-century which would have eliminated some of the bends on the Thames, thus improving and reducing the length of the navigation, all such proposals being resisted by the Commissioners.

TO THE DIRECTORS

OF THE

GREAT WESTERN RAILWAY COMPANY.

GENTLEMEN,

In reply to your enquiry relative to our investigation of the proposed Line of Railway between London and Bristol, in which you particularly refer to the practical construction of the work, and the working of it by Locomotive Engines when completed, and whether Mr. BRUNEL had taken our opinions before he made the selection between the two inclinations at Box,—we beg to state, that we have examined the whole of the important parts of the proposed Line, and consider it judiciously selected, not only as regards the execution, but also the working of the Line when executed, and that Mr. Brunel did take our opinions upon the two planes at Box.

Our advice to him was, that he should select the shorter and steeper, as by concentrating the rise in one point, with a practicable length for working, either by stationary or assistant Locomotive Engines, he reduced all the remaining inclinations upon the line to the present favourable amount; and we beg in addition to this to state, that many lines, with planes of similar or greater length, have been executed, and are now working efficiently, and that no difficulties in the execution of the work can be anticipated.

The levels of your proposed line are undoubtedly superior to those of the Southampton, or the Basing and Bath, or of any other extensive Line with which we are acquainted, and are therefore better adapted to the working of the Locomotive Engines, both as regards economy and expedition.

We are, Gentlemen,

Your obedient servants,

GEORGE STEPHENSON,
HENRY R. PALMER.

London, March 31st, 1835.

FIGURE 5. Report by George Stephenson and Henry R. Palmer - dated 31 March 1835 - to the Directors of the Great Western Railway commending to them the suitability of Brunel's proposed route for the railway between Bristol and London.
(Reproduced by kind permission of the Librarian of the University of Bristol)

CHAPTER FOUR
PARLIAMENTARY APPROVAL

In late January 1834, the plan of the projected railway with the distances marked in feet, was available for inspection at the Town Hall, Reading. This event did much to stimulate interest in the project and in February 1834, it was announced that the Directors would allocate the remaining shares to complete the subscription of 10,000 shares. In a Petition to the Mayor of Reading on 28 February 1834, over 140 burgesses requested the Mayor to convene a meeting to discuss the implications and advantages of the railway proposals. The meeting was held on 6 March 1833 and on behalf of the Great Western Railway, Saunders addressed the large body of people present, in the process emphasising the benefits of the railway to Reading and district. He said:

> 'It has been said that the trade on the Thames will be annihilated and that the river will be filled up from disuse ... but I believe that the railway will not do any injury to the Thames. The railway is principally for passengers, but, if there should be any obstruction to the river navigation, such as frost and drought, then the railway will come to the aide[sic] of the river trade'.

The meeting concluded overwhelmingly that the construction of the railway was essential for the future prosperity of the borough and of the county. Only five hands were raised against the proposal and a deputation was appointed to impress upon the county MPs that it was essential that they support the proposal.

The final plans were deposited in Parliament by the end of November 1833 (a branchline to Windsor had been dropped at an early stage, owing to violent opposition from Eton College) and the second reading of the Bill in the House of Commons was moved on 10 March 1834. After a debate of some hours, the Bill was carried by 182 votes to 92, with the Bill then being referred to a Committee. Despite all the opposition, the Committee, on the final day of the hearing, declared their support for the Bill, passing it through to the House of Commons for their approval. The House of Lords, however, made short work of the Bill and rejected the proposal on 25 July 1834 by 47 votes to 30. The vigorous opposition from influential landowners and the Thames Commissioners had finally won the day.

The Directors, realising that the opinion of the general public was increasingly in favour of the proposal were not too dismayed by this defeat. They immediately began preparations for bringing in a new Bill, this time for the construction of the whole line. They were confident of success, if they could raise the capital.

The Thames Commissioners continued with their pressure to abort the scheme. In February 1834, 100 guineas had been subscribed to support the opposition to the railway and when the first Bill was rejected by the House of Lords, the Commissioners were jubilant! At a General Meeting held at Abingdon on 6 August

1834, the Commissioners heard:

> *That comforably [sic] to the Order and Minutes of the General Meeting of the 5 October 1833, they had taken such steps as they had deemed advisable for opposing the progress of the Windsor and the Western Railway Bills, and have the pleasure of reporting with success, the former having been withdrawn and the latter having been thrown out upon the second reading in the House of Lords at a cost of £1431 defrayed by subscription to which this Commission has contributed £315'.*

The General Clerk was congratulated and received:

> *'a vote of thanks, on behalf of the whole body of Commissioners ... for the distinguished talent, and persevering energy with which he conducted and brought to a successful termination the opposition to the Western Railway'.*

However, the Commissioners jubilation was short-lived and the 'railers' would not be denied the ultimate victory.

The Thames Commissioners, becoming aware of the Directors' intentions for the second Great Western Railway Bill, took additional steps to defeat the Bill. In the early part of 1835, correspondence took place between the Commissioners responsible for the five lower river districts and the City Commissioners, whose responsibility was the control of the river from London Bridge to the City Stone near Staines. This correspondence concerned the reintroduction of the Great Western Railway Bill into Parliament and further opposition was coordinated, which was expected to cost £1500, with the City Commissioners promising £100 to the cause.

In March 1834, the City Commissioners had expressed their own anxieties over competition from railways, as the projected London & Southampton Railway would clearly add to the Commissioners' problems. Attempts to insert clauses into various railway Bills protecting the river tolls all failed and a further attempt to promote a campaign against the railways by the formation in May 1834 of a General Union of Canal Interest was too late to be effective.

Interest in the railway proposals began to stir again in Berkshire, when a meeting of subscribers met in Reading on 26 September 1834 at the office of Vines the Great Western Railway Company's broker. In the same month, a Supplementary Prospectus had been issued inviting subscriptions for 10,000 additional shares. It was stated that with the 10,000 shares already subscribed, this would enable the Directors to carry the Bill for the whole line through Parliament in the next session. This Supplementary Prospectus stated that the line was to be 116 miles in length - four miles shorter than in August 1833 and one mile less than in October 1833. A new edition of the Prospectus was issued in November 1834, with a plan showing the main line as proposed in August 1833, except at the London terminus and between Keynsham and Bristol.

A further meeting of subscribers took place in Reading and following this meeting, the Directors convened a meeting in the Merchant's Hall, Bristol on 8 October 1834. This meeting was attended by several MPs and representatives from

London, Windsor, Reading, Gloucester, Stroud, Bath, Exeter and other places. A total of eight resolutions were passed in favour of the Great Western Bill and Resolution 4 stated:

> *'that it is expedient to form local committees in the several towns and districts interested in the undertaking, in order to ensure its success'.*

Consequently, meetings in support of the new Bill were organised in almost every town of importance in the west and extensive petitions to Parliament were signed in places as distant as Truro, Bridport, Hereford and even Southern Ireland.

Nevertheless, opposition continued. An anonymous letter from 'A Landowner Upon the Line' published in a Berkshire journal on 1 November 1834 stated:

> *'... that the opposition of this and the adjoining county [Bucks], will be as active and uncompromising as that by which they were heretofore discomfitted'.*

Unperturbed, the Directors published for the next few weeks the statutory notices informing the public of the proposals for the railway, with the result that the opposing landowners of Buckinghamshire and Berkshire again met to discuss their tactics.

On Wednesday 3 December 1834, a meeting of landowners, occupiers and opponents of the project met at Salthill near Slough, the gathering concluding:

> *'that from returns which have now been made to this meeting, no doubt can be entertained that the same feeling pervades the landowners and occupiers in the County of Bucks. That in the event of a Bill being again introduced for effecting this obnoxious project ... will pursue all legal means for resisting it'.*

The meeting terminated with a subscription being set up and a committee formed for carrying the resolution into effect. It was hoped that the Bucks committee would work with the Berks committee, which it was anticipated would be shortly formed. Not to be outdone, a meeting took place on Saturday 13 December 1834 at the George Inn, Reading, the conclusion being:

> *'that this meeting concurs ... in their conviction of the inexpediency and mischievous tendency of the Great Western Railway'.*

Again, a committee was formed with the instructions that they were to join forces with other committees with the same objectives.

However, despite outward appearances, these committees had lost their thrust. Interest in the railway proposals was growing and opposition dwindling. In a letter published after the meetings in Buckinghamshire and Berkshire, a correspondent in a local journal stated:

> *'the landowners on the line of the proposed railway will probably see enough reason to keep their money in their pockets and not advance it to fight the battles of the Thames Navigation and the Kennet & Avon'.*

At the first meeting at Salthill, over 200 people had attended, including noblemen and MPs. At the second meeting, only 25 persons attended, with no dignitaries present. At Reading, the same feelings prevailed, only 12 people attending.

During the autumn and winter of 1834-35, the promoters were active creating support - financial and moral - all over the West of England and in South Wales. Brunel and Saunders were the leaders in this campaign, but they had other helpers and even some of the Directors took part. Despite a much more positive attitude to the proposed railway in most quarters, occasional forays by the opposition continued to occur. The *Berkshire Chronicle* published on 21 February 1835 a proposed basis upon which petitions should be framed and signed by all parties throughout the United Kingdom whose interests were threatened by railway communications. This communique was directed to landowners, occupiers, canal and navigation proprietors, coach, wagon and van masters, inn keepers and creditors of turnpike trusts and the like.

By the end of February 1835, the Directors' confidence appeared to be justified and it was announced to the public, that the 10,000 additional shares required by Parliament to complete the whole line of railway had been taken up. However, this public confidence concealed the true facts. There was still some reluctance on the part of the public to subscribe to the undertaking and in a letter to Vines, the Company's broker at Reading, Saunders emphasised:

> *'You must really press as STRONGLY as you can upon the inhabitants of Reading the necessity of subscribing FORTHWITH to complete our list'.*

Saunders' anxieties centred around recent proposals from the Great Western Railway's opponents in Parliament - the London & Southampton Railway Company - who were proposing an alternative railway to Bristol via Basingstoke - known as the 'BBB' - Basingstoke, Bath and Bristol.

The other firms of solicitors who were acting as brokers for the Company had also not done too well in persuading people to take up shares. Messrs Walsh of Oxford and Ormond at Wantage had not sold any further shares since the earlier issue. Similarly, at Wallingford, the efforts of Hedges - the local solicitor acting for the Company - had fallen on deaf ears. Thus, as at 18 July 1834, the only shares sold in the Vale of White Horse amounted to one issue of five shares in Wallingford and seven issues of either one or two shares in Oxford. On 18 July 1834, Saunders informed Vines at Reading that it would be:

> *'Necessary that the Parliamentary Deed and Agreement should be executed by the Proprietors residing at Wallingford and Oxford, who have not yet signed. I am desired to request that you will take steps to procure the undermentioned persons to execute it in time to transmit them to this office by Tuesday morning next. The attesting witness at Reading should be the same as Wallingford and Oxford to save expense'.*

Saunders again wrote to Vines on 23 April 1835, enclosing a book of 250 share certificates (Nos.19,001-19,250). These 250 shares were for delivery in the Reading area. However, in the same letter, Vines was requested by Saunders to find further subscribers to take 14 shares still deficient in the Reading area.

The total capital now raised amounted to £2,000,000 and a Petition for the Bill had been presented to the House of Commons. This was read a second time without opposition in the Commons on 9 March 1835 and committed, the report of the previous year's proceedings being referred to by the Committee. Shortly after the Committee had met, the Chairman announced that the public advantage of a railway had been sufficiently established by last year's report and the Committee required no further evidence on that subject. The chief opponents now were the London & Southampton Railway Company and the Eton schoolmasters, with the landowners in the Home Counties appearing to have accepted defeat. The London & Southampton pursued an active attack on the Great Western by proposing an alternative line between Bristol and London. This would be a direct rival to the Great Western and would pass from Reading to Basingstoke, Bath and Bristol. Some support for this scheme had been obtained from towns along the proposed route, but little from Bath or Bristol who preferred the Great Western scheme.

The Committee eventually decided in favour of the Great Western Bill and it was reported to the House, being read for a third time on 26 May 1835. The following day, the Bill was introduced into the House of Lords and read for the first time, with numerous petitions being presented by various peers in its favour. The Bill was finally referred to a Committee, after the second reading was carried by 46 to 34 votes on 10 June 1935. Quickly, this Committee reached the same decisions as the Commons Committee. However, although no more evidence of the need for a railway was required, the enquiry was still to continue for 40 days!

The word by word report of this enquiry is available for study and clearly it was a very irritable Brunel who was again interrogated closely by opposing counsels. One can imagine how Brunel must have felt, again confined in the oppressive atmosphere of the enquiry room and answering the same questions, instead of going about his business in the open countryside with his assistants.

Called to give evidence, was a Reading tallow chandler and grocer. He gave evidence of the uncertainty of the present communication and spoke of the delays in the delivery of the candles made by him to places such as Wallingford, Thatcham and Newbury. Zachariah Allnutt - the Receiver and General Surveyor of the Thames Navigation - also gave evidence. Allnutt had been the General Receiver for 35 years and gave details of the recent improvements which had taken place on the Thames navigation. He emphasised the fact that the Thames Commissioners made no profits from the trade on the river, that currently the Commissioners had borrowed approximately £94,000 and that the tolls had been mortgaged to repay these loans, plus interest. He expressed concern that if the tolls decreased, the loans and interest would not be able to be repaid, nor would further improvements be able to be carried out. The occupier of the Streatley and Goring mills - a Mr John Childs - expressed concern about the proposed bridge at Gatehampton and the two embankments leading to the bridge, one on each side of the river. He was asked:

Q. 'will the bridge and embankments be likely to injure your mills?'
A. 'I think they will'.
Q. 'Do you know the meadows on either side of the river?'.

A. 'Yes'.
Q. 'Are they likely to be flooded?'.
A. 'Yes'.
Q. 'Are those floods likely to be increased by the embankments?'.
A. 'Yes'.

Mr George Treacher, the Assistant Surveyor to the Thames Navigation, was questioned. He explained that his father before him had been the Surveyor for nearly 40 years. Treacher confirmed that he had worked all his life on the river and that he had been Assistant Surveyor for more than 12 years. He was asked:

'What would be the Effect on the Towns of Oxford and Abingdon and Wallingford, Pangbourne, Reading, Henley, Marlow, Maidenhead and Windsor if the Navigation of the Thames should be deserted?'.

He replied:

'I should suppose that they would lose a considerable deal of their Trade, as a good deal of Trade is carried up to these Places, and there are Canals which carry some of the Trade'.

After hearing all the evidence, towards the end of August 1835, the Committee declared the preamble proved by 33 votes to 21 votes. However, the branch to Windsor had been dropped and the Provost of Eton College had ensured that a clause was included forbidding the erection of a station at Slough or anywhere within three miles of the college. The Committee reported the Bill for its third hearing and despite some opposition from Peers, the Bill received the Royal Assent on 31 August 1835, being carried by a majority of 22 votes.

At the time of the Great Western application to Parliament for authorisation, the Bill was one of 19 other Bills waiting to receive the King's approval. The King - choosing not to attend Parliament - had issued a signed 'Commission' or declaration. This document gave the Royal Assent collectively to a number of Bills which had already cleared the various stages of the Parliamentary procedures. The contents of the declaration would eventually be read before both Houses of Parliament, officially confirming the King's approval. The Great Western Bill would be number '17' on the list of Bills finally read out and with the Norman phrase *Le Roy le veult* (The King wills it), the Great Western Railway was finally born on 31 August 1835.

The success of the Bill was received with mixed comments from local journals. One newspaper commented sagaciously on 5 September 1835:

'The Bill for carrying this measure into effect, having passed the Houses of Parliament received the Royal Assent on Monday last ... We have not heard what decision will be made by the inhabitants on the high road between Reading and Bristol, but we should advise them to prepare for the great change which the railway will affect in their trade'.

Another journal was more enthusiastic:

'We have at length the pleasure of congratulating our fellow townsmen on the completion of *their wishes. THE PASSING OF THE GREAT WESTERN BILL. After an opposition unexampled for its bitter contumaciousness, this great measure passed the House of Lords last night, without a division. The glad tidings was received in this town with much rejoicing, and the bells of the three parishes were rung right merrilie'.*

Now, come what may, the railway between Bristol and London would be constructed. The localities and their inhabitants along the line of the railway would be permanently affected by the construction and opening of the Great Western Railway and some of these effects would be positive, others negative. The Act authorising the construction of the Great Western Railway contained 251 clauses, many of them for the protection of individual landowners, canal companies and turnpike trusts, although the general stipulations of the Act would apply along the whole length of the line.

FIGURE 6. The actual Commission "By the King Himself - Signed with his own Hand," and Seal, by which King William IV gave Royal Assent to the Great Western Railway Act on 31 August 1835. *(OPC/BR)*

PART II
SELECTING THE ROUTE

'It is harder work than I like. I am rarely much under twenty hours a day at it'

FIGURE 7. Brunel's initial surveys were generally conducted on horseback, however, to ensure that nothing impeded his indefatigable efforts to survey, design and construct the Great Western Railway, the engineer had made for him a personal coach. This took the form of a 'britzka', which was basically an open carriage with a folding top and with space for reclining. The coach was unusual in that Brunel had designed the vehicle without windows - just slatted ventilators - which allowed him to snatch a few hours sleep *en route* between site visits. *(OPC/BR)*

FIGURE 8. As the construction of the Great Western Railway progressed east and west, Brunel had to travel to many different sites along the whole length of the line to inspect the numerous works which were now taking place. Indeed, as the various sections of the line opened, the engineer travelled by train to many of the intermediate sites, sometimes accompanied by Directors and other officials. For such occasions, another horse carriage of varnished mahogany was used - appropriately named 'Galloper' - the name being in large gold letters shaded crimson, the coach being loaded onto a carriage truck for that part of the journey undertaken by rail. *(OPC/BR)*

CHAPTER FIVE
BRUNEL'S SURVEYS AND GEOLOGICAL SURVEYS

T he spring of 1833 found Brunel about to commence the project for which he will probably be most remembered. The outline survey for the railway was required and it had to be completed within two months. This initial survey was a general reconnaissance of the country and the engineer had to acquaint himself with the nature of the ground over which the projected railway might finally take. He would have to carefully note surfaces and the formation of the intervening districts with their canals, rivers, streams and roads. He would then be in a position to select the route which appeared, on the whole, to have the greatest advantages.

Brunel had as his assistant surveyor during this preliminary survey, a former Bristol land surveyor - W. H. Townsend - who had been initially in charge of construction on the Bristol & Gloucestershire Railway. Townsend had also been a potential rival to Brunel as engineer to the Great Western Railway. Brunel and Townsend were later joined by another surveyor by the name of Hughes. The initial survey took the form of a general view of the country and was a cursory examination of all the alternative routes, coupled with all known information. Brunel describes this initial survey:

'On our first examination of the country I obtained all the information I could which could be collected upon the point. The levels of the canals on both lines are well known, and are ascertained. Projects have been put forward by other persons previous to that; there have been a printed prospectus of a railway from London to Bristol, and a survey made for a turnpike road; one of those took the north and the other the south of the Marlborough Downs; those I got access to, and the levels of the canals. The levels of the Kennet and Avon Canal, which takes the southern line, are about 130 feet higher than the levels of the Wilts and Berks. Canal that took the northern line. The Kennet and Avon Canal passes that summit level by a deep cutting, while the Wilts. and Berks. Canal is carried over it without any deep cutting, so that the height of the summit level on the one side of the hills is considerably greater than the height on the other. It so happened that the southern line was the first I examined, for a variety of reasons; from the turnpike road passing that way I got more acquainted with it; and the project I spoke of was for a southern line, and that was the first one I took, but it was from finding the difficulties of that line I tried the north; and I then, at a meeting of the Directors, stated the difficulties of both, and they agreed with me that embracing Gloucester and South Wales was a very important feature'.

During this preliminary survey, which commenced on 9 March 1833 and was completed punctually in May, Brunel spent most of the daytime in the saddle. At night he was absorbed in the study of maps, documents and calculations needed to establish the line of the proposed railway. The decision to construct the line either to the south or the north of the Marlborough Downs absorbed much of his time and he spent a lot of time travelling in the Vale of White Horse and the Kennet Valley. However, he did find time to do some sight-seeing. Brunel's diary records:

'Sat. April 20th - Arrived at Reading late. Went to bed. After breakfast went in search of Hughes. After some trouble found him at 'Blackboy', Shinfield, gave him maps. With him to Theal [sic] Road and into Pangbourne. Returned to Reading, went to Theale. Met a Mr. Keeps who showed me the new church. Returned to Reading; Hughes came in the evening. Gave him £5.0.0'.

Brunel frequently travelled from Reading, through Pangbourne and Streatley to Wantage. Streatley could be reached from Reading along the turnpike via Purley and Pangbourne. At Streatley there were diverse routes - ancient and modern - for the traveller to choose from. Here the turnpike forked, one passing through Moulsford and Wallingford to Oxford, the other passing along the southern fringe of the Vale of White Horse to Wantage and beyond. Brunel's diary records:

'Monday April 22nd - Started at 6 a.m. Examined the ground in the neighbourhood of Wantage - breakfasted at Streatley. Determined on the outer line winding round the undulating ground. Returned to Reading, dined, and went to Theal [sic] to meet Hughes. After waiting some time gave it up and returned'.

Brunel and his assistants during the preliminary and later stages of the railway construction, were frequent visitors to this part of Berkshire. During April 1833, Hughes - one of the surveyors - had cause to remember the area well. Hughes, following a pencil line drawn by Brunel on a map, arrived at Streatley on 25 April 1833 with his son. The pair spent a few days in the area taking levels before Hughes left for Wantage. The surveyor left his son at Streatley where he was engaged in laying down the sections taken by Hughes, ready for examination by Brunel. Brunel had previously complained about Hughes's expenses and the surveyor - clearly rattled by the engineer's comments - replied by letter from Wantage on 1 May 1833:

'I came in here last night dripping and having stood in the rain all the morning and no clothes to change. I have always two or three hours to work after I get home to catch up. I make no stop in the day and work as hard as I can till evening to conclude'.

Brunel's response has not been traced, but it appears unlikely that the engineer felt any sympathy for the surveyor. Indeed, Brunel was driving himself just as hard and was indefatigable in his efforts to complete the survey on time.

Brunel also would shortly earn the London Committee's disfavour regarding the second survey, when he exceeded his own budget. The engineer had estimated £600 for completing this survey and preparing the final plans for submission to Parliament. Saunders wrote to Brunel on 28 October 1833 on behalf of the London Committee to:

'express their regret and disappointment at the tenor of his letter which announces a considerably

*increased outlay in the expense of the survey beyond the estimate made and recently confirmed
by himself to this Committee'.*

Despite this irritating incident, the Directors would soon realise the true value of
their small, but tenacious engineer.

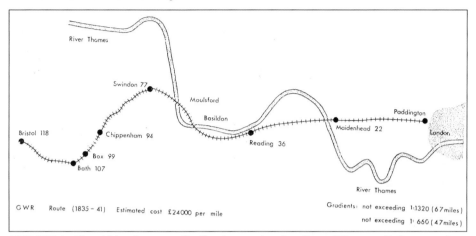

FIGURE 9. The 114 mile route finally chosen for the Great Western Railway and as
constructed during 1835-1841 at an estimated cost of £24,000 per mile. The line was laid
down with 67 miles not exceeding a gradient of 1:1320 and 47 miles with gradients not
exceeding 1:660.
*(Reproduced by kind permission of David & Charles, Newton Abbot, Devon, England,
from 'Brunel's Britain' by Derrick Beckett)*

Brunel after completing the preliminary survey, made his views known to the
Committee of Deputies who convened a Public Meeting in Bristol. Following this
meeting and the decision to form a company, a General Board of Management was
constituted consisting of two separate committees of 12 each of the Bristol and
London directors. It was at this time that Brunel was redirected to make a second
survey in a 'more regular and formal manner'. Consequently, Brunel commenced
a more accurate survey of the northern line, although further consideration was
given to the merits of the southern line. In the main, this second survey
concentrated on the area between Reading and Bath and various alternatives for
the line between Reading and London. During this survey, levels were taken to
ascertain the inclinations and the nature of the ground over which the proposed
railway would pass. The levels provided basic information regarding the amount of
'cutting' and 'banking' required, information which was essential if an accurate
estimate of the cost of the proposed railway was to be made.

However, it was during this second survey that Brunel began to realise the
problems he would experience in negotiating the path of the railway west of
Streatley. Hughes, again staying at Streatley on 24 September 1833, wrote:

*'I write to say that we intend leaving Streatley tomorrow and shall remain at Aston Tyrril for
a day or two. Mr. Bell will also leave tomorrow and either take up his quarters with us or at
Cholsey. The country between Lonningdon Farm [Lollingdon Farm (directly overlooking
Cholsey main line station)] and Streatley being so very hilly it is impossible to get rapidly over*

the ground - All of us however are doing our utmost to get on and I trust if our progress in this difficult district does not come up to your expectations when the Country turns more favourable we shall fetch up'.

The final plans deposited at the end of November 1833 showed a line of railway, which apart from slight alterations at the London end, would not vary much from the line which would finally be constructed. Before any railway scheme could receive Parliamentary approval, the engineer's estimate of the costs involved in constructing the line had to be verified. This involved a close scrutiny of the estimates supplied and an examination of the various consultants employed by the Company to undertake various technical investigations. Brunel - as the chief engineer - would be carefully questioned during the examination of both Great Western Bills which went before Parliament. Other experts would be chosen - not only for their technical expertise - but also for their adeptness in conducting themselves before sometimes very hostile cross-examination.

While Brunel and his team were initially deciding upon the line of the proposed line of railway, other calculations had to be undertaken. Borings had to be taken to determine the nature of the ground and evaluations had to be made along the length of the line for which Parliamentary approval was being sought. To determine the geological formation of the various strata, Brunel had initially used maps which were available at the time and also noted stratification in quarries and other exposed areas along the route. Now, more details of the ground were required and trial shafts and borings took place along the line of the proposed railway. This would provide important data for the engineers and the results would also be required by the investigating Parliamentary Committee. On 16 January 1834, the London Committee empowered the engineer to:

'commence the requisite borings and other examinations required to verify the estimates in Parliament'.

This instruction, of course, only applied to the two extremities of the line.

Following the defeat of the first Great Western Bill, the undismayed Directors continued during the autumn and winter of 1834-35 to drum up support. Consequently, before the end of February 1835, the second Bill had been presented to the House of Commons. On 26 February 1835, Brunel was again instructed to:

'commence the necessary borings and other examinations required to substantiate the estimates in Parliament'.

This latter instruction applied to the 'intermediate' section, i.e. the portion of the proposed line from Tilehurst - immediately west of Reading - to Corsham, near Bath.

The borings in the 'intermediate' section were under the superintendence of Mr. James Otto Heise. Heise and his assistants began their investigations in early 1835, when 12 separate borings were made at various locations in this 'intermediate' section, ranging in depth from 3-feet 6-in. at Purley, near Reading, to 78-feet 6-in. at Corsham, near Bath.

The geologist completed his investigations and Brunel authorised payment of Heise's expenses on 6 January 1836, plus a bonus of £10 as the geologist was also required to give evidence before the Parliamentary Committee for the second Great Western Bill. He gave a good account of the work he was responsible for, but appears to have been given little information about why the borings were necessary in the first place. An interrogating counsel appeared to find it incredulous that Heise had been commissioned to undertake the borings without any knowledge of the proposed works and as Heise was unable to answer any questions, except those directly relating to the soundings he had taken, he was soon dismissed.

CHAPTER SIX
LAND EVALUATION

Of all the skills necessary to construct a new line of railway, the expertise of the land valuer has failed to be recognised by contemporary historians. No mention appears of the land valuers employed by the Great Western Railway to value the land required for the projected railway and neither has any of the land valuers ever been identified in any of the histories so far written about this early period of the Company's history. The land valuer had to be a man of many skills. Sometimes, he had to use his local knowledge to persuade landowners to give their assent to the Bill. On occasions, the valuers had also to placate irate landowners and occupiers whose land had been invaded by surveyors making surreptitious expeditions. In other instances, the land valuer's expertise was ignored by the Directors, as the practice of 'buying off' opposition became more and more widespread. In some cases, the Company's land valuer was not involved at all, with the Company accepting a ludicrous private evaluation obtained personally by the owner or occupier.

The valuation of the land covered the value of the land required for the projected line of the railway and also included compensation for damages of every kind. Where a landowner or tenant's land was severed by the railway, various options were available, including a crossing over the railway; an under- or over-bridge or financial compensation. Frequently a landowner or tenant who had initially agreed to a crossing or bridge changed their mind and were quite prepared to settle for compensation only. Generally, in these cases the Company was only too ready to oblige as the heavy expenditure involved in constructing a crossing, with all the inherent dangers and the heavy work involved in constructing an under- or over-bridge was dispensed with.

A prospective land valuer for any railway scheme would ideally be a local man, with an intimate knowledge of the country and the people involved. He would also need to be a man of integrity, which would help to gain the confidence of ambivalent or totally opposed landowners or tenants. He would also have needed to be totally positive about the projected railway and confident that the project would bring great benefits to the country the line would pass through and to the people who lived there. He would need to be very calm and confident when facing hostile cross-examination before a Parliamentary Committee, charged with investigating the merits - or otherwise - of the projected scheme.

Such a person introduced himself to the Directors of the Great Western Railway in the Autumn of 1833. Daniel Lousley was aged 37 and lived with his wife Mary and their three children at Manor Farm in the village of Blewbury, situated a few miles to the south of Wallingford on the turnpike road from Reading to Wantage. Blewbury was one of seven similar small settlements throughout the Vale of White Horse which had developed because of the presence of a series of streams emanating from water springing from the chalk base of the Berkshire Downs. In the 19th-century, Blewbury was renowned for its cherry orchards and each year's annual crop, together with those from other nearby districts, were sent to market in either London, Oxford or Bath. Not surprisingly, the Directors of the Great Western Railway were not impartial to a basket of these luscious fruits and in the closing stages of the land valuer's association with the Great Western Railway, Saunders wrote to Lousley on 8 July 1839, first of all to upbraid him:

> *'I am getting very anxious about the remainder of your purchases ... Have you made any progress ... you will bear in mind that our powers to take land expires in August & where we cannot treat for it we must have a jury commissioned ...'.*

Then, continuing:

> *'I will mention to the Directors your kind intentions about the cherries, which will I dare say arrive in time for their meeting'.*

Daniel Lousley and his family farmed between 1,200-1,300 acres of land in West Berkshire, but he was also a grocer and also sold 'a vast quantity of coal'. Lousley was also well acquainted with the conditions of the local agricultural poor, as he was a member of the Wantage Board of Guardians. Lousley was also passionately in favour of the proposed Great Western Railway, as he considered:

> *'that the railway will be beneficial to this country especially as there is an account of the Poor Laws causing great discontent among the labourers, and if there was a little more work for them it would be better'.*

Lousley was, of course, referring to the fact that under the amended Poor Laws, outdoor relief had been virtually abolished and that any family seeking Relief was now removed to the Union Workhouse. Here, the family would probably be separated during their time in the institution and they would have to undertake allocated work for the duration of their stay.

The coal sold by Lousley was produced in the Somerset coalfields, being brought by canal to Abingdon and then by road to Blewbury. The cost of the road carriage increased the price of the coal by 50% and Lousley presumed that if the railway was constructed, the price of coal would be reduced. Lousley in his evidence before the Parliamentary Committee of 1835 was asked why he considered the construction of the proposed railway would benefit the inhabitants of Berkshire and particularly the agricultural poor. He informed the Committee that in his part of the country there was no wood of any consequence within several miles and that the agricultural labourers found it necessary to purchase wood for fuel. The price of carriage cost more than the original price of the wood and Lousley explained that if he and his fellow farmers wanted the agricultural labourers to cut the corn at harvest time, the farmers had to give the haulm [stubble] to the labourers to use as fuel.

Lousley went on to explain to the Committee that the area around Blewbury was generally a poor agricultural area and that the land required a great deal of manure if reasonable crops were to be grown. It was generally considered at that time, that the haulm ploughed back into the ground provided the best manure and it was considered advantageous to the farmer to have the haulm to manure his land. However, because of the necessity of giving the haulm to the labourers to use as fuel for their cottage fires, all the farmers could do was to insist that the ashes from the fires be given back to the farmer, although the farmer would make no payment to the labourers for these.

Lousley had considerable experience in land valuation. This experience had been gained over some 20 years, the majority taking place in Berkshire, but also in other locations. This experience and an awareness that the Directors of the Great Western Railway would need such expertise, prompted Lousley to write to the solicitors acting for the company in London to offer his services. His letter dated 22 October 1833 was received by Messrs Swain, Stevens & Co and the letter was duly passed to the Company secretary.

Lousley's letter and a reference from a Mr Graham of Abingdon regarding Lousley's suitability for the post of land valuer was duly considered by the London Committee on 24 October 1833. Saunders wrote to Lousley on 26 October, stating:

'that the application had been duly considered by the Directors ... I have received their instructions to thank you for the proposition you make of undertaking the survey and estimation of lands in Berkshire to be taken for the Great Western Railway Company, and to state that your application shall be duly considered before any definitive step is taken to ascertain the value of property there, affected by the line of railway. The terms in which Mr. Graham conveys his recomendation are highly satisfactory, and it will give the Committee much pleasure to be enable to comply with your wishes when the proper time arrives for giving their attention to the subject'.

At the end of October 1833, barely a quarter of the capital required to construct the line had been subscribed. The Directors decided to seek Parliamentary authority to proceed with the two extremities and plans were deposited at the end of November. Although sensing defeat, the Directors continued to promote the total project whenever possible and as Daniel Lousley had already indicated his support for the proposed railway, he was approached to assist in further promoting the scheme. Saunders wrote to Lousley on 4 December 1833, stating:

'As Mr. Hunt of the firm Messrs. Swain, Stevens and Co. Solicitors to the Great Western Railway is proceeding to Reading and Abingdon on business connected with the undertaking, it has been thought adviseable that he should take the opportunity of seeing you also, in order to gain general information, which may be useful to him from your local acquaintance.

Mr. Simmonds has represented to the Board that you will be enabled to assist the views of the Committee, and as you have already expressed your inclination in favour of the railway, I shall be obliged by your doing what is in your power to forward Mr. Hunt's operation.

He leaves London early tomorrow and will be at the Bear Inn Reading in the afternoon.

On the following day he proposes going to Wallingford and Abingdon, and will probably call at Blewbury on his road. He will at all events be with Mr. Graham at Abingdon in the course of Friday'.

On 16 January 1834, the London Committee instructed Brunel to arrange the necessary borings and other examinations required to verify the estimates in Parliament. On 27 March, the Committee considered letters from Lousley and others requesting to be considered for the positions of land valuers. The Committee resolved that the Secretary and engineer be authorised:

> *'to secure the services of Mr. Har[d]wick and Messrs. Drivers [Edward and Samuel Drivers had offices in Richmond Terrace, London] or of such other land surveyor as may seem best calculated to prove in Parliament the value of the land required for the railway'.*

The Secretary reported to the London Committee on 1 April 1834, that he and Brunel had virtually made all the arrangements for the land valuation between London and Reading. Hardwick had agreed to value the land between the proposed junction with the London & Birmingham Railway Company, near Wormwood Scrubs to Starch Green. Between Starch Green and Maidenhead, it was hoped [later confirmed] that Messrs. Drivers would conduct the valuation. The section of the proposed line between Maidenhead and Reading would be valued by Daniel Lousley. Saunders consequently wrote to Lousley on 29 March 1834 stating:

> *'I am desired by the Directors of this Company, to enquire whether you can undertake to survey and value the properties required for the line of railway between Maidenhead and the Town of Reading, and, if so, to request that you will come to London either on Monday or Tuesday for the purpose of arranging the terms of such valuation and of receiving the requisite instructions. It is of necessity that such business should be undertaken and performed without delay in order to give evidence of the value of the land for a Committee of the House of Commons about the 15th April.*
>
> *Mr. Brunel the engineer will remain in London on Monday and Tuesday for the purpose of meeting you at this office where I will thank you to address your answer by post. The Directors have determined upon this communication being made to you upon the understanding that you are favourable to the principle of the railway and can promote the success of it by bearing testimony to the general advantages likely to be derived by the public'.*

Lousley accepted the Directors' proposition and one assumes attended the meeting with Brunel.

The quantity of land valued by Lousley between Maidenhead Bridge and Reading amounted to 142 acres, 1 rood and 29 poles. The total value of the land, including all compensations, amounted to £14,231 and Lousley was paid three guineas per day plus expenses. On 11 July 1834, Saunders again wrote to Lousley requesting that an account for the survey and valuation of the land be received in London by 15 July. In addition, Lousley was instructed that his attendance before the Parliamentary Committee would be required. Following the Bill receiving the Royal Assent, Lousley did not return and complete the final negotiations as the Maidenhead to Reading section was under the jurisdiction of another valuer.

Following the defeat of the truncated scheme of 1834, the Directors quickly decided to seek authorisation for the construction of the whole line the following year. On 26 February 1835, the London Committee authorised the Secretary and engineer to secure the services of land valuers who it was considered:

'may seem best calculated to prove in Parliament the value of the land required'

and the Directors considered that if possible, the services of Messrs. Trumper, Drivers, Lousley and Hawkes be secured. From Reading to the Parish of South Stoke - directly adjacent to the bridge over the Thames at Moulsford - Messrs Drivers were appointed valuers. Daniel Lousley became responsible for the section west of the Moulsford bridge in the Parish of Cholsey, to the River Cole near Shrivenham. The total area of land to be valued by Lousley between these two locations amounted to 241 acres 1 rood 38 poles and the gross value of the land - including compensation for damages of every kind - amounted to £25,785-17s-10d. This valuation also included severance i.e. where a property was severed by the proposed railway; for crops growing on the land at the time of the valuation; for ploughing conducted shortly before the valuation; for seeds found and any other consideration.

Lousley was initially instructed by Brunel and one of his principal surveyors Mr. George Hennet. The land valuer was given a statement of the land required and accompanied by Hennet, who was described by Lousley as:

'one of Brunel's young men and a gentleman of Reading that went to lay down the line'.

Lousley commenced his assessment and he described how he conducted his valuation:

'Mr. George Hennett first put me on the line, and showed me the track I was to pursue, to set me going'.

One can imagine Hennett pointing Lousley in the direction the valuer was to take. Probably, the track was by now quite well worn, as the line of the proposed railway was now more-or-less finally determined and all the various professionals involved in the future construction would have traversed the area many times.

The valuer made an assessment every quarter of a mile of the value of the land required and he made these evaluations in every individual field the line would pass through. This valuation, taken in conjunction with the assessment of other inconveniences, formed a gross figure to the total compensation. Where it was not possible to reach the land required, say because of flooding, Lousley made his assessment from adjacent land. When making the assessment, 'enclosed' lands were worth slightly more than 'unenclosed' lands. The average value of the land by years purchase, was given as 28 years for 'enclosed' lands and 27 for 'unenclosed' lands. The final figure for compensation appears very generous, as land which was considered by Lousley worth 28 years purchase was doubled, the final figure of 56 years purchase being normally settled upon. The difference between the 28 years valuation and 56 years valuation was the sum allowed for compensation. The average worked out at 56 years purchase for land, buildings, compensation and damages.

FIGURE 10. The final resting place of Daniel Lousley - a land valuer employed on the embryonic Great Western Railway - in the peaceful churchyard at Blewbury, near Didcot, Oxfordshire and a short distance from the line of railway which he helped create.

(Author's collection)

CHAPTER SEVEN
LAND PURCHASES

The final valuations reached by Lousley regarding the value and all compensations for the land required for the Great Western Railway allocated for his attention, appears to have been generous. Indeed, Lousley admitted this when he was asked by the Parliamentary Committee in 1835:

'Are your estimates low or high?'.

Lousley replied:

'Very high; because I expected to be called over this property again'.

Despite the high valuation, it did not appear to have influenced the owners of land, particularly in Berkshire and Buckinghamshire. Virtually none of the landowners had actively supported opposition to the second Great Western Bill, but many still doggedly refused to give their assent to the project.

As with many other railway projects throughout the country, landowners whose property was on the actual line of proposed railway knew that the Directors would agree to virtually any terms. Thus, landowners in Berkshire formed a high proportion of those refusing to agree to the Bill before it was presented to Parliament in early 1835. The figures as presented to Parliament were as follows:

County	Assents	Neuter	Special Answers	Dissents
Gloucestershire, including Bristol	35	6	-	-
Somersetshire, including Bath	145	13	7	20
Wiltshire, including Branches	131	31	10	29
Berkshire, including Parts of Oxon and Wilts intermixed	143	86	33	69
Oxfordshire	30	7	2	4
Buckinghamshire	15	7	4	31
Middlesex	32	32	10	11
	531	182	66	164

Some of the 'Special Answers' received from landowners and tenants regarding the proposed railway, included the following:

'Can't be found'
'Application made, no answer received'
'declines answering'
'abroad, his agent neuter'
'too ill to be seen'

Before the Bill was presented to Parliament there is much evidence to confirm that the Directors were ready to agree to almost any proposition made by a dissenting landowner or tenant, particularly if this involved compensation alone. However, if the inducements involved practical considerations, the Directors would whenever possible, agree to most requests after first consulting Brunel. One such request involved land and buildings leased to a tenant farmer by the Dean and Chapter of Christchurch in the Parish of South Stoke near Wallingford. The tenant had requested in early 1835 that consideration be given to a deviation which would take the line away from his land. The London Committee had considered this request and Saunders, after consulting Brunel, was instructed to reply that minor alterations were feasible. However, this reply proved unsatisfactory to the tenant and resulted in a further request to the Committee - who again after consulting Brunel - prompted the following reply from Saunders:

'I have submitted your letter to the Directors who are very apprehensive that it will not be in their power to make so great a change in the line without altering the position of their bridge [Moulsford] across the river'.

Brunel had confirmed that the deviation proposed would be totally impracticable. Saunders wrote to the tenant again on 31 March 1835, stating:

'I am desired by the Directors of the Great Western Railway to undertake that they will build a proper station house at Stoke with sufficient communication across the roads, with any necessary conveyance such as planting and fencing, upon the understanding that you will now withdraw the dissent you had expressed to the Bill, and will induce the Dean and Chapter of Christchurch to give their assent to the measure. The Directors would have readily acceded to your wish, if it had been possible, of carrying the line beyond the meadow, but upon consultation with the engineers, it was found impossible'.

The mention of a station house, gives some indication of the extreme measures the Directors were prepared to take to ensure that opposition to the railway proposals was nullified. It had never been intended to build a station at this location, nor was one ever constructed.

Using various methods, the Directors were able to persuade most opposing landowners to agree to the purchase of their land. These negotiations were a continuing process and the statistics presented to Parliament in 1835 continually changed. Brunel stated, when giving evidence before the Parliamentary Committee:

'In Berkshire, the Assents are Twenty-one Miles Fifty-four Chains and a Half, the Neuters Eight Miles thirty Chains and a Half, Special Answers Four Miles Twenty Chains and a Half, making the Assents, Neuters, and Special Answers, Thirty-four Miles Twenty-five Chains and a Half; the Dissents are Eleven Miles Forty-one Chains; making a Total in Berkshire of Forty-five Miles Seventy-six Chains and a Half'.

Research confirms that between Reading and Uffington required some of the most intense negotiations experienced along the whole line of railway. Even then, certain landowners held out to the very last minute. As late as 3 August 1839, land between Moulsford Bridge and the Uffington Road - amounting to 33 acres - had still not been relinquished by owners or tenants. This land included the Cholsey West Common and Hagborne Marsh and despite the fact that the contractors building this section of the line had commenced operations in the Spring of 1838 - over 12 months before!

As the preparations for the construction of the railway west of Reading got under way, it became obvious to the Directors that the arrangements made for the legal transfer and sale of the land and buildings involved were totally inadequate. The huge number of land purchases entailed a vast amount of work for the Company's solicitors and this would increase dramatically as the land valuers concluded their negotiations with the landowners and tenants. Most of the legalities concerning land purchases east of Reading had been handled by Charles Stevens, a senior partner in the London solicitors handling the Company's business. Not because of criticism, but because of an increasing awareness of the awesome amount of legal work which was impending, Saunders wrote to the firm of solicitors on 26 October 1837, stating:

> 'Dear Sirs, I am desired by the Directors to express to you their wish that you could adopt some mode of subdividing the labours of your professional investigating into titles, so as to bring them all to an early completion & generally to obviate any delay in the business of the Company which is likely to be incurred by further purchases beyond Reading ...'.

Despite this request, no agreement was reached until almost six months later, when another partner in the firm - W. O. Hunt - was appointed to deal with the legalities of the land purchases west of Reading (to the western boundary of the London Division). On receiving this news, Saunders again emphasised the urgency of the situation in a letter to Hunt dated 16 March 1838:

> 'My Dear Hunt, As I consider from our conversation this morning that it is definitely arranged between yourself & your Partners that the purchases of land beyond Reading are to be placed under your superintendence, ... Possession of the land is much wanted & I am led to expect an early report of some further purchases where immediate possession is of urgent importance ...'.

Well prior this, the negotiations by the land valuers for the purchase of the land had got under way. Although Lousley had originally valued the land required for the railway between Maidenhead Bridge and Reading, Lousley was not given the responsibility for the purchase of this land. Instead, Driver - one of the original surveyors for the land east of Maidenhead - was given this undertaking. However, Lousley was not forgotten and on 16 December 1837, Saunders wrote to Lousley at Blewbury:

> 'The Directors have always intended, as I think I told you, when I last had the pleasure of seeing you, to place under your superintendence the general purchase of land in the part of Berkshire, beyond Stretley [sic], and Moulsford, which you formerly surveyed for them, if you would under take the business on satisfactory terms: They have not given to Mr. Driver any part of that District, beyond Molesford [sic] ... Mr. Brunel & I have assured the Directors that you will do your best for the Company's interests, & it remains for you now to propose reasonable terms for

conducting the purchase. The sum will of course amount to a good deal in the aggregate of these purchases & the Directors will expect to be charged a low percentage. Let me hear from you as soon as possible in order to prepare the business'.

On 16 March 1838, Lousley was requested to come to London to meet with Saunders and Brunel to discuss the purchase of land beyond South Stoke. The meeting obviously agreed terms, Saunders writing to Lousley on 23 March 1838, stating:

'I send you a copy of the Form of Agreement which has been used by Mr. Driver & I have ordered some to be printed with you[r] name on them which I will send down early in the week.
    The Agreement when signed must be sent to me with your report, stating any which you think ought to be known to the Directors & giving such explanation as may be requisite for the solicitors to draw up the conveyance of the land'.

Just over two weeks later, Lousley nervously sent his first two completed agreements to Saunders in London, the Secretary writing back on 9 April 1838 complimenting and reassuring Lousley in the following terms:

'I have received your letters with two agreements which seem to me to be made out in every respect as clearly as possible'.

Matters appeared to be progressing satisfactorily for the rest of that year, but early the following year Saunders appeared far from happy with Lousley's efforts. The Secretary wrote on 25 January 1839, stating:

'I am getting very anxious about further purchases of land - not having heard from you since you were in London. In fact, if you are to go on purchasing for the Company lower down the line, it is absolutely incumbent to clear off some of the outstanding negotiations, as soon as possible'.

Perhaps Saunders would have even more harsh with the land valuer if he had known why the land purchases were falling behind? During this period, Lousley was also busily engaged in surveying the Parish of East Hagborne in preparation for the Inclosure Award. However, who can blame Lousley for continuing with his normal work? After all, the completion of the Great Western Railway through Berkshire and adjoining counties was not far away. To neglect local contracts would not prove to Lousley's future advantage and he sensibly continued with this work. However, Saunders chided Lousley again on 15 March 1839, writing:

'Herewith I send, the remainder of the property plans to Affington [Uffington] with an earnest request that you will get forward with the work as much as possible'.

Lousley appears to have taken the hint as by 3 August 1839 only 13 agreements were still outstanding for the purchase of land between Moulsford and Uffington.
    Despite occasional testy comments from Saunders, the relationship between Daniel Lousley and the Company Secretary appears to have been quite warm. As

Lousley's involvement in the great enterprise drew to a close, he appeared to be considering retirement, as he mentioned to Saunders that he was considering selling his farm. Saunders expressed some interest and requested Lousley to send him details of the property. However, the sale did not go ahead and Lousley and his family continued to live at Blewbury Farm right up to the time of his death on 14 October 1853 aged 57.

FIGURE 11. An early Great Western Railway relic. A boundary post located at Ruscombe near Twyford, Berks. *(Author's collection)*

PART III
CONSTRUCTION OF THE GREAT WESTERN RAILWAY THROUGH BERKSHIRE AND THE VALE OF WHITE HORSE

'Pray don't give away our Roman remains we are collecting . . .
We have already Roman coins, pottery and teeth of elephants
no doubt of Roman education already and I should grudge the
Roman villa' [To the GWR Directors]

3 December 1837

FIGURE 12. A completed line of railway, waiting to receive ballast and rails.
(Leicestershire Museums, Arts & Records Service)

FIGURE 13. A barrow-run.   *(Leicestershire Museums, Arts & Records Service)*

CHAPTER EIGHT
CONSTRUCTION BEGINS

After the safe passage of the second Great Western Bill through Parliament, work commenced simultaneously on constructing the railway at both ends of the line. The preparatory work undertaken by Brunel and his assistants to facilitate the passage of the abortive first Bill was now used to the best advantage. However, regarding the intermediate section, virtually ignored up to this time, Brunel had now to set in motion some urgent enquiries. An example of this unpreparedness was Brunel's inability to supply plans for the scrutiny of the Parliamentary Committee of the bridges over the Thames at Gatehampton and Moulsford. When questioned by the Committee over the design of the bridges, Brunel replied:

'that each bridge would be constructed with two arches of seventy-five feet and four arches of thirty feet'.

As history records, neither bridge was built to these specifications.

The whole line of railway from London to Bristol was divided into sections or 'contracts'. Major works, such as bridges or tunnels, were also let as separate contracts. The initial calculations had ensured that for each individual contract, adequate land was purchased to ensure that cuttings could be excavated to provide enough spoil to construct the embankments. Normally, more than enough land was purchased, although contractors were usually reassured by the engineer that the maximum amount of spoil to be removed, as stated in the contract, would only need to be excavated if individual circumstances required this. After all, even Brunel could not guarantee that a particular embankment would not settle more than originally anticipated. However, in many cases ballast [gravel] was later used to stabilise and compact embankments which proved prone to slipping.

The railway had been divided into two 'divisions' - Bristol and London. The London Division originally extended westwards to Shrivenham, where the Bristol Division terminated, However, at a later date, the four-and-a-half miles from Uffington Road to Shrivenham had been transferred to the Bristol Division. The two 'divisions' were split into separate 'subdivisions', each 'subdivision' being identified by the first letter of the 'subdivision' i.e. L=London, R=Reading, B=Bristol, C=Chippenham etc. Each 'subdivision' was broken down into individual 'contracts', with each 'contract' being allocated a 'letter' and a 'number' i.e. '8L' was the infamous Sonning Cutting, which was later to be sublet in three separate contracts. In any written correspondence, the letter relating to the subdivision would always be emphasised either in bold type or with a line underneath. This ensured that any facts relating to a particular contract would not be accidentally or mistakenly recorded against another contract and this particularly related to payments to the various contractors.

The London (subdivision (L)) extended to Reading, the last contract being '8L', which extended from Ruscombe near Twyford to Reading and included the Sonning Cutting. From Reading westwards - a distance of 17-miles 20-chains - to Didcot, all the contracts (with one exception) carried a 'R' prefix, being designated as follows:

'R1' Gatehampton Bridge.

'R2' Moulsford Bridge.

'R3' The construction of the line west of the Gatehampton Bridge to the Moulsford Bridge, a distance of 3-miles 23-chains.

'R4' The construction of the line from the Moulsford Bridge to Vauxhall Farm (to the west of Didcot), a distance of 6-miles 4-chains.

The section of line between Reading and the Gatehampton Bridge, was - for reasons unknown - not allocated a contract number, but was always known as the 'Pangbourne Contract'. The plans and specifications for this contract were repeatedly delayed and as late as 20 June 1838, Brunel was still apologising to the London Directors and requesting additional time to complete the plans and allocate the contract. The section was eventually taken by the well-known and experienced contractors Messrs. Grissell & Peto, who completed the section by working 24 hours a day, the works being illuminated by giant bonfires enabling the navvies to work night and day.

The first contract in the London Division - the viaduct over the Brent Valley - was taken in November 1835. Work actually started in February 1836 and was completed in the summer of 1837. Between Maidenhead and London, several contracts had been completed by the end of August 1837. Maidenhead Bridge was commenced in early 1836 to Brunel's highly controversial design and despite a change of contractor, was brought fully into use on 1 July 1839 when the railway opened to Twyford.

In the meantime, the citizens of west Berkshire braced themselves for the invasion of their mainly rural habitat. The navvies reputation had already permeated the county, fanned by speculation and newspaper reports. In the main, Berkshire had been left untouched by the ravages of the Industrial Revolution which in northern parts had already become a hard fact of life. Thus, Berkshire had been spared the mines and slag heaps which despoiled many parts of the country and the air was still clear and not marred by huge columns of polluting smoke which hung over the fast-growing industrial towns. Similarly, there had been no rush from the countryside to the towns, as increasing numbers of people sought employment in the recently spawned factories and mills in more northern parts of the country.

In most districts which the Great Western Railway would pass through, the upheaval was awaited with some anxiety, as the scene in the 1830s was still one of pastoral tranquillity. Most of the landowners - one way or another - had eventually agreed to the construction of the railway, but there was still deep misgivings in some quarters, as the railway would disrupt both the rich and the poor and would leave a permanent scar across a long familiar countryside.

FIGURE 14. An interesting memento of the construction of the Great Western Railway was this inscribed stone built into an old brass mill at Saltford near Bristol, indicating the date when the building of the railway commenced in this locality.   *(OPC/BR)*

The problems associated with Contract '8L' - the Sonning Cutting - did not dispel any of these misgivings. The cutting, nearly two miles long and in places 60-feet deep was commenced in the autumn of 1836. For more than three years, hundreds of men - and a large number of children - laboured here, excavating the gravel and hardened clay. The local populace became aware of the privations of the labourers - caused by the work and the weather - and there were increasing local misgivings about the very young boys who were being used on the railway works.

It was a common sight in Britain in the 1830s in agricultural areas to see young children working in the fields. But, the fact that children were being maimed and killed while working on the construction of the Great Western Railway appears to have disturbed some consciences. After the introduction of the New Poor Law, the employment of women and children in agriculture increased in many parts of the country. Before the 1834 Bill, low wages were subsidised from the rates and allowances were received by poor families for their children. When this practice was discontinued following the introduction of the New Poor Law, a large family became a handicap. The father's wage could rarely support all the family members, unless supplemented by wages earned by children as soon as they were old enough to work.

Wages paid to agricultural workers in Berkshire in 1833 were a pittance! For instance, a head carter might receive 12s 6d per week, an ordinary man 10s per week, a best team boy 4s 6d per week and a woman 4s per week. Thus, it becomes clear why more and more men and boys left the fields as the construction of the

FIGURE 15. The wooden trestle bridge across the Sonning Cutting as drawn by John Cooke Bourne. *(Author's collection)*

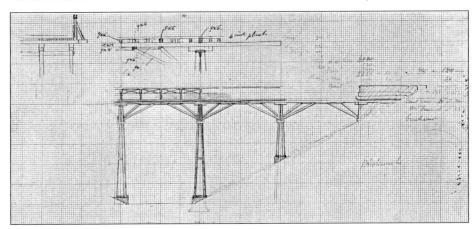

FIGURE 16. Brunel's sketch of the wooden trestle viaduct used to bridge the Sonning Cutting. Two bridges crossed the cutting at its deepest part, the western - carrying the main road - consisting of a three-arch brick structure 60 feet high. The eastern bridge was built as illustrated, this structure being the first of many similar timber viaducts Brunel would use on the railways he would become responsible for.
(Reproduced by kind permission of the Librarian of the University of Bristol)

railway got under way. Labouring on the railway works presented a rare opportunity for the agricultural labourer and many boys also followed their fathers to work on the railway. Local newspaper reports confirmed that many local men changed their employment. For some, this would be temporary, while for others, they would perhaps, transfer with their sons to new contracts either on the Great Western Railway or other railway projects.

In April 1839, Robert Wicks - aged 10 - fell from a wagon while working on the railway near Reading. He received severe abdominal injuries and died on the spot. His death immediately stirred the local clergy into action and the Vicar of St. Giles,

Reading, realising the plight of many of these children, organised a Sunday morning bible-class in the school room of the church. Four boys attended the first morning session, but once the word spread, 24 boys turned up for the afternoon session. While this gave the boys some temporary respite, the death and injuries continued unabated.

However, not all the local clergymen were so dedicated:

'in this place [Sonning] there are two clergymen, the vicar and the curate, and both frequents dinner parties almost every night. Altogether it is a much depraved place. The chief of evil lays at the clergymens' doors. At the public houses there are fights almost every night. They none of them keep the Sabbath for they work as on another day. The tailor makes clothes, the baker bakes bread, the washerwomen irons her clothes, and the men on the railway dig and do work as on another day'.

The Directors of the Great Western Railway also contributed to the labourers' problems. The contractors stood to gain a considerable bonus if a contract was completed before the scheduled date, but conversely the reverse was applicable, with the contractor having to a pay a penalty for every day the contract was behind. Consequently, there was intense pressure for the utmost effort to be expended to facilitate the early completion of the contract. The contractor would convey this urgency to the gangers, who in turn conveyed it to the navvies working under them, as all would probably share in any bonus earned.

One result of this unrelenting pressure was that Sunday working took place. The contractors did not normally encourage Sunday working, as at that period this was illegal, but neither did they discourage the practice. In Berkshire, Sunday working led to some bitter attacks by the local clergy on the Great Western Directors and in a letter to the editor of the *Berkshire Chronicle*, a correspondent expressed his concern at what he had recently witnessed:

'On Sunday last, the 24 instant [24 February 1839] I asked one of the railroad labourers, whom I met near my own residence, whether he had been to church? 'No', said he, 'I have been to work already this morning, and I am going to work again presently'. This was a little after one o'clock. Between five and six the same Sunday evening, I met three railroad men clothed in their working dress and with spades over their shoulders. I asked whether they were going to work? 'Yes' said they ... I asked, 'Why do you break God's commandment?'. 'We know its wrong (said they) and we don't like it, but if we didn't agree we should be turned out of work altogether'.

Some contractors used as an excuse for Sunday working, the fact that the contract bound them to complete the work in a stipulated time. This aspect, however, did not prevent some gangs labouring on the Great Western works at Bath in early 1839 being summoned before magistrates. The magistrates convicted them for proceeding with their work on Sundays, refusing to accept the plea that the contractor was bound to complete the works in a certain time.

In April 1839, a memorial was sent by the Clergy of Berkshire to the Directors. Saunders on 4 April 1839 was instructed to reply by the Finance Sub-Committee of the London Committee, who had met and considered the content of the memorial. Saunders wrote to the Rev. J. W. Yates, Vicar of St. Mary's Church, Reading, stating:

> *'The Directors will use every exertion to discourage and prevent the desecration of the Sabbath by the employment of labourers on the works, excepting where in cases of emergency or indispensable necessity it may be impossible to dispense with it.*
>
> *They unite cordially and unanimously in the desire to promote the due observance of the Lord's day, on the part of every individual engaged on the works on the line, and, with this in view, the London Directors have instructed me to write to every contractor engaged in their division, which extends to Uffington, requesting them to take immediate and effectual measures for prohibiting any work on the Sabbath Day which it is possible to avoid'.*

Saunders also received the following instructions from the Directors:

> *'A circular be addressed to the several contractors on the London district expressing the earnest desire of the Directors that they should abstain from all works on Sundays which are not indispensably necessary - and even in these cases should endeavour as much as possible to limit the employment of Men to such times of the day as cannot interfere with the hours usually set apart for Divine Service'.*

It must be noted that the Directors effectively left a loophole and a contractor, by pleading that the work was unavoidable, could justifiably continue Sunday working. Although the Directors' directive applied to the earlier contracts which had already been let, to the Directors' credit, an extra clause was incorporated in future contracts, including the ban on Sunday working. Unfortunately, there were only two new contracts outstanding at this time - '1S' and '2S'!

CHAPTER NINE
RIOTS

It appears that although considerable numbers of local labourers were employed on the railway works, a substantial number of the workforce also came from other parts of the kingdom. Probably, these men had followed a contractor from contract to contract or even had moved with the contractor from a construction site not associated with the Great Western Railway. Similarly, men may have moved quite independently from one site to another, attracted by the rumour of higher wages. The labourers were referred to as 'tramps' or 'navvies' in Berkshire and many local traders were reluctant to allow credit to these nomadic men. A letter to a local journal on 12 October 1838, sums up these feelings:

> 'Mr Editor. Can any of your readers inform me whether it be true that there is a combination formed by what are termed tramps; who have undertaken the work under the present contractors not to allow any Berkshire men to work on the line, but only those who tramp about from Lancashire and other places? If it be true, tradesmen in the Borough [Reading] and other places should be cautious how they allow men to get on their books, who are here today, and gone tomorrow'.

A few days prior to the opening of the railway to Twyford, problems arose with the contractor - William Ranger - who was responsible for Contract '8L'. This contract was for the construction of the railway from Ruscombe to Reading and included the deep cutting through Sonning Hill. The *Berkshire Chronicle* sympathetically reported:

> 'During the past week the town of Reading has been in a state of great excitement and apprehension in consequence of the whole of the men employed on the line between this town and Twyford having suspended their customary labour ... For sometime past it was generally understood that the contractor for the portion of the works nearest this town was in considerable difficulties, but it was not until Friday evening, the usual pay day, that it was stated that the fortnights wages then due to the men could not be paid. The men, upon hearing this, were considerably exasperated and did some trifling injury to the works, and also assaulted one of the clerks, but this last offence was entirely owing to the indiscretion of that person in his treatment of the men ...'.

The inhabitants of the town grew increasingly frightened after the navvies hung around for several days and the Mayor eventually sent for military assistance from Windsor. Some 20 minutes after the Mayor's messenger - a police officer - arrived at Windsor, a squadron of Horse Guards was despatched and the soldiers' appearance late Tuesday evening in the town, caused further excitement. Eventually, short of money, the strikers were quickly reduced to begging from the local people who responded very generously. In the meantime, the soldiers guarded the railway works, until on the Friday, the Mayor and Town Clerk addressed a meeting of the strikers. A letter from the Directors was read and the men were promised by the Company that if they returned to work at the end of the day, they would receive three days wages and the same on Saturday and Monday. The Town Clerk also promised that he would advance six days arrears of wages from his own resources. The men briefly discussed the proposals with their leaders, accepted the terms and quickly returned to work. This episode appears to have raised the local peoples' opinion of the railway labourers, who according to the *Reading Mercury* had previously had:

> *'but an indifferent opinion of the character of railroad labourers'.*

The Company were eventually forced to take all William Ranger's contracts away from him (including those in the Bristol district) and splitting the Ruscombe-Twyford section into three separate contracts.

The railway eventually opened between Twyford and Reading on 30 March 1840, terminating at Brunel's uncharacteristically ugly, one-sided station at Reading. The London Committee on 14 March 1839, had initially approved Brunel's original drawings for the Reading station, but a month later on 11 April, rejected the same plans because of the estimated costs. Nonetheless, the residents of Reading were very pleased with the arrival of the Great Western Railway and the opening to the town was clearly an event to be celebrated. A local journal describes the scene thus:

> *'The town of Reading was much enlivened from an early hour in the morning in consequence of the extension of the railway to that place; numbers flocked from the surrounding country, and the town had the appearance of a grand holiday. Many of the inhabitants availed themselves of a cheap and expeditious ride to Twyford; and some went as far as Maidenhead and Slough; and a few actually went by the first train to London and back to breakfast before 10 o'clock. The station was thronged the whole of the day by respectably dressed persons eager to view the arrival and departure of the trains. The extreme beauty of the first spring day - the splendid scenery the station commands - the presence of hundreds of elegantly dressed females rendered the whole proceedings of a highly interesting nature'.*

As the Great Western Railway progressed beyond Reading, further incidents occurred. During the construction of the line, the intention was that the navvies' labours were to be confined to the land staked out as belonging to the Company. This, in theory, allowed cultivation to continue as normal on either side of the line, but the labourers were not satisfied with this arrangement and trespassing and encroaching on adjoining land was a frequent occurrence. While the landowners and tenants faced with this problem appeared to be reasonably tolerant, perhaps, they had little choice in the matter? However, matters came to a head on 4 April 1840 at Wantage, when landowners and tenants met to express their concern at continuing trespassing. They said they were prepared to overlook the navvies' nefarious activities during the winter months, but they were now concerned about their growing crops. Cogswell - the Company's resident engineer on that part of the line - reassured the farmers that he had been instructed that if:

> *'mild steps and remonstance failed he was to use his discretion as to a better means of enforcing*

the Directors' orders'.

Problems also arose at Pangbourne. This was despite the reputation of the contractor for this contract - Messrs Grissell & Peto. This partnership was described by Brunel in 1846 as:

'probably the largest contractor in the world'.

Grissell & Peto's financial status enabled them to pay their labourers weekly (Brunel considered this unnecessary, recommending instead fortnightly payments), the navvies being able - once they were paid at the end of each week - to indulge in drunken orgies of violence. At least under Brunel's doctrine, the men would have had to budget and this should have prevented some of the excess drinking witnessed. The *Reading Chronicle* reported on 20 October 1838:

'the peaceful and beautiful village of Pangbourne has been of late subjected to every species of annoyance by the riotious and disgraceful conduct of the labourers employed on the railway in or near that place. The churchyard has been more than once desecrated by fights and riots, until at length the civil power was completely set at defiance, and prisoners rescued from custody by their companions'.

At the same time, similar incidents were occurring at Whitchurch a small hamlet situated to the north of Pangbourne, as well as at Twyford to the east of Reading and special constables had to be sworn in by local magistrates. A local journal commented:

'the magistrates have now received from the Home Office effectual assistance in the presence of a small police force, since which a degree of quiet has been restored to which the village of Pangbourne has long been a stranger. Still they have not been able to prevent numerous robberies from gardens orchards and fowl-houses in the neighbourhood'.

The 'assistance' mentioned in this report was implemented by the use of special constables specially sworn in by local magistrates. The Municipal Corporations Act 1835 ensured that the major task of a borough was the maintenance of law and order and for the first time, an embryonic police force took the place of the 'watchmen', the former ancient custodians of the peace. A Corporation was now elected by ratepayers and its members were bound to appoint a professional police force to ensure some semblance of peace. The Watch Committee also had the power to appoint special constables at times of crisis and constables so appointed, became the responsibility of and paid for by the Corporation.

The early 19th-century saw a sustained increase in the construction of major public works - which included railways. The Municipal Corporations Act 1835 did not provide for special constables to be engaged who could be charged to a particular works or contractor and consequently a statute was passed in 1838 which allowed for the appointment of special constables and their payment by the Directors of an individual company. The Bill was entitled 'An Act for the Payment of Constables for Keeping the Peace Near Public Works (1 & 2 Vict.c80)'. The preamble to the Act stated:

'great mischiefs have arisen by the outrageous and unlawful behaviour of labourers and others employed on railroads, canals, and other public works, by reason whereof the appointment of special constables is often necessary for keeping the peace, and for the protection of the inhabitants, and the security of the property in the neighbourhood of such public works, whereby great expense have been cast upon the public rates of counties, and the districts chargeable with expenses'.

The Bill ensured that a railway company's directors and shareholders were liable to pay the costs of any special constables appointed by the magistrates for maintaining the peace. However, history indicates that this power was little used, as railway companies particularly, considered that the appointment of special constables was at best, only a way of suppressing a riot once it had started. A more likely explanation for the infrequent use of the statute, however, was the fact that companies were totally opposed to these powers and protested vociferously whenever the powers were invoked. Also, as the tempo of railway building increased, many magistrates became shareholders in their local railway company and it is hardly likely that they would feel disposed to incur costs which would lead to diminished dividends.

The Great Western Railway Company was no exception and there were immediate protests as soon a special constables were sworn in at the Company's expense. On 18 January 1839, Saunders wrote to William Andrews, the Clerk to the magistrates at Reading appealing against the appointment of special constables at Twyford and Pangbourne, which were chargeable to the railway company at five-shillings per constable per day. Saunders explained:

'The Directors have always been willing to nominate as constables such persons as may absolutely be required for the preservation of peace on their works and are now quite prepared to do what is needful to that end, but they do, strongly remonstrate against the forced employment of men, as constables at 5/- per day, over whom no sort of control is exercised and who are much more calculated to excite than to repress any disturbance, if it should arise ...'.

These comments from Saunders, however, do not appear to be based on fact. The constables appointed by the Pangbourne magistrates had been seconded from the Metropolitan Police Force and were clearly experienced officers. Two of these officers - Cleaver and Forder - were stationed at Pangbourne and were reported on Saturday 9 March 1839 as having investigated the theft of a sheep's carcass. The two officers - with the aid of a bloodhound - unfortunately lost the scent of the culprits, who had cleverly crossed a sheep walk which confused the dogs.

However, there was no change in the situation and the Company continued to be charged for the employment of the specials. The Bill allowed for the employment of a maximum of 12 special constables at any location and at Twyford and Pangbourne, six constables had been appointed at each location and these were on duty, seven days a week. At Twyford, two of the officers were paid 5s per day and the other four 5s-6d, for being on duty during the night. At Pangbourne, the Company was charged £1-15s per constable each week.

On 30 May 1839, Saunders appealed to the Hon. Fox Maules M.P. at the Home

Office, requesting that the situation be drawn to the attention of Lord Russell the Home Secretary. Saunders emphasised that the Company had always found that:

'as special constables the chief gangers, most already powerful employees of the works which has been invariably tending with complete effect in maintaining the best order and prevent riot and disorderly behaviour. The men so nominated have great control and influence over the labourers ... the Company have already a large constabulary force of the very best description of men, who receive 19s a week and their clothes and most numerous applications are made for such appointments'.

Saunders also warned that any special constables not sanctioned by the Company would be trespassing if they entered any of the construction sites!

It would not be until 29 July 1839 that the Secretary was able to inform the London Committee of any change in the situation. Saunders reported that he had recently attended a magistrates' meeting at Reading. The conclusion had been that the magistrates had consented to waive the reappointment of any special constables which were chargeable to the Company. The magistrates also agreed to withdraw the order against the Company for the payment of the wages of the special constables during the previous month. To obtain this concession, the Company had agreed to the appointment of a policeman to superintend the special constables already appointed by the Company. The Directors quickly resolved:

'that a policeman be appointed for the purpose of preserving the peace and protecting property in the Pangbourne district during the continuance of the works at 21/- per week, with instructions to place himself under the orders of Mr. McDonnell the assistant engineer and to make weekly reports to the magistrates of the division under whose authority he is able to act whenever required'.

For a time, there were no further newspaper reports of any riotious behaviour on the part of the navvies in the Pangbourne area.

However, later in the same year and as the works progressed through the Thames Valley, further disturbances occurred at Goring, west of Pangbourne. After complaints from the local magistrate, Saunders wrote to the resident engineer with the request that a suitable ganger or other person be appointed policeman to keep the peace. A letter of reply from the engineer dated 4 November 1839 reveals an interesting situation:

'My Dear Sir, I am sorry to say that I can find no ganger or person connected with the works whom I can recommend as fit to be entrusted with the powers of Constable. The fact is that the Contracor's [sic] men are very ill paid and altogether of an inferior class of labourers, many of them being taken from the agricultural population of the district. The Company's servants upon the contract consist of a man and a boy who are both pretty closely employed.

I have seen Mr. Fell [Vicar] and have explained into the real state of the Parish of Horing [Goring]. Mr. Fell is usually non-resident and a very serious feud exists between himself and his Parishioners on the subject of a popular Curate whom he removed in the Spring. There was much rioting in the Parish in consequence and the Paronsage [Parsonage] House in particular was the object of attack. I mention this because I think Mr. Fell over estimates the amount of rioting and places it, as is usual, to the score of the Navigators.

If the Directors will let me have one GOOD Policeman I think I can undertake to say that there will be little rioting on GWR.

This arrangements will satisfy Mr. Stone the resident Magistrate.

I am Aware of course that this makes an additional expense to the Company, but on the whole I think, considering the ill condition of the Contractor's Gangers & Agents and the Company's very scanty staff that the plan I recommend will be the only feasible one'.

This letter appears to throw into doubt Saunders' earlier statement regarding the suitability of the gangers for the post of policemen. It also reveals the vulnerability of the labourers in attracting notoriety to themselves. However, it must be said that the opportunity to engage in a local fracas - which may not always have been of the labourers' making - may have endeared itself to a number of, perhaps, bored navvies looking for some excitement, particularly on pay day and on weekends!

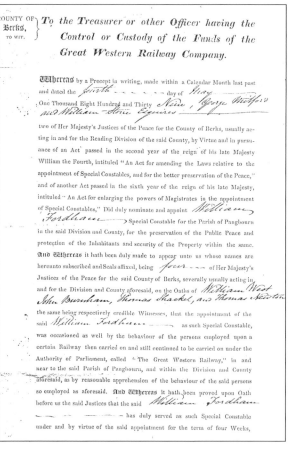

FIGURE 17. Warrant by Reading, Berkshire magistrates - dated 4 May 1839 - confirming the appointment of a William Fordham as Special Constable for the Parish because of '... the behaviour of the persons employed upon a certain Railway [GWR] ...'.

(OPC/BR)

CHAPTER TEN
CONSTRUCTION BEGINS WEST OF READING

T he completion of the Sonning Cutting eventually allowed the Great Western Railway access to Reading on 30 March 1840. From Reading the line would veer away from the Kennet Valley and the southern flank of the Berkshire Downs and pass in a north-westerly direction through the Goring Gap. This unique geographical feature is situated between the southern extremity of the Chiltern Hills and the northern flank of the Berkshire Downs. From ancient times, travellers had taken advantage of this natural break in the spiny backbone of England and the Thames Valley was one of the first parts of England to be inhabited. Neolithic man about 2000BC, established along the ridge of the Berkshire Downs - the Ridgeway Path - the main highway of prehistoric man. The path ran along the ridge of the hills to Streatley, before plunging down to the Thames crossing and continuing on its way. From Goring, the line of railway would take - for a short distance - an almost due north direction. This brief digression would quickly resolve itself, the railway resuming its generally westerly direction as the line neared Didcot and on through the fertile Vale of White Horse towards Swindon. From the opposite direction, the line would edge its way eastwards until the Bristol and London Divisions finally met.

The first contracts to be let for the railway westwards beyond Reading were for the two bridges over the River Thames at Gatehampton '1R' and Moulsford '2R', the advertisements appearing in local journals on Saturday 18 March 1837. The next contracts to be advertised were for the works between the Gatehampton and Moulsford bridges - '3R' - and for the works from the Moulsford river bridge, westwards to Didcot '4R'. The two final contracts in the London Division westwards from Didcot to Uffington Road - '1S' and '2S' - were advertised on 7 February 1839.

Local journals reported on 14 July 1838 the progress of the line west of Reading:

> *'the works on the Great Western Railway are now in activity between Reading and Wallingford ... The bottom of Shooters Hill at Pangbourne is being cut through'.*

One of the most formidable obstacles on this section was the excavation at Shooters Hill directly west of Pangbourne. This necessitated the removal of part of the northern slope of the chalk down, which at this point ran steeply down to the banks of the Thames. This excavation was in full view of the public as the turnpike road leading to Oxford and Wantage was compressed into a narrow strip of land between the River Thames and the slopes of the hill. The excavation was about three-quarters of a mile in length and the spoil removed would be used to form the embankments on either side of the bridge over the Thames at Gatehampton. By 27 October 1838, the hill had been excavated at both ends and soil had also been removed from the summit.

West of the village of Pangbourne, a brick bridge of three arches was being constructed to carry the railway over the turnpike road and it was here that an incident occurred, the first such recorded incident on the embryonic Great Western Railway system. On Tuesday 24 September 1839, Wombwell's Menagerie left Reading to travel to Oxford and then to Birmingham. When the slow-moving procession of caravans reached the newly constructed archway, unprecedented problems occurred. The smaller caravans passed easily through the structure, but unfortunately, a large caravan which contained the performing elephants, stuck fast under the arches of the bridge. After considerable delay, the caravan was eventually dragged free and there being no alternative route, was compelled to take a long detour to reach its destination. Luckily, the elephants were not affected by their unfortunate experience.

The scene at this time in western Berkshire was one of intense activity and the River Thames was being used to its full potential. Materials for the construction of the railway were being brought by barge to various sites, which in many cases were directly adjacent to the river. Local scenes familiar to generations, changed almost overnight as the labourers attacked the chalk hills and bridged valleys. Turnpike roads were diverted - temporarily or permanently - while brick arches used to carry the railway over or under the roads sprang up lonely and isolated to await the encroaching embankments. Temporary accommodation was built to accommodate the influx of labourers who had arrived to construct the railway and stables for the numerous horses required.

Local tradesmen quickly took full advantage of the opportunities presented to them. The local populace soon began to experience shortages of various items - including food - the limited stocks going to the highest bidder which was frequently an agent acting for the railway contractors. Local solicitors and magistrates became involved in disputes between landowners, labourers, contractors and even the Great Western Railway Company itself. Local journals eagerly reported the progress, accidents and disputes which were taking place and some incidents received national importance - or notoriety - according to the particular circumstances.

Local physicians and hospitals found themselves helplessly embroiled as they attempted to stem the tide of serious injuries and deaths which occurred to the men working on the railway. The scenes enacted in west Berkshire in the late 1830s had never before been witnessed by local people, as despite the grandeur of the scheme, much human suffering was also being witnessed. Numerous accidents occurred to the men and boys working on the railway between Reading and Didcot. Similarly, the two viaducts at Gatehampton and Moulsford appeared to be particularly vulnerable, high winds seriously affecting the men working on the lofty scaffolding surrounding the structures. This, coupled with rising waters which raced around the foundations of the bridges, placed the skilled artisans seriously at risk, working

FIGURE 18. The ancient crossing point to the village of South Stoke across the River Thames at Moulsford. At this point on the river, the towpath changes sides and in the days when barges were towed by teams of horses, the horses had to be conveyed by ferry to the other side of the river to continue their journey hauling the laden barges. Today, this scene has changed little and the Beetle & Wedge Hotel remains a prominent landmark on this part of the Thames. The ferry point here and at Little Stoke - a few miles away - were known to be regular landing places for barges and it is likely that during the period when the Great Western Railway was being constructed a short distance away, this scene was considerably busier than in this tranquil scene. *(Derrick Stockham-Jones)*

as they were in exposed and very precarious positions. On Monday 7 January 1839 during a period of very high winds, a bricklayer working on the Gatehampton Bridge was blown into the river and before assistance could be rendered, 'he sunk to rise no more'. An inquest was held nearly a month later on 11 February 1839 after the man's body had been found many miles away at Caversham, near Reading.

The Great Western Railway Company made no provision for the injury or death of any of the men involved in the construction of the line. On most of the works, the men themselves paid into a sick club which enabled the navvies to retain a local doctor who could respond to their needs and which also enabled sick pay to be paid. Peto - one of the contractors on the Pangbourne contract - later confirmed that it had proved impossible for himself to take charge of these sick clubs, as the men were most reluctant to trust their sick club funds to their employer. However, the money in the fund was normally kept at the site office on the individual works and the men - if they became sick - had to sign for any cheques they drew. Peto commented that the labourers felt this to be a great honour, as it was very unusual for men of the labouring classes to receive a cheque.

The practice on the Great Western Railway was that every accident, as it occurred, had to be reported to the resident engineer and through him to Brunel, who 'as a matter of duty' used to enquire into the causes of an individual accident. Brunel could also recommend following an incident how similar accidents could be avoided. In 1846, Brunel was called before a Parliamentary Select Committee on

Railway Labourers which was enquiring into railway labourers' welfare. He was shown a list of names of men and boys admitted to the Bath United Hospital following accidents on the construction of the Great Western Railway in the Bath area [working on the Box Tunnel], between the period 30 September 1839-17 September 1841. The list was compiled by the house surgeon at the hospital and was exclusive of all persons slightly injured who were classed as 'out-patients'. The number of admissions during the period numbered 136 and included 14 eventual fatalities. Brunel did not appear too dismayed by these figures and when asked by the Select Committee was he not surprised:

> *'that a list like this is a startling thing, as connected with the construction of a great work?'*

Brunel replied:

> *'No; I think it would be a small number of accidents considering the large number of men employed for between two and three years, and doing a very large quantity of work; I believe that if the same number of men had been employed in twos and threes on parish roads, scattered over the country, the number of accidents would have been as large if not larger'.*

Initially, most of the men injured during the construction of the Reading to Didcot section of the railway were usually transferred to the Reading Dispensary, which was situated at the time in Chain Street. The Dispensary was founded in 1802, when a group of local doctors provided - free of charge - advice and medicine to poor patients. After May 1839, injured railway labourers were also treated at the newly opened 50-bed Royal Berkshire Hospital situated on the London Road in Reading. The hospital had been built on land donated by Lord Sidmouth and designed by architect Henry Briant. Donations of £13,000 were raised to build the hospital and fit it out, with subscribers being able to recommend patients to be cared for by its surgeons and physicians. However, it would not be until a particularly serious accident occurred in Sonning Cutting in July 1839 that the

FIGURE 19. A modern-day view of the front facade of the Royal Berkshire Hospital which opened in 1839, the same time as the Great Western Railway was being constructed through Berkshire. *(Author's collection)*

FIGURE 20. Trimming the sides of an embankment.
(Leicestershire Museums, Arts & Records Service)

London Directors donated 100 guineas towards the expenses of tending to people injured in this accident. The Directors also sanctioned a miserly 10 guinea annual subscription to the hospital's funds.

The London Directors did not appear to have adopted a particularly benevolent attitude to the men who were indirectly working for the Company while toiling on the railway works, or to the hospitals along the line of railway who were trying their utmost to deal with an almost constant stream of injured workers. Despite the very serious injuries which occurred, the Directors on numerous occasions refused to sanction payment to local doctors who had responded to the injured men. The London Committee adopted this rigid stance from the outset and the Bristol Committee - who at first paid local doctors' bills - were eventually and reluctantly forced to adopt the same stance. Instructions were issued by both Committees that all seriously injured workmen must be taken to the nearest local dispensary or hospital to which the Company had subscribed. This had serious implications for the labourers who became injured, as they were now bundled into carts and - if necessary - hauled long distances over rough roads. Such treatment usually ensured that any chance the injured had of surviving their injuries became even more remote due to the time delay and the rough treatment they received while being transported.

Two incidents occurred in 1838 which highlighted the detrimental effects of this policy. In late October, a labourer by the name of Brown who was digging chalk at Pangbourne, died from his injuries after falling 30 feet following the collapse of the chalk bank he was working on. The navvie suffered serious back and thigh injuries and was immediately taken to the Dispensary in Reading by horse and cart.

An inquest recorded a verdict of 'accidental death', but also noted that the man had been alive while passing St. Mary's Church, Reading. The implication being that, if the injured man had received treatment sooner, his chances of survival would have been been greater. The Company was criticised for failing to provide treatment on the spot for such injured men, which it was felt would have ensured higher survival rates amongst the injured labourers.

Another serious accident occurred at Pangbourne later the same month, following which, a local surgeon Dr. Stephen W. Kidgell, complained about the lack of sensitivity of the railway authorities. The physician stated that as he himself was away from home, another surgeon who lived with him and who acted as his locum, promptly attended the scene of a dreadful accident on the railway works. The attending doctor felt that the temporary huts used as accommodation by the labourers and where the patient was placed following his accident were totally unsuitable for the treatment of such appalling injuries. The surgeon had requested that the injured man be removed to a more suitable place where the patient could be attended to, but this request was refused, the injured man being immediately conveyed to the Reading Dispensary. Following this incident, Dr. Kidgell warned that:

> *'I shall not in future think it proper to undertake the great responsibility of such accidents, unless the patient be removed to some desirable home or lodging, as the huts in which many of the railroad labourers live are totally inadequate for the reception of such formidable and appaling [sic] accidents'.*

Despite further accidents, the Directors failed to be moved by the plight of the labourers and right up to the time of the opening of the line, injured labourers continued to be taken to the nearest local medical facility to which the Company had made a subscription - whatever the distance involved.

FIGURE 21. The Bull Inn at Streatley, little changed from the days when Brunel was a regular visitor and when the inn was used as the 'Railway Office' during the time of the construction of the Great Western Railway.   *(Author's collection)*

CHAPTER ELEVEN
GEOLOGICAL AND HISTORICAL FINDS

The construction of the Great Western Railway proved a unique opportunity for local geologists and archaeologists, as the deep excavations which would take place would reveal many interesting geological and historical mementos and as today, some would seize the opportunity - however brief - to investigate the various finds. There was also a speculative element involved and dealers could be found scouring the excavations for specimens of fossils and the like which could be offered for sale. Some enquiries were hasty and incorrect opinions were formed. Also, some artefacts were destroyed before investigations could take place, but luckily Brunel with his team of resident engineers won the support of the Directors and everyone did their best, as far as they could to promote the preservation of the various finds.

As early as 3 December 1837, Brunel had plans for a museum situated directly adjacent to one of the stations on the line. An unusual postscript to a letter written by Brunel states:

> 'PS. Pray don't give away our Roman remains we are collecting really valuable geological and general museum to be attched [sic] to the railway establishment. We have already Roman coins, pottery and teeth of elephants no doubt of Roman education already and I should grudge the Roman villa'.

As the excavations revealed their links with the past, many of the finds were initially protected to allow investigations to take place. Thomas E. M. Marsh, a 19-year-old trainee civil engineer on the Great Western Railway at the time, was held responsible by Brunel for the recording and removal of the remains of a Roman villa found at Newton St. Loe near Bath. Entries in Marsh's surveyor's notebook - now preserved in Bristol City Museum - show that he worked intermittently on the site between 29 October and 24 December 1837. During this time, he produced plans and sections of the villa buildings and drawings of the mosaics found, including a full-size tracing of the now famous Orpheus pavement. Marsh, much later in January 1900, recalled the events:

> 'I was professionally engaged on the works of the Railway when the discovery was made.
> There was every desire on the part of the Railway Company to preserve as far as possible all that could be preserved or removed. The walls of the building were traced and all opened out under my direction and supervision. All being cleared out and exposed to view and every care taken for its protection.
> It was an object of great interest to visitors so long as it could be permitted to remain.
> I then removed the tesselated floors. The two most perfect were taken up in sections with the

least possible disturbance for relaying. This was successfully done by the plan adopted in frames and plaster of Paris.

These floors were subsequently removed to the Keynsham Railway station to be relaid there. The larger floor in which was the central figure of Orpheus and animals was relaid and successfully completed. The other floor remained in the sectional frames ready for relaying'.

Marsh also disclosed that:

'I have a full size tracing of the centre portion of the principal floor in which the figures are depicted. This I prepared as a precautionary measure in case of the falling apart of the tessera of that portion which would be difficult to restore with exactness'.

As Marsh indicated, the pavement depicting Orpheus - a famous mythical poet - charming a circle of wild animals, would become one of only nine examples of Orpheus mosaics known in Britain. In 1851, the mosaic was removed from the Keynsham station and donated to Bristol Museum.

Near Bristol, three tunnels situated close together had to be cut through hard rock. In excavating the westernmost tunnel, two very large specimens of nodules - often found in Pennant sandstone - came to light. The resident engineer for this particular contract was G. E. Frere, an able engineer with scientific interests and who would later become an FRS. When these unusually large nodules were found in 1837, it was Frere - encouraged by Brunel - who saved them from destruction. Brunel then arranged for the nodules to be placed on pedestals, one on each side of the eastern portal to the tunnel which was finally finished in 1842. Brunel was encouraged in this particular preservation by a local amateur geologist - W. Sanders - who was very interested in the geological features revealed by the cuttings and tunnels excavated between Bristol and Bath and it was Sanders, as a gesture to encourage their preservation, who paid for the erection of one of the nodules.

One of the nodules was later moved from the entrance to the tunnel and placed on the platforms of St Anne's Park station, Bristol. When the station closed during the 1970s, the nodule was left to be invaded by weeds and spreading undergrowth and the possibility of attack from vandals. Because of this threat, efforts were made to preserve the stone and Sir Alfred Pugsley - President of the University of Bristol - with the cooperation of R. J. Collins, the British Rail Civil Engineer at that time, arranged for the transfer of the nodule to the grounds of the University. In 1983, the nodule was officially presented to the University and today stands in the garden at the front of the Queens' Building.

Bristol Museum, in its collection of fossils, includes several which are scientifically important and which were found during the construction of the Great Western Railway. Some of these exhibits were donated by Joseph Chaning Pearce, a surgeon of Bradford-on-Avon and included in this collection are fossils from the Wiltshire section of the railway excavations found in the Cocklebury Hill cutting at Chippenham. Also in common with several other museums, the Bristol collection includes fossils from pits excavated to provide the material for the embankments for the section of line near Christian Malford east of Chippenham. From further east along the line of railway, the Bristol collection includes some marine reptile bones, collected from the Kimmeridge clay of the Studley Hill cutting, Lydiard Tregoze near Swindon.

J. C. Bourne, in his 'History of the Great Western Railway', tells of other finds made between Goring and Moulsford:

> 'the grey chalk here full of fossils and pyrites forms the embankment which the railway approaches Moulsford Bridge; the subsoil, however, is covered up with a thick deposit of gravel which elephants' and sharks' teeth and various diluvial remains have been discovered'.

However, the *piece de resistance* for Brunel was the discovery of a fairly complete skeleton of an ichthyosaur - a marine reptile from about 200 million years ago. This skeleton was found during the excavating of the Lower Lias rocks of the Saltford cuttings and Brunel - already an honorary member of the Bristol Institution for the Advancement of Science, Literature and the Arts, founded in 1823 - donated the skeleton to the Institution in July 1841. From its inception, the Institution (later the Bristol Museum) had been involved with the scientific discovery and collection of fossil ichthyosaurs and plesiosaurs from the West Country. Consequently, a remarkable collection of 'Sea Dragons' existed in the Bristol collection, until during the Bristol Blitz of 24 November 1940, when the collection was virtually wiped out after the building housing the collection was hit by incendiary bombs and reduced to a burnt-out shell.

The area between Reading and Didcot revealed many antiquities, but unfortunately many of the finds were not preserved, as the labourers themselves used some of these for their own benefit. At an unknown location, some navvies unearthed a Roman urn which contained some 60 coins and it was reported that the men lost no time in sharing out the coins amongst themselves. Brunel was personally very excited about any artefacts that were discovered and he determined to preserve and eventually display as many of the finds as possible.

The area west of Reading to the fringes of the Vale of White Horse was an area with more than a tinge of history. The numerous battles which had taken place over the centuries and the existence of various civilisations would never be completely eradicated by the march of time. The elements themselves on occasions revealed some of these links with the past, as also did ploughing and other agricultural activities. There is much proof remaining of the earlier inhabitants of the Vale of White Horse and the Thames Valley, as for many years, stone implements shaped by men of the Palaeolithic and Neolithic ages, bronze axe heads, swords and spearheads, pottery, weapons and brooches of many ages have been dredged from the Thames and found in the soil. For centuries, the Thames had acted as a natural moat and protected against hostile invasion from the north of the country. Consequently, there are many reminders of the civilisations that either lived or passed through the area.

A report in *Archaeologia*, volume 28 for 1840, refers to the discovery by navvies working on the Great Western Railway at Shooters Hill near Pangbourne of five skeletons. However, a report in *Archaeological Journal* Volume I refers to nearly 100 skeletons. These interesting discoveries had occurred in the late summer of 1838, local journals reporting on 27 October 1838 that:

> *'the labourers have in this work turned up many testimonials that this hill was once the scene of a severe engagement. From six to eight feet in the chalk, they have found human skeletons, cannon balls, pike heads and an ancient spur; and within the last fortnight horseshoes so numerous to fill a two-bushell measure. One of the men struck the pickaxe through a watch the case of which was gold'.*

The report expressed the opinion that the site was a reminder of the period of Charles I, who had advanced and retreated many times from Oxford to Reading and from Reading to Newbury. However, a local archaeologist - Richard Allnatt of Wallingford - disagreed with this theory. On 1 November 1838, he commented in a local journal:

> *'There can be no doubt, from the specimens of warlike weapons which have been disinterred, and from other testimonials, that the summit of this hill was the area of fierce contests, but I am inclined to believe that they are of much higher antiquity than that assigned to them by your correspondent; and that, in fact, the skeletons which have been brought to light by the spade of the excavator, are the remains of Roman Soldiers who fell during the sanguinary conflicts between these invaders and the ancient Britons. The bones, as far they have been discovered, are disposed in nearly a straight line, and are in a state of high preservation, not embedded in the chalk as stated, but immediately overlying it in the loose alluvial superstratum; and in the graves, scattered among the bones, have been found between thirty and forty Roman coins, and several small sepulchral urns of elegant and classical devices. Some of the vases are preserved entire, but others were broken at the time of their removal. The coins are of gold, silver, and brass, of the reigns of Domitian, Constantine, Julian the Apostate, Constantius, Gratiannus Licinius or Lupicinius, the Pro-prietor (who was invested with soveriegn authority) and several others; and I am informed by Samuel Peto, esq., one of the Contractors, that some of the graves contained evident traces of charcoal, but no bones, thus indicating that funereal honors had been paid to the deceased warrior, and that his remains, previous to interment, had been offered as a holocaust on the shrine of the Deity of War.*
>
> *These facts, I conceive are conclusive as to the nature of the organic relics. The high state of preservation in which the bones occur, cannot be urged as an objection to their antiquity, as any one must know who has ever looked into the cabinet of the geologist; and I have before me at the moment of my writing, the remains of antidiluvian quadrupeds dug from the same stratum - viz., the gravel - unchanged in their nature, except indeed that they have undergone a slight modification of their consistuent proportions, owing to the decay of the animal matter, and the subsequent usurption of its place by the carbonate of lime'.*

In early 1839, the *London Medical Gazette* published a report of Allnatt's findings, with engravings depicting the nasal bones, the upper jaw and the ampulla potoria or supposed drinking cup, which Allnatt considered the urns found in the graves to be. In early February 1839, further reports were printed concerning facts which had only now come to light concerning these discoveries, confirming that:

> *'a small copper coin fell from the interior of one of the skulls when raised by the workmen, which was probably the sestertius placed in the mouth of the deceased plebeian, to pay the fare of the infernal ferryman of the River Styx'.*

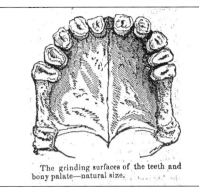

The grinding surfaces of the teeth and bony palate—natural size.

FIGURE 22. The grinding surfaces of the teeth and bony palate from the skull of one of the five Roman soldiers found by navvies excavating the Great Western Railway at Shooters Hill near Pangbourne as reported in the *London Medical Gazette* 1839.

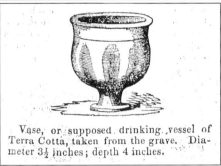

Vase, or supposed drinking vessel of Terra Cotta, taken from the grave. Diameter 3½ inches; depth 4 inches.

FIGURE 23. One of a large quantity of terracotta vases - or drinking vessels - taken from the graves of the Roman soldiers found at Shooters Hill. Also found in and around the graves were spear-heads, spurs and battle-axes of British and Roman manufacture and a large quantity of coins of various Roman emperors.

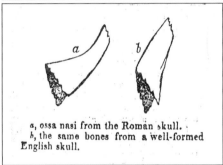

a, ossa nasi from the Roman skull.
b, the same bones from a well-formed English skull.

FIGURE 24. Illustrations by Dr. R. H. Allnatt M.D. of Wallingford following the discovery of the skeletons at Shooters Hill. The doctor concluded that the Romans must have had extreme 'pug noses' compared to the English race.
(The Wellcome Institute for the History of Medicine)

Alnatt also discounted the suggestion of cannon balls being discovered. He claimed that the objects considered to be ammunition, were in fact spheroidal nodules of iron pyrites - a natural geological phenomenon. Similarly, he felt that the remains of the watch pointed to more nefarious activities, referring of course to the activities of highwaymen. He stated:

'tradition has immortalised this spot as the scene of the notorious Turpin'.

Indeed, this could well have been the case. Shooters Hill was as notorious as Finchley Common on the Great North Road and other places such as Watford Gap, Blackheath, Kennington and Putney Commons as places where highwaymen and footpads lay in wait for innocent travellers. Travellers passing to and from Wallingford and Oxford to Reading were likely to have been of a wealthy nature and would have made good pickings for such robbers.

Alnatt also commented at a later date about the fine examples of chalk flints found as the railway was cut near Pangbourne. Flints are very commonly found in deposits of chalk and it is generally considered that flints are formed from sponges, which dissolved and solidified again along lines of weakness in the chalk. To the west of Pangbourne - near Purley - a few flints had been found about 20 feet below the surface, but, it was to the area to the immediate west of Pangbourne, that Allnatt was referring. Here, a profusion of layers of flints were found and Brunel would make good use of these deposits, for it was from this site that the flints used for the Pangbourne and Moulsford stations would be collected. Allnatt reported that:

> *'splendid specimens of silicious deposits, many of them embracing large and perfect branches of white coral indeed of such frequent occurrence is this peculiar structure in the flint, as to encourage the belief that the chalk deposited in this bed of the ancient sea might have been originally derived from the detritus of a coral reef'.*

Further discoveries continued to be reported as the railway works progressed, including the finding of a Roman coin depicting the Roman Emporer Vespasian, found as soil was being removed from the site of one of the piers of the Gatehampton Bridge. This coin was presented to the Philosophical Institute of Reading.

Also revealed, was the foundation of a Roman villa, including two mosaic pavements which were found in a cutting between Pangbourne and Goring. According to the *Reading Mercury* of 8 December 1838, MacDonnell the resident engineer immediately ordered fencing to be erected around the site to ensure it was protected to allow investigations to be made. This was also reported in *The Times* for 10 December 1838, this account also including a description of the square mosaic. Paintings made at the time show two tesselated pavements, which probably formed the floors of a Roman villa consisting of tesserae about one-inch square, buried 12-14 inches below the soil. Also found at the same site were two skeletons and a coin.

At the time, the mosaics were broken up and no further attempt was made to investigate the site, but in 2001 Channel 4 Television's 'Time Team' conducted further investigations at the site after aerial photographs had revealed a series of crop marks in the field alongside the railway. Despite plenty of finds, there was no sign of the main villa and it had to be eventually concluded that the villa had probably been obliterated by the construction of the original line of the Great Western Railway, a situation made worse by the later widening of the line.

CHAPTER TWELVE
THE LINE OF THE RAILWAY BETWEEN READING AND DIDCOT

In August 1838, the half-yearly meeting of shareholders of the Great Western Railway took place at Bristol, when figures of the estimated total construction costs per mile were given. The Reading to Didcot section - a total of 17¼ miles - was estimated at £25,629-5s-6d per mile and this amount was the second lowest figure for the whole line of railway between Bristol and London. Brunel's earlier estimates of the costs of construction for this section were reasonably accurate, with the final construction costs amounting to £7,000 less than the engineer had expected. With the exception of one other section in the London Division, only the Reading to Didcot section cost less to construct than the engineer had originally estimated.

From Reading, the railway would take a north-westerly direction, following the ravine of the Thames westwards along the river's west bank to Goring situated 44½ miles from London (Paddington). The line would not follow the river's course exactly, as Brunel had planned his line to cross the land between the bends of the river, thus shortening the route and eliminating sharp curves, a course previously advocated some years previously by the canal faction when they fruitlessly tried to persuade the Thames Commissioners to improve the navigation on the Thames. The railway would in places run along a narrow gorge worn out by the action of the river, embraced by the water on one side and chalk cliffs on the other. At Goring, Brunel's railway had to pass through the only gap in the spiny backbone of England - the Goring Gap - which for a short distance separates the Chilterns from the Berkshire Downs. From Goring, the railway would cross the Thames twice; by a bridge at Gatehampton [also referred to as Gathampton or Basildon] and two miles further on, by another bridge at Moulsford.

From Goring to the Moulsford Bridge, the railway would pass through several cuttings, cut through the lower chalk, which at this location was hard and pure white. From Goring and Streatley, the eastern edge of the great Vale of White Horse is reached, with the valley opening rapidly and the high ground on the left passing off westward to form the Berkshire Downs. To the right and almost at right angles, the western outcrops of the Chilterns pass in a north-westerly direction until out of sight.

The railway would now enter a completely different geographical aspect, the green and fertile valley of the Thames being left behind at Moulsford, the river continuing alone to Wallingford and beyond. Almost abruptly the scene changes.

FIGURE 25. With the Chiltern Hills in the background, a steam-hauled 14-coach train passes over Brunel's viaduct over the Thames at Moulsford.　　　*(Author's collection)*

To the west, the Berkshire Downs stretches between Streatley and Uffington, with the Downs serving as the southern boundary of the great Vale of White Horse. To the north, the Thames forms a boundary between Berkshire and neighbouring Oxfordshire, while between the two spreads the patchwork of meadow and ploughland which forms the main constituent of the Vale.

Travelling westwards after leaving the Goring Gap - whether by road or rail - one immediately becomes aware of a change of mood. The lush, deep wooded river valley changes to a more harsh environment and the blunt, northerly scarp of the Downs sometimes presents an extremely bleak aspect. One feels immediately more vulnerable on the exposed roads. There is scant shelter, only small clumps of trees and a few scattered farms. On the rounded hills, a sense of isolation prevails. The weather, at times can be extreme, with rain driving in sheets and wind blowing almost unhindered. In contrast, during the summer thermals rise from the great mass of golden grain fields, while in times gone by an almost funereal atmosphere would prevail, huge columns of smoke rising into the air from farmers clearing their fields of stubble. Still clinging to the hills today can be seen the terraces which act as as a reminder of a time long before the coming of the railway, when local people had to be self-sufficient.

The railway, after crossing the Gatehampton Bridge, would continue on the Oxfordshire side of the river through Goring and Streatley, the route from Goring to the Moulsford bridge being almost due north. The northerly direction of this section of line led to speculation that Brunel would not have taken this wild swing to the north by choice and Mr William Morris, proprietor and editor of the *Swindon Advertiser* in his book 'Swindon, Fifty Years Ago (more or less)' published in 1885 stated:

> *'the promoters were driven to change their course on leaving Reading and to take a much more northern route and hence the detour which looks so remarkable on a Great Western Railway map'.*

The detour mentioned in this article, around the northern slopes of the Berkshire Downs, was one of the reasons for the Brunellian main line being dubbed 'The

Great Way Round' by the Company's competitors. However, there is no evidence whatsoever to assume that the detour was caused by the objections of landowners or tenants along the route. It would have been possible to have located this part of the line closer to the foot of the Downs and still maintain the same levels and with virtually the same cuttings and embankments. However, by so doing, the line would have had to cross innumerable roads and tracks, which at the base of the Downs were particularly concentrated. This would have required a vastly increased number of crossings and bridges with the inevitable increased costs. Also, the railway as finally proposed by Brunel, was ideally situated for the construction of the short branch to Oxford and communications with Gloucestershire. However, all the speculation about the north-westerly route, is answered by Brunel himself in an entry from his diary:

'Monday April 22nd 1833. Started at 6 a.m. Examined the ground in the neighbourhood of Wantage - breakfasted at Streatley. Determined on the outer line winding round the undulating ground'.

Leaving behind the last cutting west of Goring, the railway would reach the river crossing via a short embankment, where after crossing the Moulsford Bridge in the Parish of South Stoke, crossed into the Parish of Cholsey. From the west bank of the river, the line would cross a short embankment to the site of the Moulsford station, the station buildings being constructed directly adjacent to the Reading-Oxford turnpike. After leaving the station at Moulsford, the railway passed under the turnpike road, continuing to the north of the village of Cholsey itself via a deep cutting through the grey chalk marl of the East Common Field, which almost like a finger, pointed north-east to Wallingford. From the westward end of the cutting through the East Common Field, the line continued on an embankment formed over a grassy moor which frequently flooded.

From Cholsey village, the railway, now perched on an embankment - ran through a short cutting before passing from the Parish of Cholsey and now intersecting the Parishes of North and South Moreton and the villages of the same name. In so doing, the line between Cholsey and the Moretons would divide the two natural promentaries - to the south, Blewburton Hill (110m) and directly opposite and to the north of the line Cholsey Hill (74m). From the short cutting through the southern extremities of the Cholsey Hill, the line would continue on an extensive embankment to South Moreton, where another extensive cutting through the chalk marl would lead to the final embankment before Didcot.

From Moulsford to Didcot, the setting of the railway undoubtedly presents a more rugged appearance and if one compares this section of the line with that passing through eastern Berkshire, there are immense differences. The traveller using the railway east to west - or vice versa - will obviously be most impressed where the river flows side-by-side with the railway. However, the southern aspect of the railway from Moulsford to Didcot cannot fail to impress for entirely different reasons. With a backcloth of chalky, rounded hills, one can with a little imagination picture some of the past events which have taken place in these parts.

PART IV
CONSTRUCTION

'I don't know how the weather has been with you. We have had two tolerable days but otherwise it is dreadful - out of doors work - cuttings and culverts are all at a stand - all flooded. Unless very fine weather comes soon I don't know what's to become of us' [to Saunders].

November 1839

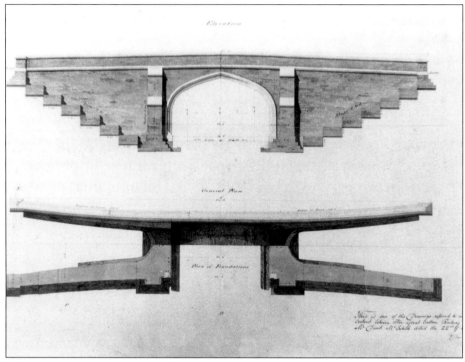

FIGURE 26. Elevation and plan of typical over-bridge in the Bristol Division. This Gothic style was used by Brunel for all the bridges between Bath and Bristol, this particular bridge being part of the contract taken by David McIntosh.

(Reproduced by kind permission of the Librarian of the University of Bristol)

CHAPTER THIRTEEN
THE SCENE BEFORE THE ARRIVAL OF THE NAVVIES

The Great Western Bill had finally received the Royal Assent. The die was cast and the railway would be constructed in its entirety. The last vestiges of opposition evaporated, as any remaining hostile landowners or tenants could now be eradicated by invoking the compulsory powers contained in the Act. Clause VIII empowered the Company, its agents or workmen to enter a property and engage in any business involved in the construction of the railway. Clause IX allowed for a fine of between £1-£5 for any person found obstructing any person employed by the railway company. The same applied to any person who pulled-up or removed any stakes driven into the ground for the purpose of setting out the line of railway. What then lay in store for the districts directly affected by the construction? Were the inhabitants prepared for the invasion by the labourers? Had the local people ever experienced anything previously which resembled the impending upheaval?

As previously described, the area was adequately served by road and water communication. Being situated almost in the centre of a rectangular area served by water-borne traffic - the Kennet & Avon Canal and the River Kennet navigation to the south and east, the Thames to the north and the Wilts & Berks Canal to the west - assured the area received the benefits of the Industrial Revolution which had taken place in other parts of the country. However, in those days of limited travel very few of the local inhabitants had ever had the opportunity of witnessing the construction of earlier canal or railway schemes. Although various improvements had taken place on the Thames navigation in fairly recent times, none of these works would match the immensity of the impending railway construction through the area. Turnpike roads had been similarly improved of late, but again these would not compare with the now imminent construction of the railway. How then, would the inhabitants of the area cope with the arrival of the railway contractor?

Immediately after the safe passage of the second Bill through Parliament, work began simultaneously at both ends of the line. This was possible because of the earlier instructions to Brunel in October 1833 to concentrate his surveys on the sections between Bristol and Bath and London and Reading. Brunel frequently referred to the section of line between Reading and Bath as the 'intermediate' section and in a report to the Directors dated 14 September 1835, Brunel stated:

'The arrangements which I have here recommended for proceeding with the two extremities of the line need not in anyway interfere with the progress of the intermediate portion of the works upon which happen to be quite independent of any parts east of Reading or west of Bath, except that the stone which will be quarried in making the shafts for the Box Tunnel may I have reason to expect be advantageously employed in constructing the bridges and other works at Bath as

well as upon the intermediate line'.

Brunel recommended to the Directors, that the 'intermediate' section consisted of:

'a number of comparatively small excavations and embankments'

and that:

'that no time should be lost in commencing'.

On 26 May 1836, Brunel reported that 13 miles of the line was under construction - eight miles at the London end and five miles at Bristol. There were 1,100 men at work, with 600 at London and 500 at Bristol. This was the scene as work commenced on the two extremities of the line.

For a time, the local populace of the areas along the intermediate section of the line between Reading and Bath had a breathing space before the frenetic activities of the men building the railway overwhelmed them. Fast and furious, the positive and negative effects of the railway's construction in other areas were becoming apparent. All too soon, local officials became aware that their particular responsibilities would be put severely to the test, the approaching maelstrom drawing ever nearer. Similarly, local tradesmen began to realise the unique opportunities which would be open to them as the construction of the railway became more and more imminent.

Local clerics of many denominations were becoming very aware of the irreligious activities of the railway labourers in other locations along the line and many must have wondered about their own role in the future scene? For a time at least, the Bristol Committee appears to have adopted a more sympathetic approach to both the physical and spiritual well-being of the men and boys indirectly employed by them. On 14 June 1839, the Secretary of the Bristol Committee was instructed to communicate with F. Landon Esq. of the Pastoral Aid Society of London, to request their assistance in seeking the services of a clergyman and for whose services the Company was prepared to donate £80 per annum, towards:

'providing the advantages of religious care for the workmen between Bristol and Bath'.

There were no such considerations from the London Committee. In the London Division it was left to sympathetic local clergy, such as the Rev. H. W. Lloyd, Vicar of Cholsey to administer to the spiritual needs of the railway labourers. The Rev. Lloyd, because of where he lived and because of his various responsibilities, could not avoid becoming aware of the privations of the railway labourers. The railway would be constructed through his parish and very close to the village of Cholsey. As part of the Rev. Lloyd's duties, he had to conduct Sunday Morning Prayers at Cholsey Church at 10.30am and then travel the short distance to the Moulsford Church to take a service at 1.30pm, returning to Cholsey to take Evening Prayers at 3.30pm. The vicar had to cross the railway excavations twice during his travels each Sunday and he gradually became well-known to many of the men and boys working on the railway.

FIGURE 27. Excavating a cutting.
(Reproduced from 'Our Iron Roads', F. S. Williams 1852)

Prior to the construction of the Great Western Railway, local clergy had the responsibility of ensuring that the general morals and behaviour of local people conformed to the norms of the period. Any serious infringement of the normal rules of behaviour were dealt with - in theory - by a Sheriff's Officer and watchmen, although in many cases, serious breaches of the peace were dealt with by the short-term swearing-in of local constables who were tasked with bringing felons before the local magistrate. In the 19th-century, few problems occurred during the day in towns, except possibly brawls between drunks and vagrants. However, during the night a different order reigned and felonies of all descriptions occurred in the unlit streets, while in the country, marauding highwaymen could be occasionally be found lurking.

Watchmen were officially tasked to describe the weather, call the hours and apprehend any felons. In practice, this latter part of their duties rarely took place, as watchmen could be frequently found drunk and many would hide themselves away as far as possible from any trouble. Originally, the watchmen used to patrol towns and watch for fires during the night, the combustible buildings and narrow streets being at great risk and fire-fighting capabilities poor to say the least. Thus, the watchmens' cries were essential if citizens were to avoid burning to death in any conflagration and if a fire was to extinguished before the whole town caught alight.

Following the Municipal Corporations Act of 1835, Watch Committees had to be appointed in each borough and a professional police force appointed and maintained. The first meeting of the new Watch Committee took place at Wallingford on 1 January 1836, when it was decided to appoint:

> *'3 persons as constables for preserving the peace within the said Borough by day and night - that one of such men shall also be considered, in addition to his ordinary office of constable, as Superintendent'.*

Each constable was consequently provided with:

> *'lanthorn, belt, rattle, and staff of office'.*

Thus, during the period of the construction of the railway, there were only three policemen in the vicinity and responsible for the safety of the Borough of Wallingford. It must also be emphasised that the Wallingford officers responsibilities were strictly confined to the borough itself. All the outlying parishes where the railway was being constructed still had no police officers to enforce the peace and these areas for some time yet would have to rely on the appointment of special constables for serious infringements of the peace.

The railway labourers when they arrived at a particular location, in the main proved to be prolific drinkers of beer and indeed would be encouraged to do so. On some railway construction sites, railway labourers would be forced to accept - instead of regular wages - tickets which could be exchanged for food or goods at the contractor's own shop which would handily be situated close to the construction site. This system was known as the 'Truck' system, to which the law offered no protection. Despite various Acts of Parliament making the system illegal in factories, the legislation did not apply to railway works. Brunel stated that he abhorred the arrangement and the engineer tried to ensure that the Truck principle did not operate during the construction of the Great Western Railway.

Brunel, when called to give evidence before the Select Committee on Railway Labourers in 1846, explained how he had tried to prevent the system operating. He stated, that before a contract was signed, he had included a clause 'expressly against the truck system'. This clause stated:

> *'The contractor shall truly and strenuously endeavour, to the utmost of his power, to prevent the introduction of the truck system upon the works, and to this effect he shall not, by himself or his agents, directly or indirectly, allow of the sale of provisions or any other articles to the workmen, either by parties exclusively privileged or in payment of wages or for any other consideration than money, and shall not in like manner allow of any control or inducement being exercised over the men with reference to their choice of market or of prices or of the mode of payment. And, moreover, with the same view, the contractor and his agents shall cause all men employed, directly or indirectly, under him to be paid at least once a fortnight, and in cash, and on no account shall the whole or any portion of wages be paid or any advance made to men by tickets or orders upon victuallers or in any way whatever except in cash'.*

However, there is evidence to indicate that Brunel - despite his best intentions - did not totally achieve his aims in this respect. At Pangbourne, a labourer unsuccessfully sued a ganger, claiming that he had been paid by ticket instead of wages. The case was dismissed by the local magistrate as the various Truck Acts did not apply to railway works. Additionally, a close examination of the Contract '4R' document, still extant today, confirms that the clause banning Truck payments which Brunel mentions, is not included.

The Great Western Railway Directors also took the responsibility of ensuring that the labourers were fortified after their days work, selected innkeepers being chosen to supply beer at the Company's expense direct to the construction site. Documents known as the 'Navvy's Refresher' or a 'draft at sight' were used for this purpose and when presented to a beer retailer, he would ensure that free beer was supplied to the men. The document was in two halves, one half being retained by the Company official at the time of issue, the other half by the retailer. Nevertheless, even if the supply of beer from this source dried up, there were ample supplies in the area. Wallingford at this period boasted two breweries and the town had 17 inns, taverns and public houses in addition to 16 beer retailers. These latter establishments, were licensed and sometimes beer was also brewed on the premises. At Cholsey, there were three inns and seven beer retailers and at Moulsford there was at least one public house.

Food and other materials would have been relatively easy to come by in the area and, for instance at Cholsey there were three bakers and shopkeepers, two butchers and two boot and shoemakers. At Moulsford, supplies would have been more difficult, but the ample facilities at Wallingford would be available, including 10

FIGURE 28. Contract '1R'. Original plans and elevations of the Gatehampton viaduct. Clearly shown are the Bath stone voussoirs which Brunel originally intended to use, however, the 14 large stones - either side of a keystone - were never used, brick being substituted for the decorative Oolitic stone. *(OPC/BR)*

bakers, nine butchers, a fishmonger, nine grocers and a profusion of other trades and professions - including a truss maker!

This then was the scene at the time of the arrival of the men who would construct the Great Western Railway through the area. There were more than adequate facilities available locally which should have ensured that the excesses of deprivation witnessed in other areas where railway construction was taking place could be avoided. There was probably enough accommodation available to house the main force of workers, as many ordinary people were only too willing to open up their own homes temporarily to take advantage of this unique opportunity. A young and energetic vicar had recently been appointed, who should have been able to take care of the spiritual and other needs of these, albeit, temporary members of his flock - if he was given the opportunity. An embryonic police force was standing guard and could be reinforced quickly should the need arise.

CHAPTER FOURTEEN
THE NAVVIES

The navvies moved into the Parish of Cholsey in the Spring of 1838 and their numbers would be soon swollen by the arrival of artisans whose skills would be required for the formation of the bridge over the Thames at Moulsford and for the construction of the Moulsford station. The local people, by now, had become used to the procession of men of various professions following the well-worn track which marked the line of the Great Western Railway through the Parish, the path of which had been recently emphasised by the siting of flag-staves. These staves were used by the surveyors to mark the prominentaries along the route and wooden fencing indicated the boundaries of the land taken over by the railway company.

There are no records to confirm the exact number of labourers who temporarily moved into the Parish of Cholsey at this time, but the Rev. Lloyd the Vicar of Cholsey recorded:

'a large company of these workmen were located in my parish for nearly two years'.

Some of the labourers were to remain in the parish after the line had been completed and the description 'navigator' appears several times in the 1841 Census. For others their stay would be longer, remaining to this day buried in Cholsey churchyard.

Contradictory to speculation, there appeared to have been no serious breaches of the peace or any 'riots and randies' for which the navvies would be remembered in other areas. There are no records of any special constables being sworn in to quell riots, nor of any incidents of poaching or the like in the area. The only incident where it was hinted that the railway labourers may have been involved was an incident at a village - to the west of Cholsey - during Christmas 1838. A paper mill at South Moreton was partly destroyed by fire despite the attendance of the local fire brigades. The incident was not considered to be accidental and two persons were eventually apprehended, although it was not confirmed if they were attached to the railway fraternity.

J. T. Bedborough was the main contractor for Contract '4R', which stretched from the west bank of the Thames at Moulsford to Didcot. Bedborough was a man of considerable talent and his entrepeneural nature had earned him many enemies in Berkshire. His ability to make large sums of money, even before the arrival of the railway contracts, ensured that much criticism was directed his way by, perhaps, less enterprising people or people of a jealous disposition. Bedborough mixed in high places and coming from Windsor had been involved in the reconstruction of the town which had been instigated by King William IV. Despite an ability to make enemies, Bedborough appears to have been a man of high principles and there are no reports of the labourers who worked for him being abused in any way.

FIGURE 29. An embankment in the process of being formed. Note the dual tip-head, the temporary rails and the youthful age of some of the navvies.
(Leicestershire Museums, Arts and Records Service)

Only one complaint about the labourers on Contract '4R' working on Sunday was made by the Rev. Lloyd, the Vicar of Cholsey. This complaint, concerning a sub-contractor - not Bedborough - was made in the Autumn of 1840 and involved the labourers working on a farmers' occupation bridge which would provide access to land severed by the railway. Saunders responded to the complaint on 3 September 1840, stating that the Directors expressed their regret that any work should have been permitted on the Sabbath and that the resident engineer had been ordered to prevent any reoccurrence.

It appears that Bedborough had adhered strictly to the Directors' wishes following earlier complaints from clergymen in Berkshire about Sunday working. The Directors on 6 April 1939 had written to all the main contractors in the London Division stating:

> *'The Directors have recently received a memorial from the resident Clergy of several parishes in the Counties of Berks. and Oxford, through or near to which the railway passes, requesting them to use their best endeavours to prevent the desecration of the Sabbath, by the employment of men on the Companies' works on Sunday I am desired to intimate to you the very urgent wish of the board that you should cooperate in that object (as far as is possible to do so) on the contract you have taken, excepting only in cases of emergency or of indispensable necessity & even then I am to express a hope that you will limit the occupation of men to those hours which are not usually set apart of divine service.*
>
> *The Directors feel assured that you & the other contractors will cheerfully aid this very important regulation, the observance of which is the common duty of all concerned in the works*

FIGURE 30. A navvie gang - levelling soil on the top of a high embankment - take a break from their labours for the photographer.

(Leicestershire Museums, Arts and Records Service)

of the Company to promote'.

However, this was but one of several complaints made about Sunday working. In the autumn of 1839, the Venerable Arch Deacon Clarke of Milton Rectory, Abingdon had complained about the contractor Jackson allowing his men to work on the Sabbath on Contract '1S'. The contractor denied that this was an infringement of the Directors' previous instructions, as he stated that it was essential work only which had taken place in the early hours of the Sunday morning. Saunders replied to the Arch Deacon on 11 October 1839 explaining the contractor's reasons for the desecration. Saunders also praised the minister for his efforts in trying to curtail such activities and also for promoting religious teaching for the railway labourers in the Arch Deacon's parish.

Early 1840 found complaints still being received about Sunday working. The Rev. W. Simeon Bucknell of the Grove Parsonage, Wantage had occasion to complain and Cogswell the contractor for Contract '2S' was instructed by the Directors to submit a report to them. He reported that the burning of ballast required a continuous supply of clay and fuel to keep the fire in. If this operation was suspended - even for a few hours - the whole operation would have been rendered useless. Saunders replied to the minister on 27 March 1840, stating:

'I trust you find some benefit derived from your communication and if all the good which both you and your neighbouring clerical friends as well as the Directors would wish to promote cannot be accomplished at this moment, I think I can promise that at no very remote period when the works shall be complete and the line revert to the Company's control, there will no

occasion for future reproach on the ground of desecration of the Sabbath'.

It would appear that Bedborough himself was a god-fearing person and the added influence of the Rev. Lloyd appears to have ensured that the Sabbath was not desecrated to any extent by the labourers working on the railway in the Cholsey area. The lack of any reported serious incidents, however, may point to the fact that the labourers who moved into Cholsey lived in a reasonable fashion and this appears to be confirmed by the Rev. Lloyd, who although he was concerned about the mens' spiritual welfare states:

> *'they appeared to be living without God in the world; and yet I ought to bear my testimony to their general civility and good behaviour to my own parishioners, as also to myself'.*

Despite this testimony, the Rev. Lloyd also confirms that there was almost a total resistance on the part of the labourers to reconsider their spiritually-damning way of life, at least initially. However, the Rev. Lloyd eventually left his mark on the men and his influence on the labourers must have been considerable. That the labourers - in the main - did not attend Sunday worship was immaterial as the minister, in his own way and with considerable fortitude, eventually won the hearts of many of the men.

FIGURE 31. A memorial in a Reading churchyard to Henry West - a workman aged 24 - who lost his life during the construction of Brunel's station at Reading on 24 March 1840.
(Author's collection)

CHAPTER FIFTEEN
THE DEATH OF 'HAPPY JACK'

The Parish records of Cholsey confirm that John Starlen [Starling] - aged thirty-six: - 'a native of Norfolk, but was a workman on the railroad', was buried in the churchyard at Cholsey on Sunday 3 March 1839. This brief entry in the Rev. Lloyd's handwriting, masks a most disturbing and emotional experience for both the minister - who was well used to death - and the labourers, who similarly were no strangers to the shadow of the grim reaper. However, the death of John Starling would establish the Rev. Lloyd's reputation with the members of his temporary flock and, hopefully leave a permanent impression on them regarding their future spiritual well-being.

The minister's relationship with John Starling was particularly close and during the months the two men knew each other, a close spiritual bond was to develop. Following the death of the labourer, the minister instigated the publication of a text which he hoped would persuade other workmen in similar situations to change their spiritual outlook and which would help to divert them from their wayward way of life.

The Rev. Lloyd immediately after the death of Starling, considered how he could more effectively influence the men working on the railway works. The minister was concerned that few of the men had any feelings about religion and little regard to outward morality. The Rev. Lloyd, however, gave the men credit for their civility and good behaviour during their stay in the parish and he also comments about the mens' general civility to himself. The minister believed that the men were:

'not ignorant of scripture, nor wholly insensible to their awfully dangerous condition'.

The minister did not forget the mens' employers and both the Great Western Railway Company and the contractors received their share of criticism, the Rev. Lloyd feeling that they should affect more influence over the men they employed, particularly with regard to their spiritual welfare.

The minister made determined efforts to provide spiritual guidance for the railway labourers. He was in the habit of visiting them in their lodgings in the village with the purpose of leaving religious texts. It was in such a lodging house that the minister met John Starling, who was originally a native of Weeting, near Brandon in Norfolk. The Rev. Lloyd was not able to clarify when Starling had moved away from his home, but he learned that following the death of the navvie's wife, the man had suffered depression and finally decided to leave his family and friends.

Starling had eventually obtained a new identity - a common occurrence among the railway labourers - with the men either earning or being given a nickname by their workmates. Some of the labourers kept these names throughout their working lives, while others changed them every time they moved to a new contract.

Sometimes, the nicknames were a deliberate attempt by the men to forget their links with the past. In other cases, the new name - given or taken - implied exactly the opposite. In the case of Starling, the name taken was 'Happy Jack' and the Rev. Lloyd suggests that this name implied that Starling appeared a very unhappy person to his workmates and to all who came in contact with him.

FIGURE 32. The Rev. Henry William Lloyd, Vicar of Cholsey cum Moulsford 1837-1873. *(Wallingford Museum)*

During their first meeting, the minister noted Starling's physical appearance and was convinced that the labourer had consumption [tuberculosis] and that his condition was serious. The Rev. Lloyd questioned the man, who confirmed that he had just returned from the doctor as he had been unwell with a cough for some time. The minister, satisfied that Starling's physical wants were being attended to, began to question the labourer about the condition of his soul. Starling then became very angry, replying that he did not consider that he had many sins to answer for. He stated that he had no debts, held no grudges against any person and he did not consider himself any worse than anybody else. Lloyd, however, continued to preach at the man, whereupon Starling hastily picked up his hat and fled from the lodging house.

Shortly after this confrontation, Starling was admitted to the Oxford Infirmary, returning to Cholsey some five weeks later. The labourer immediately returned to work on the construction of the railway, but was forced to give up completely and finally after only three days. During his stay at the Infirmary in Oxford, Starling had struck up a good relationship with another minister who appears to have made quite an impression. When the Rev. Lloyd heard of Starling's worsening condition, the minister determined to attempt to talk to the man again. Before he could do so, however, he was pleased and surprised to receive a request from Starling for the minister to visit him at his lodgings.

The minister found Starling in bed and noted that the man's physical condition had deteriorated further. However, this time he found Starling more disposed to conversation. The terminally-ill labourer had given up all hope of physical recovery and he appeared to have accepted the fact that he would soon die. He also felt that because he had sinned so much during his earthly life, he had no hope of spiritual salvation. The minister endeavoured to show him the nature of true repentance, visiting him regularly at the lodgings for about five months. The sick navvie usually sat on a wooden, high-backed chair with his dog at his feet in front of a blazing fire, the minister sat opposite him. On other occasions, the minister sat on a wooden chest by the side of Happy Jack's bed. Gradually, during his visits, the minister learned about the man's past life, Starling telling the minister:

> *'I have often taken on the Saturday night two pounds, week after week, and on the Monday morning had not sixpence left, and in the course of the week have pawned some of my clothes for more liquour. The man with whom I lodged proposed at last I should give him a certain sum every week to provide me with some victuals, which I agreed to do, but the rest was spent in drink, till finding I had scarcely any clothes to wear I resolved to save up a little to buy some'.*

The minister heard that the only occasions the navvie had attended church was when the railway labourers had carried the corpse of one of their colleagues to be buried and on these occasions most of the men were drunk. Starling related how he continued drinking, despite a warning from a doctor that drink would eventually kill him if he did not discontinue his excesses. He told the minister about his family, as he felt he had not been a dutiful son and that he had asked a neighbour to write to his parents informing them of his illness. Eventually, his mother had replied.

The condition of Happy Jack continued to deteriorate and at this time he prayed heartily and constantly, being frequently heard during the night asking God to have mercy upon him. He developed a hatred of sin in others, admonishing a companion who shared a room with him for profanity. In the end, these outbursts became so frequent, that his companion had to leave the lodging house. For the last few days of Happy Jack's life, he was entirely confined to his bed.

On Monday 26 February 1839, the Rev. Lloyd visited him in the morning. Finding Starling unable to talk much, the minister stayed with the sick man for some time, praying for him. However, the minister did not feel that the man's condition had deteriorated significantly.

The following morning - 27 February 1839 - the minister learned that the navvie had died at 5 a.m. that morning. Apparently, he was sensible to the last and had continued to pray all night. The Rev. Lloyd, although he had been expecting this sad news, asked himself whether his efforts had been enough to prevent Happy Jack's soul being lost? The dead labourer's companions - as was customary - made all the arrangements for the funeral and it was decided that Sunday 3 March 1839 would be the day of the interment. Great excitement was evident in the neighbourhood when it became known that a navvie's funeral was to take place. It was the labourers' custom not only to maintain their own sick, but to bury their own dead. To show their respect for their departed companion, all the labourers would attend the funeral, wearing white smock frocks and with bows of white ribbon on their hats.

The day of the funeral dawned, a beautiful early Spring day with the sun shining, unchilled by any easterly wind. A large body of the railway labourers had gathered together and the Rev. Lloyd wondered if this would be the only opportunity he would ever have to address so large a number of this class of men? The streets of Cholsey were filled, people from Wallingford and neighbouring villages crowding in for the funeral and the cottage where Happy Jack had lodged - and died - surrounded by a large crowd of his fellow labourers. However, the minister noted that the assembly did not appear to be treating the impending funeral in as solemn a manner as he might have wished for.

When the vicar arrived at the church, he found a great crowd of people all seemingly eagerly awaiting the arrival of the corpse. Eventually, the procession left the cottage, the cortege slowly wending its way from the village green to the churchyard. The procession included approximately 100 railway labourers and also a considerable number of villagers and onlookers. As the funeral party entered the churchyard, the crowd formed an avenue on both sides of the path leading to the entrance to the church. As many as possible crammed inside the church, until it was filled to every corner, but despite this, some hundreds were forced to remain in the churchyard, unable to gain admittance.

To the amazement of the congregation, the Rev. Lloyd took the unprecedented step of making an impassioned plea from the pulpit. The minister was clearly taking advantage of the unique opportunity which had ensured that many of the railway labourers had entered his church for almost certainly the first time. The minister commenced his sermon by saying:

> *'My Brethren, I am unwilling to allow the solemn scene which is now before us, to pass away without making a most urgent and affectionate appeal to each and all of you.*
>
> *Some one might perhaps be inclined to ask, Why do you now deviate from the usual practice upon such occasions or think it peculiarly needful to offer any remarks upon the demise of our brother, whose remains now lie before us? I will at once tell you my reason for so doing. It is not because I have any particular or interesting anecdote to relate, respecting the last days of the departed or because there is any uncommon circumstances connected with his death; far from it. It is a case, I fear, of common, of daily occurrence in the annals of mortality.*
>
> *My principal reason for addressing you is simply this. Our departed fellow-creature was one of that large company of persons, for some months past, have been occupied in this parish in an extensive work, and who thus, for a limited period, composed a portion of my flock; but who have scarcely ever given me an opportunity of addressing to them publicly the gospel words of invitation and advice; and who have seldom if ever, attended this or any other place of worship on the Lord's-day. Knowing therefore, brethren, that it was your custom to follow to the grave the remains of one, who was your fellow-labourer and companion, I felt unwilling to let this opportunity pass, without, at least, endeavouring to call your attention to the all-important concerns of eternity, and to offer to you some friendly and pastoral advice ...'.*

The minister then preached a lengthy sermon specifically aimed at the navvies' wayward ways. This dissertation was received very attentively according to the Rev. Lloyd, who states:

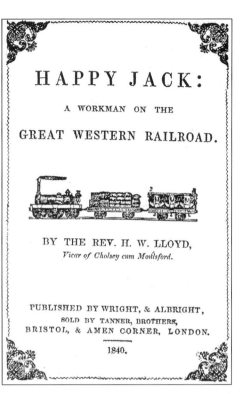

HAPPY JACK:

A WORKMAN ON THE

GREAT WESTERN RAILROAD.

BY THE REV. H. W. LLOYD,
Vicar of Cholsey cum Moulsford.

PUBLISHED BY WRIGHT, & ALBRIGHT,
SOLD BY TANNER, BROTHERS,
BRISTOL, & AMEN CORNER, LONDON.

1840.

FIGURE 33. The front cover of the small text written by the Rev. H. W. Lloyd, Vicar of Cholsey cum Moulsford in 1840 and intended for distribution among the navvies working on the construction of the Great Western Railway through the Parish of Cholsey. *(OPC/BR)*

'I never officiated at a burial or preached to a congregation, composed in part of railroad men, where more attention appeared to be paid, although poor Starling had not one relative to attend his remains to the grave. I observed not a few amongst his companions who showed themselves interested in the account I gave of his long illness and appeared touched with remorse at their own mode of life'.

The minister in his very long sermon, mentioned specific transgressions and particularly 'Disregard of the Sabbath' and 'Drunkenness'. The labourers were not the only ones to be mentioned in the Rev. Lloyd's sermon, the contractors and the Great Western Railway Directors not escaping his wrath:

'the evil example which is set you by many of your employers, who have been better educated, and move in a higher station than yourselves; the utter neglect which has been shown to your spiritual welfare by those connected with this work, particularly claim the pity, the prayers, the exertions of every true Christian'.

Before Happy Jack's remains were finally committed to the ground he knew so well, the Rev. Lloyd recalled the sick labourer's words to him:

'The first time, sir, I saw you, I hated to hear you speak; but now I would sooner hear you than any one else in the world'.

Starling was finally buried, the crowds continuing to weep by the side of his grave.

The Rev. Lloyd later wrote directly to the railway labourers and in the introduction to his printed text, he stated:

'My Brethren, In presenting to you, in this printed form, the exhortation I made from the pulpit at the interment of your late companion, John Starling, I do so, with the earnest hope, that you will receive them as the offering of one, who has your spiritual welfare at heart.

It is true I have spoken openly and plainly, but I have not told you of your disease without pointing you to the remedy; and he only, remember, is your real friend, who warns you of those dangers with which you are surrounded, and cautions you of that misery which hereafter awaits you; and however much you may dislike me for my plain and open language, I will venture to say, that midst all your companions, your friends or your relatives you have not one who more earnestly wishes to promote or who more constantly prays, for your spiritual welfare and happiness, than your faithfull friend and pastor.

Cholsey Vicarage, March 17, 1839 H. W. LLOYD'.

The Rev. Lloyd also officiated at the interment of another navvie, a William Hulse, aged 35, 'A native of Gloucester a workman on the railroad'. However, at this burial there appears to have been none of the emotional and charged scenes seen when Happy Jack was buried.

FIGURE 34. Cholsey church from the north-east as it probably appeared during the construction of the Great Western Railway.   *(Wallingford Museum)*

CHAPTER SIXTEEN
THE EFFECTS ON THE DISTRICT

The Rev. Lloyd's comments to the railway labourers at Happy Jack's funeral summed up the minister's concern about drunkenness. The minister told the men that he considered the disregard of the Sabbath as generally the first step taken on a downward path. He felt that any man who despised this hallowed day had no hope left, as the individual concerned had no true concern for his own soul. The minister had advised the men that when he proposed the observance of the Sabbath Day, he did not merely mean that the men had to attend church, but that they had to totally cease work for the day. He meant a total cessation of all worldly pleasures and company and the dedication of the day to the service of God. In the minister's opinion, drunkenness was the next most serious crime:

'There is not one sin in the catalogue of human vices, which more effectually or more speedily ruins a soul than this'.

The response of the Rev. Lloyd to the spiritual needs of the railway labourers in his parish was impressive, however, there is no evidence to indicate that significant efforts were made to influence the labourers from any other source. In other parts of the country, clergymen and missionaries - with the encouragement of the railway companies - were working directly amongst the navvies. A general complaint appeared to be that the men were ignorant regarding the use of money. Many did not know what to do with their earnings - apart from visiting the beer shop - and one minister experienced no difficulty in selling to the navvies on another railway scheme, 350 bibles (costing 6d to 1s 6d each according to size), 200 prayer books and 200 hymn books.

It appears fairly certain that the railway labourers working on Great Western Railway Contract '4R' were not allowed to work on the Sabbath. This forced break from their exertions ensured that the men had the opportunity to spend the excess of their wages, many - after their lodging and sick club money - had been paid, having a surplus of money available. In some more isolated areas where the railway had been constructed, there was nothing else to do, but spend money on drink and this frequently led to the riots for which the railway workmen would earn an immortal reputation. For instance, the *Reading Mercury* reported that on 17 August 1839:

'the village of Hanney, near which the works of the GWR are in progress, was on Sunday, the scene of considerable disturbance and riot. It would appear that the navigators as the men are called had been very abusive to the villagers, who feeling greatly annoyed, mustered a strong party and after some hard fighting, succeeded in ejecting them from the village. It was expected that the same would occur the following night but other than one or two skirmishes, nothing further occurred'.

It was the normal practice of the period for all public houses and retail beer houses to be closed for the sale of beer (travellers could still be received) during the hours of the afternoon service at the local church. At Cholsey, the Rev. Lloyd held evening prayers at 3.30 p.m. at St. Mary's Church and consequently, the local hostelries were compelled to close between the hours of 3-5 p.m. However, following on from two incidents, a landlord and a publican were both served with summonses following an infringement of the licensing regulations. The evidence of 'James Greenwood, Constable of Cholsey' - a local farmer and only sworn in as a special constable for a limited period - brought Joseph Willmot, the licensee of a public house (the Brentwood Tailor) and James Franklin - 'a seller of Beer, Ale and Porter, by Retail' - before magistrate Francis Walcot J.P. at the Town Hall, Wallingford on Friday 16 November 1838. In evidence against Joseph Willmot it was stated that:

> *'Under provisions and Authority of an Act to Regulate the Granting of a Licence to Keepers of Inns, Alehouses and Victualling Houses, did keep your said House so licensed as aforesaid, other than and besides the reception of travellers during the usual hours of the afternoon Divine Service in the Church of the said Parish of Cholsey on Sunday November 4 1838'.*

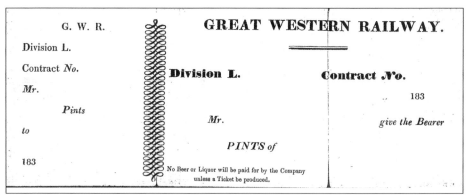

FIGURE 35. Beer docket issued to men engaged upon the construction of the Great Western Railway. The document - known as the 'Navvies Refresher', was the medium by which selected beer sellers along the line of railway were authorised to 'draw' upon the Company's credit.   *(OPC/BR)*

At Wallingford, the embryonic police force appeared to maintain the peace without any serious breaches, until on 10 March 1838 the Superintendent resigned, simultaneously and coincidentally perhaps, with the arrival of the railway workmen in the area. A new Superintendent was appointed on 19 April 1838, an appointment which it was hoped would stiffen the two constables under his supervision. Unfortunately, following a serious incident in the High Street, Wallingford on Saturday 23 March 1838, the Watch Committee concluded that both constables were highly culpable after the two men had been accused of neglect of duty. Because of lack of evidence, no further action was taken against the two regarding this incident, nor with regards to a second incident which occurred on 10 June 1839 (one of these constables was later to retire from the police force on the grounds of ill health). The new Superintendent himself was not to escape unblemished and after serving a warrant on Saturday 17 August 1838 - in front of the Mayor - he was dismissed from his post after being accused of 'great cowardness and neglect of duty'. The evidence points to the fact that during the period when the railway labourers were in the area, the local police force had to face - on occasions - some considerable hostility. The fact that the constables and their superiors were often accused of 'neglect of duty' is perhaps, not surprising when one considers the anxiety experienced by the policemen in trying to execute their duty.

FIGURE 36. A typical scene before the arrival of the Great Western Railway changed the scene forever - Reading Corn Exchange c.1823.   *(Author's collection)*

Although there are reports of disruption caused to local communities by the railway labourers during the period of the construction of the Great Western Railway, there is also evidence that in the main, the arrival of the navvies was a positive experience for some local communities and individuals. Although the earnings of the labourers was not significant individually, collectively the money the men spent in the location was considerable. In addition, the more-or-less total ban on the 'truck' system imposed by Brunel ensured that the money earned by the men would be spent as each individual wished, each free to buy commodities and services from who he liked and not confined to the contractors' own facilities.

With regard to accommodation available for the workmen, this varied from location to location. At Pangbourne for instance, purpose-built 'cottages' were built by the contractor, while in the Cholsey to Didcot area it appears that most of the labourers found accommodation in the houses of the local population.

However, despite the fact that there were no serious shortfalls in accommodation, it could not be assumed that all the workmen wished to avail themselves of such comforts! Brunel himself, when questioned by the Select Committee on Railway Labourers in 1846, confirmed:

'I remember perfectly well, when the large works were carried out at Hanwell [Contract '1L'], Messrs. Grissell & Peto were the contractors for the viaduct: Mr. Macintosh [sic], one of the largest contractors for the contractor for the earthwork close to it; they were not able to obtain lodgings thereabout. There were some 700 or 800 men employed. And yet there were large numbers sleeping under the hedges at night, while a considerable number walked from London to the work. How could you provide for a case of that kind? There was lodging in the neighbourhood, but owing to the fine weather and a desire to save money, a large number of labourers used to sleep under the hedges'.

Another former Great Western navvie told the same Select Committee about the 'vans' used for accommodation during the construction of the line. These 'vans' consisted of accommodation for a man and his wife (who did the cooking) and - separated by a partition - sleeping space for four labourers. When the Committee questioned the navvie about these vans, he confirmed there were cooking facilities and fireplaces and that they were:

'Very, very hot in the summer; forced to cook the victuals outdoors'.

Although there are few reports to indicate that the railway labourers constructing the railway through Berkshire slept rough, this would have almost certainly been the case with some individuals - particularly during warmer weather.

The Minutes of the Wallingford Union for the period, confirm that during the time of the construction of the Great Western Railway, no Poor Relief was given to the railway workmen, nor were any of the men admitted to the Union workhouse. This supported Brunel's experiences and when giving evidence before the 1846 Select Committee, he was asked:

'Do you not conceive that parishes may sometimes suffer from having thrown upon them the temporary support of a large number of men, who, having been defrauded of their wages by persons in the employment of a company or rather under an agreement with the company, may be thrown upon the resources of the Parishes?'.

Brunel was able to reply:

'I do not believe such cases have occurred'.

One reason for this was the railway labourers' determination to look after themselves and their work-mates during difficult times. When a new contract was commenced and the men arrived for the first time in a new locality, they immediately set up a 'sick club'. This was necessary because of the miserly attitudes of the railway company - particularly the Great Western - who totally ignored the mens' physical welfare.

To deal with their minor injuries and when they fell ill, the men usually chose a local doctor to care for them, the doctors' fees being paid from 'sick club' funds. Following the establishment of the 'sick club', the men would pay their subscriptions - about sixpence a week - for which an individual would receive about 12 shillings per week if he became sick or injured. Occasionally, this amount proved excessive and with certain individuals it was enough to encourage a man 'to swing the lead' and remain sick longer than was necessary. In some cases, if a man was killed on the works and was known to have a dependent family, a small payment was also made to next-of-kin.

Those labourers who were seriously injured on the works were normally taken - if at all possible - to the nearest medical facility to which the Company had paid a subscription. As the donations were always very small, they would not compensate the hospital authorities for the expenses they actually incurred and although the removal of the injured to hospital suited the Directors of the Great Western Railway, the arrangements did not suit the hospital authorities.

At the peak of the construction of the railway through West Berkshire, the labourers were being seriously injured with increasing frequency, which prompted Dr. Edward Boulger - the House surgeon at the Royal Berkshire Hospital, Reading - to write to the Board of Guardians of the Wallingford Union, requesting a weekly subscription of seven shillings a week to cover the costs of caring for the injured labourers. This request was ignored by the Union, as were several more similar requests from the hospital authorities made during the time the railway was being constructed through the area.

PART V
THE RAILWAY WORKS

'I remember perfectly well, when the large works were carried out at Hanwell, Messrs. Grissell & Peto were the contractors for the viaduct; Mr. Macintosh, one of the largest contractors for the contractor for the earthwork close to it; they were not able to obtain lodgings thereabout. There were some 700 to 800 men employed. And yet there were large numbers sleeping under the hedges at night, while a considerable number walked from London to the work' [to the Select Committee on Railway labourers 1846].

FIGURE 37. One of the two nodules found during the construction of the Great Western Railway and now located in the grounds of Bristol University.

(Author's collection)

THIS STONE IS ONE OF TWO LARGE NODULES
OF SANDSTONE FOUND IN 1837 DURING THE
EXCAVATION OF THE G.W.R. TUNNEL No.1
NEAR ST. ANNE'S AND PRESERVED THERE BY
I. K. BRUNEL
PRESENTED TO THE UNIVERSITY OF BRISTOL
BY BRITISH RAIL (WESTERN REGION)
IN APRIL 1983

CHAPTER EIGHTEEN
JAMES THOMAS BEDBOROUGH

James Thomas Bedborough was involved in controversy even before he was born and his lowly beginnings are recorded in the Parish records of New Windsor. On 21 January 1787, the baptism of James Bedborough is recorded for posterity, his creators being: 'Father - Bedborough', 'Mother - Ann Durbridge'. At that time, a Bedborough family was already well established at New Windsor, however, the mother's lineage is unknown. James Bedborough's beginnings are simply recorded in the parish register 'Son of Ann Durbridge (bastard)'.

Due perhaps to his dubious start in life, Bedborough appears to have attempted to make an impression on everyone he came into contact with. His sometimes forthright and dogmatic self-assertedness was, perhaps a sign of the strenuous exertions he made to ensure that he made a place for himself in history. Married in the early 1800s, his wife Sarah bore him their first child in 1808. Once again, Bedborough appears to have tried to ensure that he and his family would not be forgotten, as the couple had 13 children between the years 1808-1834. He was trained as a mason and had established a successful business in Windsor, with establishments in Thames Street and Sheet Street. Bedborough was deservedly prosperous and the family moved to several locations in Windsor. By 1845, the family had moved to a prestigious house in the grounds of Upton Park (east of Slough) and close to the railway that Bedborough had helped to construct.

Despite success, Bedborough and his family were to experience some sad times. At the time when the Directors of the Great Western Railway were seeking Parliamentary permission to construct their railway, Bedborough's youngest son was born. Frederick started life on 12 December 1834, being James Bedborough's youngest and last-born child. He was to live only 14 months and just as Bedborough was preparing to launch himself wholeheartedly into the construction of the Great Western Railway, Frederick passed away with the funeral taking place on 8 November 1835.

Bedborough had a formidable reputation throughout Berkshire and he was also fanatically pro-railway, being particularly keen on bringing a railway to his home town of Windsor. In 1833, the first specific proposal to bring a railway to Windsor was made, but it would be until 1849 that two railway companies - the Great Western and South Western - eventually reached the town. Bedborough, a Liberal Councillor of Windsor and Mayor of the town in 1846, was one of the civic leaders of the town for many years. All the evidence concludes that Windsor's leading citizens were fully aware of the importance of a railway to the town and Bedborough could be found at the vanguard of all the efforts made to expedite various schemes.

Bedborough appears to have had his first personal contact with the Directors of the Great Western Railway on 5 September 1834. Bedborough, with the engineer and other representatives of the abortive London & Windsor Railway Company - formed on 10 January 1834 to expedite the construction of a railway between London and Windsor and points west - met with the London Directors for the purpose:

> *'of suggesting the proprietary of carrying the line [London & Windsor] under the Long Walk at Windsor, as a means of inducing the influential inhabitants of the town to unite with the Great Western Railway'.*

The Directors were not impressed by the deputation's arguments and:

> *'considered it inexpedient to entertain the proposition'.*

FIGURE 39. Reproduction of an old print showing Brunel's bridge over the Thames at Maidenhead in the course of construction. *(The Railway Magazine)*

Bedborough was open in his approval of the construction of the Great Western Railway and at a meeting to discuss opposing the scheme, held at the Windmill Inn, Salthill near Slough on 19 November 1833, James Bedborough established himself as a man of courage and principle. Along with only three other people, Bedborough voiced his approval of the proposed Great Western Railway, compared to the near 200 others present who vehemently opposed the project. Amongst the violent disapproval voiced by the vast majority at this meeting, it would have needed a brave person to have an opposing opinion in favour of the scheme!

In 1839 negotiations took place for an abortive 'Windsor and Slough' line, followed in October 1844 by the Windsor Junction Railway Company, which was abandoned in August 1845 following opposition from the Crown. The following month, the Windsor, Slough and Staines Atmospheric Railway Company was formed with James Bedborough as a member of its provisional committee. This scheme was rejected by Parliament in May 1846. However, following these failures, the Crown Commissioners attitude softened, with the result that in June 1847, the South Western Bill received the Royal Assent, followed by the Great Western in August 1848.

James Bedborough had remained in the forefront of most of these protracted negotiations and his tenacity - with his fellow citizens - would eventually succeed.

FIGURE 40. Dumb-bell Bridge - a local nickname from the first days of the Great Western Railway - took the name because of the structure's similarity to the weight-lifter's dumb-bell (a short bar with a weight at each end). This nickname is still recalled today on the sign outside an adjacent hotel located immediately to the west of the bridge which carries the railway over the A4 east of Maidenhead, near Taplow.   *(Author's collection)*

However, the question must be asked, was Bedborough's dedication due to an altruistic attitude to his town or was there, perhaps, an ulterior motive? Bedborough was a controversial person and he was constantly in the public eye. He held many posts in local institutions, but occasionally these interests would attract some negative reaction from his fellow citizens, some questioning his benevolent intentions. For instance, following controversy in March 1835 when an Assistant Overseer of the Parish of New Windsor absconded with the receipts of the last two parish rates, Bedborough - as churchwarden - found himself implicated, although no action was taken against him.

He became a very well known local builder and amassed a large fortune from the many projects he became involved in. Locally, he appeared popular and for instance, in 1833 he was on the Committee of the Royal Windsor Dispensary. However, in Berkshire as a whole, he appeared to attract almost derision at times, these feelings probably generated by jealously because of his financial successes. In 1833, letters in Berkshire's journals openly sneered at Bedborough after he had completed alterations to Windsor Castle, when it was claimed that he had 'netted £60,000 profit'. In the same year, he was made a Freeman of the County of Buckinghamshire and was also involved in the reconstruction of the town of Windsor, involving connecting the extremities of the town by forming a new street from Peascod Street to Sheet Street.

The Industrial Revolution and various Parliamentary Reforms had allowed men - such as Bedborough - to develop their entrepenurial abilities to the full. The inherent restrictions imposed by Britain's agrarian economy, had been largely overcome, with the previously dormant capabilities of many of the country's new breed of engineers and industrialists beginning to reshape the country. Bedborough would prove a great survivor and would mix with royalty. In early April 1842, he would present an ornamental trowel to Prince Albert after the foundation stone of Holy Trinity Church, Windsor was laid by the Prince.

When the construction of the Great Western Railway commenced, Bedborough quickly secured contracts in the London Division and following the completion of these, he attempted to secure contracts further west, which would ensure that his labour force was kept intact. Prior to the completion of Contract '4R', he submitted tenders for '1S', which was the continuation of the railway from Didcot to the Wilts & Berks Canal in the Parish of Ardington (five miles 68-chains) and for '2S' which ran for seven miles 78-chains from the Wilts & Berks Canal to the Uffington Road - the limit of the London Division. Both bids proved unsuccessful and Bedborough then tried to secure contracts in the Bristol Division. In June 1839, he submitted tenders for Contracts '14B', '2C', '3C', '7C', '3S' and '4S'. Again, all these tenders were unsuccessful. However, for some reason Bedborough on 8 June 1839, was allowed to submit an amended tender for '7C'. This proved acceptable to the Directors and ensured that Bedborough's labour force working on Contract '4R' at Cholsey had the opportunity to move west to work on this new contract.

CHAPTER NINETEEN
TENDERS

The 17-miles and 20-chains of line between Reading and Didcot had been divided into three separate contracts. In addition, the two viaducts over the Thames at Gatehampton (Basildon) and Moulsford were the subject of two separate contracts. The most expensive contract would be the 'Pangbourne Contract' - not allocated a contract number for some unexplained reason - at a final cost of £76,975-14s-10d. The main contractors for this section of line, which stretched from the western outskirts of Reading to the east bank of the Thames at Gatehampton, would be Messrs. Grissell & Peto.

The contracts for both the bridges over the Thames at Gatehampton and Moulsford - '1R' and '2R' - would be taken by William Chadwick, who had already achieved considerable esteem for his construction of the railway bridge over the Thames at Maidenhead with its two very flat elliptical brick arches of 130-ft. span. Contract '3R' was for the construction of the earthworks for the section of line between the Gatehampton and Moulsford bridges and this contract was taken by a local man - Richard Custance of Goring - at a final cost of £26,455 0s 6d.

Following the publication of the advertisements for Contracts '3R' and '4R', the Directors received the tenders at their offices on 22 March 1838 and satisfied with James Bedborough's submission and sureties, the Directors accepted his price of £59,570 for Contract '4R'. However, when the works were completed, because of 'extras', the final amount of Contract 'R4' amounted to £62,861 13s 5d. Upon being informed by Saunders that his tender had been accepted, Bedborough wrote back, questioning the wording of the specification. Saunders wrote back reassuringly on 27 March 1838 stating:

'You are to form all the embankments according to the requirements of the engineer's specifications to the full dimensions whatever may be the quantity of each required. The cuttings are to be made in such a manner as to furnish the adequate quantity of earth requisite to form the embankments but it is not expected that you are to widen the cuttings to the extent specified in the engineer's specifications unless you find it necessary to do so for the purpose of completing the embankments, roads, approaches, etc.'.

On 30 April 1838, Bedborough, satisfied with the reassurances he had received, duly signed the Contract document (40 handwritten pages); Brunel signing on behalf of the Great Western Railway, the signing being witnessed by Thomas J. Westwood, a clerk working for the Company's solicitors Swain, Stevens & Co. The Contract, being a legal document, required government stamp duty to be paid. Similarly, the 10 sheets of plans were also dual signed by Brunel and the contractor. These plans gave the contractor all the information he required, including details of the maximum depth of material to be excavated, the maximum height of the embankments and the sites of the various works and bridges to be constructed. The set of plans had been lithographed and Bedborough and the Company's assistant engineer for the contract each had their own copies, although the originals, with Brunel's and the contractor's signatures, were deposited at the Company solicitor's offices. The assistant engineer's copy, kept at the local Railway office at the Bull Inn, Streatley would provide an easy and handy reference for all parties.

It is notable that Bedborough, when signing the Contract document, described himself as an 'Excavator'. Bedborough had to provide a surety of £4,000 which had been arranged as a joint bond from a John Ramsbottom 'Esquire' of London [unidentified] and Thomas Jenner 'Gentleman', a surveyor and auctioneer of Windsor. Bedborough's previous contract in the London Division had been '5L', which included the construction of Brunel's famous 'Dumb-bell' bridge, the oblique bridge over the Great Western turn-pike road, east of the town of Maidenhead. Bedborough was also initially the contractor for '6L', Brunel's controversial bridge over the Thames at Maidenhead.

On the last day of May 1838, the Directors made a trial run down the now almost finished line from London to Maidenhead. The contracts in this section were now almost completed and the contractors who had been successful in obtaining new contracts had probably already moved their men and equipment further to the west. It is likely that many of the men employed by Bedborough on his previous contract now moved on to the Cholsey area, to continue their herculean task on the contractor's new contract '4L'. How many men were involved is unknown, but almost certainly, the highways of Berkshire saw large numbers of tramping railway labourers moving west at this time.

As already mentioned, Bedborough attracted more than his fair share of controversy. He was also not immune to upsetting people for various reasons and included in this group of people with grievances were Brunel and the Thames Commissioners. It would appear that Bedborough and Brunel were cast from the same mould. Both were impulsive and both had scant respect for authority if this did not suit their own purposes. As early as December 1836 while working on his earlier contracts east of Maidenhead bridge, Bedborough had run foul of the river authorities following his authorising his workmen to dredge a quantity of sand from the river bed without first seeking the Thames Commissioners' permission through their surveyor. Bedborough, after enquiries had been made by the surveyor, was eventually charged £2 a ton for his illicit haul. A similar complaint was received in September 1839, which again confirmed that the contractor had illegally obtained ballast [gravel] from the river at Old Windsor. This action was considered by the Commissioners to be in deliberate violation of the instructions already given to Bedborough by the General Surveyor. As Bedborough's actions were considered 'injurious to the navigation', the Surveyor was instructed to take immediate steps to curtail Bedborough's activities. Of course, as Bedborough was working for the Great Western Railway at the time of both these incidents - the river authorities great rival - it is hardly likely that the Commissioners would be sympathetic to Bedborough's surreptitious activities.

The Secretary to the London Committee also became entangled with

Bedborough. On 3 March 1839, a London Journal - *Paul Pry* - of 55 Holywell Road, Strand published an article suggesting corruption on the part of Bedborough. The article dealt with the dismissal of a clerk employed by the Great Western Railway at the Company's offices at 2 Cornhill, London. The clerk had been recently dismissed for 'drunken habits' and the journal suggested that Bedborough had been involved in corrupt practices with the clerk. The Directors demanded an explanation and Saunders was ordered to inquire into the situation. Saunders wrote to Bedborough on 9 March 1839 stating:

> *'respecting the conduct of some clerk in the office of Great Western Railway, in supposing transacting with you as a contractor for works on the line. 'The accusation however is in every respect circumstantial, and even quotations, are introduced from supposed letters, signed by your name.*
>
> *'You will, I am sure, naturally feel I am entitled to the most candid and unreserved information from you'.*

Bedborough cooperated fully with Saunder's enquiries and the Secretary, apparently satisfied that no misconduct had taken place, on the 30 April 1839 returned all the documents submitted by Bedborough to assist the enquiry, with apparently no further action being taken.

As previously mentioned, Bedborough also ran foul of Brunel on several occasions, these disagreements eventually leading to a long-running dispute between the two for payment for work completed. The contractor, while working on various contracts had been under the direct supervision of a resident engineer - Hammond - who was himself directly responsible to Brunel. Thus, Bedborough, as one of the contractors working on contracts in the London Division was under the scrutiny of both Hammond and Brunel. The contractor was responsible for '5L', the section of line leading to Brunel's unique bridge which was being constructed over the Thames by William Chadwick (Contract '6L'), just east of the town of Maidenhead. Bedborough's contract included Brunel's 'Dumb-bell' bridge, a skew bridge - constructed of brick - which carried the railway over the main London road (now the A4). Despite the fact that the line between London and Maidenhead had opened in June 1838, a dispute between Brunel and Bedborough simmered on until late 1839.

It was the normal practice for a cash bonus to be given to contractors who finished their contracts early and on the Great Western Railway a contractor could earn £5,000 if the contract was completed six weeks before the stipulated date. This reduced to £3,000 if the works were completed four weeks ahead of schedule. Bedborough had completed all the works on '5L' before the contractual date and the contractor assumed that he had earned a bonus. Brunel disagreed strongly and on 22 October 1838 the engineer explained to the Directors in London the reason why he opposed any extra payment. Brunel had formed a very low opinion of Bedborough's work force, particularly those workmen responsible for the brickwork which formed the arches of the bridges on this section of line. The engineer informed the Directors that much defective brickwork had been found in

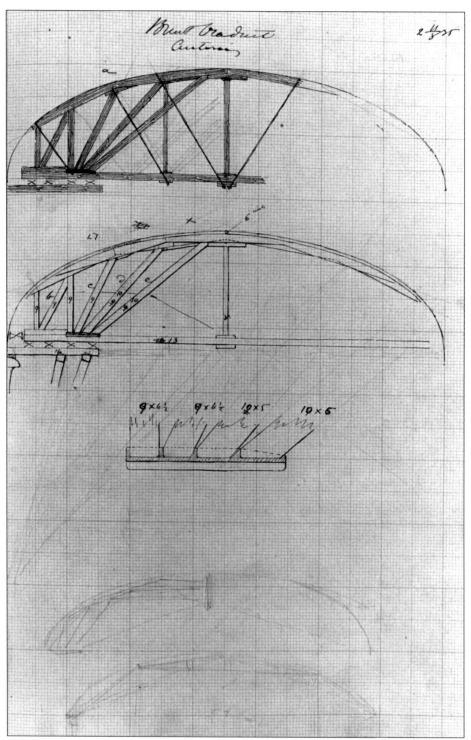

FIGURE 41. Brunel's original sketches for the centreings to be used for the construction of the Brent (Hanwell) viaduct.

(Reproduced by kind permission of the Librarian of the University of Bristol)

'5L', including one arch in a cutting near Slough which had already fallen down and another which had given way to such an extent that the arch required demolishing and rebuilding. Brunel also confirmed that two other arches were in a similar condition and had been condemned. However, what caused Brunel the most concern, was the construction of the 'Dumb-bell' bridge. Because of Bedborough's apparent inability to ensure that the bridge was constructed to Brunel's strict requirements, the engineer had taken the construction of this important structure away from Bedborough and transferred the contract to William Chadwick, the contractor for the Maidenhead railway bridge.

Bedborough, however, continued to insist that '5L' had been completed early and therefore qualified for a bonus. Brunel argued that if he had not transferred the construction of the 'Dumb-bell' bridge to William Chadwick and some of the rebuilding to other contractors, the contract would not have been finished on time. Brunel stated:

> *'Bedborough certainly immediately adopted means for expediting the earthwork but in the brickwork he was always very backward principally for the bad workmanship requiring the work to be rebuilt, and consequently much of the brickwork remained still to be completed or replaced'.*

The dispute was to simmer on until February 1843. However, this on-going situation did not prevent Bedborough from obtaining further contracts on the Great Western Railway and clearly the contractor's expertise eventually improved enough to satisfy Brunel. Indeed, when Bedborough in early 1840 indicated to the engineer that he was virtually destitute, Brunel wrote to Saunders on 22 January 1840 stating:

> *'My Dear Sir, Mr. Bedborough writes to me that he is very much pressed for money - There is rather a large balance now due to him on R No. 4 as we have reason to be satisfied with his present mode of proceeding, I should recommend that his present request be answered'.*

Despite this apparent improvement, Bedborough continued to press his claim relating to '5L'.

At a meeting of the Great Western Railway Traffic Committee held at Steventon on 22 September 1842, a further appeal for payment from Bedborough was read out. The Directors consequently instructed Saunders to inform Bedborough that he was to submit full details in writing of the dispute between himself and Brunel. At a further meeting of the Traffic Committee held at Steventon on 20 October 1842, the meeting was attended by a Henry Darville who was acting as an intermediary on behalf of Bedborough. Darville when questioned, discounted claims that he was a professional legal adviser, claiming that he was simply a friend of Bedborough and had attended the meeting in the hope of settling the long-standing dispute.

Darville was a Liberal colleague of Bedborough on Windsor Council and he was also a partner in the Windsor firm of solicitors, Darville & Geary (this firm were later in 1845 to become the solicitors acting for the abortive Windsor, Slough &

Staines Atmospheric Railway, which included on its provisional committee James Bedborough). At the meeting at Steventon on 20 October 1842, Brunel eventually suggested 'an amicable settlement'. Failing this, the engineer could only suggest that the claim be referred to Mr. Charles Stevens, one of the solicitors acting for the Great Western Railway.

The dispute appeared to widen as the Company continued to withhold payments to Bedborough, not only for the disputed Contract '5L', but for work done more recently on other contracts, including '7C' and '4R'. However, on 9 February 1943 Brunel was able to inform the Directors:

> *'That he had concluded an agreement with Bedborough subject to the conditions previously stated on all matters in difference relating to the work performed under Contracts 7C, 5L , 4R, 4S'.*

The final settlement agreed for work completed on these four contracts amounted to £22,000.

The delaying tactics used by Brunel to deal with the contractor Bedborough, however, were not unusual or excessive. The record for such action is without doubt, Brunel's point-blank refusal to countenance payment for work undertaken on Contracts '3L' and '9L' by contractors Hugh & David McIntosh, for work undertaken in 1837. Brunel's stubbornness would continue to prevail until 1865, when the Great Western Railway Company were forced by litigation, to pay to the McIntosh estate (Hugh was by this time dead), the sum of £100,000 and 20 years accrued interest, plus costs!

Despite Bedborough's apparently dubious reputation - regularly reinforced by negative comments in Berkshire journals - there is no evidence to confirm that the contractor abused the men who worked on his contracts on the Great Western Railway. Similarly, no disputes have been traced between Bedborough, his sub-contractors or gangers and the men working under them. Bedborough appears also to have been a great innovator and a man not afraid to use the latest technology. Well prior to the railway coming to West Berkshire, mechanisation and steam power were already being used to supplement the navvies' efforts in constructing the nation's river and canal network, with steam engines being used for a number of purposes, including pumping, piling and dredging. The Thames Commissioners, meeting at Wallingford on 10 November 1836, learned that:

> *'J. T. Bedborough, the contractor for the Great Western Railway bridge at Maidenhead, having made application for the sale or loan of the steam engine belonging to the Commissioners now in store at Marlow it is resolved it be now offered to him for sale price as shall be considered right by Mr. Easton, of The Grove, Great Guildford Street, London'.*

The Commissioners were consequently informed at their meeting on 14 February 1837 that Bedborough had purchased the steam engine for £500.

CHAPTER TWENTY
CONSTRUCTION COMMENCES

The Spring of 1838 saw the line of the Great Western Railway, to the east of Brunel's great bridge over the Thames at Maidenhead, being prepared for opening to public traffic. Brunel's graceful viaduct over the Brent Valley at Hanwell - the first contract to be let by the Company - had been commenced in February 1836. Twelve months later all the arches had been turned and the whole structure was ready for use in the summer of 1837. The majority of the works being completed along this 22 miles 42 chains section, the line was prepared for opening and on 31 May 1838 an inaugural train ran from Paddington, to a 'temporary' station at Maidenhead. The train consisting of the *North Star* locomotive - and six carriages - two each of 'first', 'second' and 'third' class - carried the Directors of the Company, a large party of their friends - including several MPs - and such other persons considered worthy of a place.

The first public service train, between the terminus at Paddington and Maidenhead would run four days later on 4 June 1838. Again, this train would be hauled by *North Star*, the service leaving promptly at 8 a.m. and attaining a speed of 36 mph. One of the railway's Directors travelled on this train and recorded the events of the day:

> 'Our railway opened to the public this morning. I went to Maidenhead by the first train and came back by the third, which started from Maidenhead at 10.15. I was disappointed with regard to the speed, as we were 1 hour and 20 minutes going down and 1 hour and 5 minutes coming up. If from the 65 minutes we deduct 4 lost at Drayton, 3 at Slough, and 4 between the two places and in slackening and getting up speed, there remain 54 minutes for 23 miles or 25.5 miles per hour. We carried altogether to-day 1,479 people and took £226'.

As the contracts to the east were completed, the contractors and navvies would move to contracts in the intermediate section and to the west. Messrs. Grissell & Peto - who had been responsible for the Brent viaduct - would construct the line between the west of Reading and the Gatehampton bridge - the 'Pangbourne' Contract. Hugh McIntosh, who had constructed the embankment approaching the Hanwell viaduct from the east - Contract '9L' - and his son David McIntosh, who had the responsibility for the embankment west of the viaduct - Contract '3L' - would take over from the disgraced contractor William Ranger and complete his three contracts in the Bristol and Bath area. James Thomas Bedborough who had completed Contract '6L' would construct the line from west of the Moulsford bridge to Didcot - Contract '4R'.

Bedborough's work force moved into the Parish of Cholsey in the spring of 1838. The year began with snow and severe frosts and ice, eight-inches thick was recorded on the Thames. A subscription had been raised in the nearby Borough of Wallingford for the poor people and coals and meat had been distributed to those

FIGURE 42. Above: The Hanwell viaduct under construction, as illustrated in a drawing by G. H. Andrews. Below: Some of the detail from the same drawing.

(Alan Mott/The Institution of Civil Engineers)

families in direst need. The cold weather continued and on 21 April further snow fell. Luckily, a reprieve from the Arctic conditions quickly took place and on 2 May, thundery showers with a noon temperature of 70 degrees was recorded.

Prior to the labourers commencing their task, the centre line of the railway and the boundary on either side had been marked out, despite the fact that not all the land negotiations had been completed. Although some prolonged negotiations with some of the more recalcitrant land owners and tenants were still necessary, this would not prevent the Company commencing operations. Authorisation was included in the Great Western Railway Act allowing representatives of the Company to enter property not already owned by the Company for the purposes of surveying and marking out the line of the railway. Clause VIII of the Great Western Bill gave the Company powers to commence the construction and Clause IX detailed the penalties available to any person found guilty of impeding the railway's activities. Additional clauses detailed the powers available to the Company for dealing with landowners or tenants who refused to quit their lands or buildings, after being served due notice to do so.

Following the Royal Assent being received, the construction of the line began almost immediately and on 3 September 1835, Brunel had written to the Bristol lawyers and the Company's surveyor confirming that he had been instructed to set out the line between London and Reading and Bristol and Bath. Brunel had added:

'We shall have our flags flying over the Brent Valley tomorrow'.

This statement was interpreted by many, that by 'flags', the engineer suggested bunting associated with a celebration. Of course, Brunel meant nothing of the sort. On 14 September 1835, Brunel had informed the Directors of the procedure he would adopt when setting out the line prior to the arrival of the main force of labourers. He stated that initially and with the consent (or not) of landowners or tenants, any woods or trees on the land would be cut down. The surveyors would then follow on, with the precise task of determining the exact path of the railway, marking principal points or prominentaries with tall staves decorated with triangular flags. These 'flags' would be visible for considerable distances and would

FIGURE 43. Clearing trees preparatory to commencing earthworks.
(Leicestershire Museums, Arts & Records Service)

aid the surveyors in determining the line's path.

The surveyors also had to assist the contractor in setting out the sites of the bridges and other structures, as well as the boundaries on either side of the line. In theory, all work would be confined within these boundaries, normal agricultural activities going on in the fields on either side of the railway. The local farmers - tolerant to the navvies poaching and other activities during the winter months - became more sensitive during the harvest period and notices appeared during the late summer of 1839, warning that anyone found encroaching on areas of growing crops, would:

'be deemed wilful trespassers and dealt with accordingly'.

However, local pastimes appeared little affected by the construction of the railway and a ploughing match - in very wet conditions - was held on 9 November 1839 in a field at Cholsey which had been recently intersected by a deep railway cutting.

CHAPTER TWENTY-ONE
CONTRACT '4R'

The 17-miles 20-chains of line between Reading and Didcot had been divided into three separate contracts. In addition, the two viaducts over the Thames at Gatehampton [Basildon] and Moulsford were the subject of two separate contracts, although eventually both were let to the same contractor - William Chadwick - who had already achieved fame for his inspired construction of Brunel's railway bridge over the Thames at Maidenhead.

The most expensive section of the railway to construct - and also the longest - between Reading and Didcot was the 'Pangbourne Contract'. This contract would stretch from Littlejohns on the western outskirts of Reading, to the viaduct which was being constructed across the Thames at Gatehampton. Unusually, this contract was not allocated a contract number, but was always referred to as the 'Pangbourne' contract and almost certainly this was because of Brunel's tardiness in preparing the plans for this section of line. Brunel was constantly apologising to the Directors for being behind and the contract for this section was eventually taken by Messrs. Grissell & Peto at a final cost of £76,975-14s-10d. This contract had to be completed by day and night working with the works lit by huge bonfires.

Contract '3R' was for the section of line between the two viaducts over the Thames at Gatehampton and Moulsford and this contract was taken by a local man - Richard Custance of Goring - at a final cost of £26,455 0s 6d.

Contract '4R' - which stretched from the west bank of the Thames at Moulsford to Vauxhall Farm near Didcot - did not involve the formation of any large structures, neither were there any geological problems, such as underground springs which would cause problems for the men labouring to complete the works. The ground through which the line would be cut, would consist in the main of 'chalk marl' [soft chalk and soil] from which the embankments would be formed and small deposits of gravel and sand. Brunel had defined in detail in the contract document for Contract '4R' that the work consisted of four embankments and four cuttings. The largest amount of material to be excavated would come from the cutting through the Cholsey Common Field [Cutting No. 1] and which would provide the majority of the spoil needed to form the embankments. The engineer had tried to ensure that the spoil excavated would be sufficient without having to resort to side cutting.

As well as the £4,000 surety guaranteed jointly by James Ramsbottom and Thomas Jenner, the Company would require further financial guarantees from the contractor. These further guarantees were raised by deducting amounts owed to Bedborough for some of the initial work done on the contract. At the end of the first 14 days, Brunel or the resident engineer would sanction payment for work completed during this period, with 80% of the money owed for this period being paid to the contractor and the remaining 20% being retained by the Company.

This system would continue until a total of £4,000 had been accrued. Once this amount had been retained by the Company, all money owed to the contractor for work done every 14 days, after first being agreed by Brunel, would be paid.

Following the total completion of the contract; if the contract had been completed on time and to the standards insisted upon by the engineer, 50% (£2,000) of the money retained by the Company would be paid to the contractor one month after being sanctioned by the engineer. As the contractor was totally responsible for the maintenance and repairs of all the works for a period of 12 months after completion, the remaining £2,000 would be held by the Company for this period. Only after completion of this further 12 months would the engineer sanction payment of the remaining £2,000 and then only if the works had been maintained and repaired to the satisfaction of the engineer. This last sum was, surprisingly, eligible for 4% interest, allowed for from the time of the completion of the contract, to the time the money was finally paid to the contractor, one month after the expiry of the maintenance period.

The terms of the contract ensured that the contractor had virtually no scope for digressing from the terms of reference laid down in the contract document. Bedborough would be responsible for enclosing the land to be used for the railway works; the excavation and forming of all earthworks; the erection of both temporary and permanent fencing; the diverting of roads and the construction of all bridges, drains, culverts and other masonry and he was also responsible for the supply of all labour, materials tools, implements and the like. The only exclusion being that the contractor was not responsible for the ballasting and laying of the permanent rails.

Bedborough, under the terms of the contract, was obliged to supply at least one competent foreman for the whole of the works. However, the Company had the right, if necessary, to demand his replacement and to replace him with a person of the Company's choice. Similar stipulations applied to the workmen and if the Company was of the opinion that not enough men were employed on the contract, they could demand that more men be employed at the contractor's expense. Any complaints regarding inferior materials or workmanship were the contractor's responsibility and faulty workmanship - from what ever cause - would be charged against the contractor.

There were certain priorities regarding the construction of the section of line between Moulsford and Didcot and after the initial notice to commence work had been served on the contractor, he had 10 days in which to commence the work. Bedborough was ordered to concentrate on the various works at the eastern extremity of the contract, namely between the bridge over the Thames at Moulsford, to a point 200-yards west of the Wallingford-Reading Turnpike. This strategy would ensure (a) that the traffic using the busy turnpike would not be disrupted for too long a period and (b) that the earthworks forming the site of the station layout at Moulsford [Wallingford Road] would have adequate time to consolidate before the station buildings were commenced. The designated section had to be completely finished, ready for ballasting and the laying of the permanent rails within 10 months from the initial receipt of notice to commence the works. Failure to complete this section on time would involve the contractor paying a accruing penalty for every week the works were late.

The contractor had been warned that disruption to the two turnpikes affected by the line of railway had to be kept to a minimum. At the eastern extremity of the section, the line would sweep under the Reading-Wallingford-Oxford turnpike, while at the western extremity, the line would pass over the Wallingford-Faringdon turnpike at Hagborne Marsh near Didcot. The Great Western Railway Bill did not include clauses offering protection to individual turnpike roads, but general stipulations were included in the Bill which would apply to all highways affected by the line of railway. Clauses XCIV and XCV gave the minimum requirements for public carriage roads and for a bridge carrying the railway over a road:

'a clear and open space under every such Arch of not less than Fifteen Feet'

was the minimum width required. A stipulated minimum height to road arches had to be provided, as:

'from the Surface of such Road to the Centre of such Arch of not less than Sixteen Feet'.

Similarly for bridges carrying roads over the railway:

'Width as to leave a clear and open Space between the Fences of such Road of not less than Fifteen Feet'

plus:

'a good and sufficient Fence shall be made on each Side of every such Bridge, which Fence shall not be less than Four Feet above the Surface of such Bridge'.

Brunel's insistence that the works at the eastern extremity of the line must have priority resulted in a report being made on 14 July 1838 that:

'on Cholsey Downs through which the railway will pass a chalk embankment has been thrown up, a quarter of a mile in length, formed of excavations from the upper part of the Downs'.

Thus, traffic on this important turnpike road from Reading through Wallingford to Oxford was interfered with as little as possible and only minor complaints were received from the Trustees. However, Brunel had obviously not attached the same urgency to the less important Wallingford-Faringdon turnpike and the Trustees of this road were continually making complaints about various aspects of the railway works interference with the road traffic.

Where any of the works interfered with the free use of an existing road, a good and sufficient road had to be formed on one side of the existing road and maintained during the period of the occupation. This temporary road had to be of generally the same dimensions and condition of the normal road and had to meet the requirements of the Surveyor of Highways of the Parish or:

'other persons interested in the road have a right to demand'.

The temporary road had to be enclosed with a temporary fence for the duration of the detour. When the new bridge was completed - over or under the railway - the new road had to be maintained until the surface became consolidated at the level marked 'road line' on the contractor's drawings.

In the case of a road being carried over the railway by a bridge, the approaches to the bridge had to have a gradual inclination of normally 1:20. These approach roads had to be - unless specified otherwise - at least 21-ft. wide at the road surface and the embankment slopes had to have a slope of $1^{1}/_{2}$:1. Permanent drains had to be installed along the foot of the embankments, which would link up with the drains to be constructed along the embankments and through the cuttings. Along the top of the approach roads, a post and rail fence, with a hedge, had to be installed. Where a road had to be carried under the railway, the approach roads had to have a gradual inclination of 1:15 and a side inclination of $1^{1}/_{4}$:1. The width of these roads or cuttings at road level had to be 24-ft. (including footpaths) and in all cases, the new road to be formed had to be:

> *properly installed and shall in every respect of quantity and quality of materials be at least equal to the existing road*.

During the construction of bridges, the contractor was responsible for any compensation which might become necessary following delays in the construction. If the contractor required the temporary use of any land beyond that provided by the Company, the contractor had to:

> *procure the same at his own cost*.

Over the arches of all the bridges in the contract, Brunel directed that a bed of concrete be laid and the surface brought up level with the crown of the arch or to such other levels as shown on the drawings. Under all foundations, a bed of concrete had to be laid to a thickness specified by the engineer and all material excavated from foundations had:

> *to be thrown into the nearest embankment*.

In cuttings where bridges were to be constructed, the chalk had to be dressed to a sound surface and all wing-walls or abutments had to be built close to the natural bed of chalk with a thin joint of mortar between. Another priority was that immediately the contract was commenced, all brickwork of arches, culverts and the like, had to be proceeded with straight away. This would allow the brick structures the longest time possible to mature and settle before the approaching earthworks enveloped them. Frequently, the main contractor would subcontract such structures and temporary accommodation would often be built adjacent to the site to house the sub-contractor's equipment, animals and men. Because of the priority to complete all brickwork, it was a common occurrence to find completed, isolated brick structures standing by themselves - almost like Victorian follies - waiting for the earthworks on either side to reach and cover them.

As part of Contract '4R', a red-brick arch had to be constructed at Hagborne

Marsh, to carry the railway over the Wallingford-Faringdon turnpike road (now the A4130). A sub-contractor - Pritchard - had taken this contract and built a thatched stable 75-ft. long to accommodate 24 horses. Despite the fact that the railway would not be opened over this section until nearly 12 months later, the brick arch over the road was completed by the middle of July 1839 when surplus materials, the stable and the horses were all put up for sale.

Bedborough's contract had stipulated that the completed works must be finished within 14 months after the contractor had received the initial notice instructing him to commence work. Failure to complete the contract on time would ensure that he faced escalating financial penalties. The fixed penalties were: £50 for the first week late and £100 for the second week (making a total of £150 for the first two weeks the contract was late). If the contract was three weeks late, this would invoke a penalty of £150 (making a total of £300 for the first three weeks) and so on. Following the completion of the works, the contractor was responsible for a period of 12 months for all maintenance and repairs deemed necessary by the engineer. Failure on the part of the contractor to undertake any remedial work required would involve the Company undertaking the repairs - at the contractor's expense.

The Company were responsible for the initial marking out of the ground: the centre line of the railway, as well as the boundaries on either side and the sites of all structures, arches, culverts and the like. Despite this, the contractor was still held totally responsible for the accuracy of the setting out, even though he would have been assisted by the Company's engineer, with the contractor having to provide all necessary equipment, including flag-poles, stakes, pegs, tools and labour. The

FIGURE 44. The front of the document for Contract '4R' between the Great Western Railway Company and the contractor J. T. Bedborough.
(Author's collection)

Company for their part, provided original drawings of all the works, although contractors were allowed to make copies - at their own expense.

After the land had been marked out to the satisfaction of the engineer, the boundaries on either side of the centre line of railway had to be enclosed by temporary fencing. This consisted of split oak posts, not less than 6-ft. 6-in. in length and of at least 14-sq.in. in cross section. The posts were placed 9-ft apart, with at least 3-ft. 9-in. of the post protruding above the ground. Each post was mortised to receive the ends of four horizontal oak or larch rails. These horizontal rails were supported by an intermediate small post of oak or larch, which was firmly nailed to each rail. This temporary fence had to be firmly installed and was intended to prevent sheep and cattle straying onto the works and also to prevent trespassing. The fencing was also linked with cross fencing at those locations where bridges had to be constructed or where passages had to be left to allow communication between adjoining lands. Similarly, drainage of the lands occupied had to be protected, with temporary drains being connected to link existing waterways until permanent drains and culverts were ready to take over this function.

As the progress of the works permitted, temporary fences had to be replaced with permanent fencing. The contractor was authorised to re-use those parts of the temporary fencing which were considered:

'to be of the requisite strength and quality and uninjured by previous use'

to construct the permanent fencing, which had to extend along the whole of the contract and on both sides of the line of railway. Where the various bridges or drains crossed, permanent fencing had to be built around the foot of the slopes. Permanent fencing would consist of an oak post and fence rail placed along the extreme boundary of the Company's property. Inside this boundary fence was a ditch for drainage and a hedge of quick [hawthorn], planted at the foot of the slopes.

The fence would consist of oak posts 7-ft. 3-in. in length and equal in sectional area to a scantling of at least 5-in. x 3 1/2-in. The posts would be placed 9-ft. from each other (centre-to-centre) and would stand 3-ft. 9-in. above the surface of the ground. Through each post, there were four mortises to receive the ends of the four rails. The horizontal rails had to be either split oak or larch, equal in sectional area to a scantling of 3 1/2-in. x 1 1/2-in. The rails had to be 10-ft. in length with the ends scarfed, so as to fit the mortises cut into each post. Half-way between the posts, an oak or larch stay, 5-ft. in length x 3-in. wide x 2-in. thick, had to be installed. The stay had to be sunk 1-ft. 6-in. into the ground and then firmly nailed to each of the horizontal posts 'with good ten-penny nails'. The posts and stays had to be firmly fixed in the ground, with the ends of the rails firmly driven into the mortises. To prevent splitting, around the top of each post was nailed:

'a piece of new iron hoop, one-inch-and-a-quarter wide and weighing one-pound to three feet'.

Inside the permanent fence, a ditch had to be formed and the material excavated in forming this ditch had to be used to form a mound between the edge of the ditch and the embankment of the railway, the slopes of the mound having to be faced with turf. Any spoil excavated from the ditch which proved surplus had to be 'conveyed to the nearest embankment'. The best of the soil excavated from the ditch had to be placed in the middle of the mound, which would ensure that the quicksets [hawthorn] would be encouraged to root in the quickest possible time. The quicksets had to be at least three years old and to have already been transplanted for at least two years. The plants had to be planted in a double-row, with at least 15 quicksets to a linear yard. and the planting had to proceed as quickly as the progress of the earthworks and 'the nature of the season will admit of'. At the bottom of the embankments, drainage tiles were laid through the 'Quick mound'. These tiles had to be no further apart than 20-yds, which would ensure that all the water draining from the slopes of the embankments, drained into the ditches.

During the progress of the works and until the expiration of the 12-months maintenance period, the quicksets had to be cleared and weeded at least twice a year. If the contractor found that any of the plants had failed to take root during this period, these had to be replaced with 'three year old living Quicksets'. At the same time, any broken posts, rails or stays had to be replaced 'by new ones equal in quality to those originally used'.

The total contents of the embankments to be formed in Contract 'R4', were estimated at 495,000 cubic yards. These quantities were calculated from longitudinal sections taken along the centre line of each embankment. The upper surface of the embankments had to be either 33-ft. or 35-ft. in width and when forming the embankments, the contractor had to tip enough spoil to allow for shrinkage of the material. As the embankments proceeded and became consolidated, the slopes had to be carefully trimmed to an even surface and to the angle stipulated, then covered in turfs of not less 8-in. in thickness and:

'with the green sward outwards and well pressed into place'.

However, if the engineer did not consider the turfs saved during the excavations were not of sufficiently good quality, then top soil, also from the excavations, had to be used instead and sown with grass seed. The soil had to be distributed over the surface of the embankment to a thickness of not less than 8-in. and after the lumps had been broken down, the surface had to be neatly trimmed before the seed was sown. The mixture of seed was to be Rye grass mixed with clover in equal quantities, with not less than 5-lb. of seed to be used per acre. During the maintenance period of 12 months following the completion of the contract, the contractor was responsible for resowing any areas where the seed had not taken.

The method of tipping spoil to form the embankments was a relatively simple operation, with wagon-loads of material excavated from the cuttings being brought on temporary rails to the end of the embankment to be tipped. However, as the embankment approached any of the newly-built brick structures, particularly those with delicate wing-walls, this operation was suspended, all in-filling having to be done by hand. Blocks of chalk - especially set aside from the excavations - were carefully stacked by the labourers against the wing-walls, the remaining spaces being filled by washing-in gravel, sand or small pieces of chalk.

The forming of embankments, as with all the work associated with constructing the railway, carried a certain amount of risk and on 8 June 1838, it was reported that William Holdacre aged seventeen had been killed at South Stoke. The youth had been:

'Employed to drive carriages or wagons along the road to convey materials; that on the 8th as he was unhooking the horses chains from carriages (then heavily laden with clay) the horse turned out of the proper track, and threw deceased down across a rail, when the wheels of passing carriages ran over the lower part of his body and so injured him that death ensued shortly after'.

The four cuttings included in Contract '4R' had to be excavated through mainly chalk marle, which would be used to form the embankments and smaller deposits of gravel and sand. All the cuttings had to be excavated to 12-in. below the 'line of rails' which allowed for the ballast and the permanent rails. The slopes of the embankments had to be finished to the angle stipulated in the specification and neatly finished, either in one continuous slope or in 'benches' if the engineer decided that the geological conditions suited this latter course of action.

In the London Division, because of the frugal attitude of the Directors, Brunel was not allowed the same freedom regarding the choice of materials as he had in the Bristol Division. However, this did not mean that the materials used on Contract '4R' or any of the other contracts in the London Division were not of the best quality. All the contracts stipulated exactly what materials could be used and the contractor would have to replace any materials which were not up to the standard required. For instance, all the bricks used throughout were:

'to be sound hard well burnt and well shaped Stocks of the very best quality - the best in point of colour and shape to be carefully selected for the exterior work and attention must be paid that those be of one uniform colour and general appearance'

and if it proved impossible to obtain bricks of a high enough quality for the face works:

'used bricks of a superior quality must be procured on purpose'.

All bricks had to be bedded sound, without striking with a trowel and in the interior of the work, the mortar had to be used sufficiently thin to enable the workmen to flush the joints up full, without grouting (grouting was normally prohibited, unless specifically ordered by the engineer). The bricks:

'in each course to be well bonded and the different courses to cross joint so as to make the most sound and perfect work and the joints throughout the work to be kept as thin as possible consistently with sound work and all exterior joints in the soffets of the arches or elsewhere to be well pointed with mortar prepared for that purpose'.

Similarly, the mortar had to be of the same high quality. The mixture had to consist of one portion of lime (measured dry) to two-and-a-half or three portions of clean, sharp river sand. Concrete had to consist of five parts gravel and one part lime. In certain parts of the work, such as upper courses of brick or any work which would be exposed to the weather, Roman Cement consisting of one portion of cement to one-and-a-half of sand had to be used. All the mixtures of materials before use had to pass through a 'pug mill', which would thoroughly blend the various constituents together.

All stone used had to be either of the Bramley Fall or Bath stone variety and all material had to be approved by the engineer before being used. The stone had to be of a good colour and free from stains or other defects. All coping stones had to be at least 2-ft. in length and to average not less then 2-ft. 6-in. The stones had to be fixed to each other by cast-iron dovetailed cramps (a metal bar with flattened ends), which required a dovetailed hole to be chiselled in each end of each coping stone to take the cramp, which had to be 1-in. square at the smallest part. The cramps had to be let into the stone for at least 2-in. and the space around filled with Roman Cement through a channel left for that purpose. The exterior facing of all stone had to be:

'fair tooled - the joints to be fine picked with a chisel of an inch-and-a-half all round'.

Cast iron would consist of clean, well shaped castings with the engineer having the right to subject each casting to tests before the castings were used. No defective casting would be allowed to remain, not even if the casting had already been fixed. All the ironwork had to be well cleaned and then painted with 'three coats of strong oil paint'.

In building wing-walls to bridges or any other battering [brickwork where the top was narrower than the bottom], the contractor had to take particular care. These structures were very fragile and adverse weather conditions could affect them very quickly. It would take only a little wind or heavy rain to cause the structure to fall or distort and the contractor had to ensure that wing-walls and the like were shored-up whenever necessary. Arches had to be constructed using centreings [wooden frames in the shape of the curve of the arch] and these had to be:

'of the most substantial description and must sustain the weight of the superincumbent brickwork without sensible flexure'.

No centreing could be 'struck' [loosened] without the prior agreement of the engineer and even then, if there was any distortion of the structure, the contractor was ultimately responsible for any remedial work required.

PART VI
THE BRIDGES OVER THE THAMES AT GATEHAMPTON AND MOULSFORD

'I have taken all due steps to ensure the security of the navigation during the construction of the bridge - and at considerable expense - and in a much more complete manner than I believe you yourselves would have provided had you been executing the work' [to the Thames Commissioners].

29 August 1836

FIGURE 45. Above: A tranquil scene on the Thames at Maidenhead as men and horses rest from their labours, while overhead a broad-gauge passenger train passes by on the newly opened bridge.

(Reproduced by permission of the Royal County of Berkshire, Department of Libraries Archives and Tourism)

Inset: Plaque on the Maidenhead bridge. *(Author's collection)*

CHAPTER TWENTY-TWO
WILLIAM CHADWICK

Early in 1837, advertisements appeared in Berkshire journals relating to the two bridges which would be constructed over the Thames at Gatehampton and Moulsford:

> '2R For the construction and entire completion of a bridge across River Thames near Moulsford in the County of Berks, together with land arches and other works connected therewith. Drawings and specifications of the above works exhibited at 17 Cornhill and at Maidenhead and printed forms of tender may be had at the said offices on or after the 30th instant March'.

This advertisement and a similar one for Contract 'R1' for the Gatehampton Bridge were the first announcements by the Directors of the Great Western Railway for contracts west of Reading. The London Directors also announced that they would be pleased to receive tenders at their office at 17 Cornhill, London at noon on or before Thursday 20 April, but they also stated that they would not necessarily accept the lowest price tendered.

It is not known whether other tenders were received for the construction of the two bridges, but there appears to have been an unusually long period between the advertisements appearing and the confirmation by the Directors that a contract had been agreed. The advertisements for Contracts '1R' and '2R' had been issued by the London Directors on 9 March 1837 and published on 18 March 1837, but it would not be until almost a year later - 1 February 1838 - that Saunders was instructed to write to a William Chadwick of Adelaide Place, near London Bridge, stating:

> 'I am desired to acquaint you that the Directors having had under their consideration today your tender for the construction of the two bridges over the Thames beyond Pangbourne agreed to accept it upon the terms mentioned - Contract to be drawn up in the usual manner with the customary stipulations'.

Saunders appears to have assumed that William Chadwick was acquainted with the procedures for tendering for contracts on the Great Western Railway, and of course this was the case. Both Brunel and the Directors already had good cause to have complete confidence in William Chadwick's ability in specialising in the construction of bridges. Chadwick at the time was the contractor for the bridge across the Thames at Maidenhead ('6L') and this outstanding engineering success had already set new records for engineering and construction practices in the 19th-century. Brunel's final design for the Maidenhead bridge would consist of four semi-circular land arches on each side of the river, linked by two elliptical arches both of 128 feet span, the two larger spans firmly anchored on a central island in the centre of the river. The extreme flatness of the arches constructed in brick had aroused both extreme criticism and acclaim - both during and after the bridge's construction - but despite some initial problems, Brunel's daring and Chadwick's ability, resulted in a structure which confounded all critics.

As both sections of the railway edged both east and west, Chadwick had become increasingly responsible for the construction of bridges along the line. This had arisen because of the inexperience of some the main contractors, which had resulted in numerous complaints about shoddy workmanship and even some structures having to be demolished. Also, because both Brunel and the Directors had great faith in Chadwick's abilities, as the construction of the railway progressed, Brunel and Chadwick appear to have developed a mutual understanding regarding the other large bridges which needed to be constructed along the line of railway. Latterly, there was a notable lack of advertisements for contractors to tender for bridge construction, Chadwick becoming totally responsible for this category of work. One such structure was the skew-bridge over the River Avon at Bath. The Directors experienced difficulties in obtaining the 500 tons of iron originally specified by Brunel, who then decided to build the bridge in timber (perhaps in an effort to speed things up). Again, Brunel used William Chadwick for this complex contract. However, it was only due to another contractor's poor workmanship and financial paucity, that allowed Chadwick the original opportunity to earn such a reputation.

James Thomas Bedborough of Windsor had originally been allocated Contract '6L', which was for the construction of the railway bridge over the Thames at Maidenhead and the approach embankments. However, Bedborough - despite a local reputation for building work in the environs of Windsor - failed dismally to meet Brunel's high standards. He also appears to have overstretched his financial resources. Work on the Maidenhead bridge commenced early in 1836 and Bedborough's work came under the scrutiny of Hammond - the Resident Engineer at the bridge site - who almost daily reported the problems he was finding to Brunel. No delays could be allowed with the construction of this very important bridge and the Thames Commissioners, having failed to block the construction of the railway, applied pressure in other ways, complaining about the obstruction caused to the navigation and tow-path in the vicinity of Taplow.

Following continual worrying reports from Hammond, Brunel visited the works on 4 December 1836 and the following day, wrote to Bedborough expressing his concerns about what he had found. The letter lambasted Bedborough in no uncertain terms:

'The progress in the dams of the Maidenhead bridge is not merely slow but most unsatisfactory to me. There does not appear any probability that in their present state they can be sufficiently water-tight, particularly the western coffer-dam. For the safety of the construction of the foundations I shall be obliged to call on you to drive another row of piles or take such steps as necessary to make the coffer-dam fit for its purpose as required by the contract. I must remind you that the defect arises in great measure from you not having taken out the gravel before driving the piles as you were advised to do so by Mr. Hammond'.

Despite Brunel's admonitions, the situation did not improve. Brunel concerned over any delay to the construction of the railway, tried to relieve the situation by removing the construction of the approach embankments from Bedborough and allocating this work to another contractor. Again, there was no improvement and Brunel terminated Bedborough's contract for the construction of the river bridge on 17 March 1837, transferring the contract for the work to William Chadwick. Prior to this - on 4 March - Saunders had written to the Company's solicitors instructing them to transfer the contract to Chadwick. Despite the change of contractor, worries again surfaced about the river bridge being delayed and Saunders had to write to Chadwick in an effort to speed matters up. Chadwick responded to the Secretary's frustration on 22 November 1837, saying:

'I assure you that the whole work will be completed within the time stated in the Contract notwithstanding a loss of 8 months by my predecessor'.

Thus, Chadwick's first contract on the Great Western Railway appears to have been '6L' - the railway bridge over the Thames at Maidenhead. However, Chadwick - belatedly - also became responsible for the adjoining contract - '5L' - which included Brunel's famous 'Dumb-bell' bridge at Taplow, which carried the railway by a way of brick skew-bridge across the main London road (now the A4) to the east of Maidenhead. Again, the original contractor for this bridge had been Thomas Bedborough, but because of shoddy workmanship, Brunel removed the contract from him and transferred the work to William Chadwick.

On 29 September 1937, further problems arose at the Maidenhead railway bridge construction site, which would be later repeated during the construction of the two major river bridges further west at Gatehampton and Moulsford. Complaints had been received by the Thames Commissioners from the bargemasters who used the river, concerning the centreings - the huge masses of timber which supported the superstructure of the bridge during its construction. These structures - depending on the level of the river - caused severe inconvenience to the barges as they went about their business on the river. The Commissioners consequently decided that the General Clerk:

'be instructed to adopt proper steps for enforcing the immediate removal and of the restoration of the towing path under the arch'.

However, the centreings, despite being first eased on 8 October 1838 due to rebuilding required following distortion to the eastern arch (which was also the navigation arch) would remain in place until early 1840.

The esteem to which Brunel felt for William Chadwick is evidenced by his recommendation to the Institution of Civil Engineers in late 1840, that Chadwick be elected a member of the organisation. Brunel stated in his proposal that from personal knowledge, Chadwick was a person in every respect worthy of that distinction:

'on account of his being a Contractor for Engineering works of magnitude'.

With Brunel's prestigious proposal - and with the backing from five other members of the Institution - Chadwick was duly elected an Associate Member on 23 February 1841.

Unsurprisingly Chadwick was to continue his relationship with Brunel, becoming the main contractor for the engineer's Hungerford suspension bridge, a footbridge across the Thames. Brunel had commenced the design of this bridge in 1841 and it was eventually opened on 1 May 1845, quickly proving very popular with Londoners. However, even Chadwick's close relationship with Brunel would not protect him from a tongue-lashing after work on the bridge fell significantly behind schedule:

> *'I am determined to have the bridge ready for the 22nd [March 1845] and I shall hold you responsible for any expenses I may be driven to incur in completing the works which is so much behind the contract time'.*

The bridge was later demolished and replaced by the present railway bridge connecting Waterloo and Charing Cross. Today, the statue of Brunel - situated at the junction of Temple Place and the Victoria Embankment - looks upstream to the remains of the Hungerford Bridge, parts of which were used in the construction of the Bristol Clifton Suspension Bridge.

Chadwick would continue his work for the Great Western Railway long after the line had opened between Bristol and London. He was actively involved in the construction of the branch to Oxford in 1843-44 - probably for the construction of the only two engineering works of any importance on the line - the timber bridges over the Thames at Appleford and Nuneham.

Chadwick's relations with the Directors of the Great Western Railway appear to eventually soured following the various proposals to construct a line of railway to Windsor and after he had aligned himself with the rival railway company - the South Western. At a meeting held in Windsor on 5 August 1847, he publicly stated:

> *'what the people of Windsor wanted in the way of railway communication with the metropolis was a line that would give them what the Great Western did not possess - a central terminus in London'.*

At the same meeting he proposed:

> *'that this meeting, thinking it desirable for the inhabitants of Windsor that they should have a better terminus in London than that afforded by the Great Western at Paddington, do resolve that a deputation be appointed to treat with the South Western'.*

CHAPTER TWENTY-THREE
BRUNEL AND THE THAMES COMMISSIONERS

Brunel prior to the passage of the second Great Western Bill through Parliament, appears to have given little serious thought to the final specifications of the two bridges over the Thames at Gatehampton and Moulsford. The plans submitted by the engineer to the investigating Parliamentary Committee did not depict the details of these structures and Brunel when asked about the dimensions of the arches of these bridges, stated that each bridge would consist of two arches of 75-ft and four arches of 30-ft. This specification is clearly very different from the final measurements of the two bridges which were eventually constructed with four elliptical arches of 62-ft. span.

Brunel, because of the Directors' earlier instruction initially concentrated his efforts on the two extremities of the line. Consequently, when the second Bill finally received the Royal Assent, Brunel was hard pushed to complete all the specifications for contracts in the intermediate section of line between Bath and Reading. Probably, it was this unpreparedness which caused the delay of almost 12 months between the advertisements appearing for tenders for the two bridges over the Thames at Gatehampton and Moulsford and the Directors accepting William Chadwick's tender for both bridges.

The unrelenting pressure faced by Brunel at this time was immense, which may have explained the tardiness exhibited by the engineer towards his old protagonists - the Thames Commissioners. Brunel had first crossed swords with the Thames Navigation Committee during the construction of the Thames tunnel, which would be constructed using two shafts, one on each side of the Thames at Rotherhithe and Wapping. Marc Brunel (Isambard's father) had been appointed engineer to the tunnel project early in 1823, using his recently invented tunnelling shield (re-designed before work commenced). Marc Brunel had appointed John Armstrong, a very experienced Northumbrian engineer as resident engineer with Isambard as his assistant. Upon the illness of his father in the spring of 1826, followed shortly after by Armstrong also becoming ill, Isambard found himself totally in charge of the project. The problems associated with the excavation of the Thames Tunnel are well recorded, but at the age of 20 it would be Isambard who would effectively run the whole operation. In April 1827, the tunnel flooded and between 15 May-28 September both Isambard and his father tried every means at their disposal to plug the hole in the bed of the river. The various methods tried out inevitably affected the passage of the river traffic and as Sir Alfred Pugsley in his book 'The Works of Isambard Kingdom Brunel' writes:

'The Thames Navigation Committee had to be appeased'.

FIGURE 46. A modern view of Brunel's Maidenhead bridge.   *(Author's collection)*

It is also likely that Brunel and the Thames Commissioners paths crossed again during the construction of the Hungerford Suspension Bridge. Brunel had first begun to design the footbridge in 1841, finally opening on 1 May 1845. The bridge had two piers sunk into the bed of the river and the whole structure had been constructed by William Chadwick, the contractor responsible for many of the bridges and viaducts on Brunel's Great Western Railway.

The Commissioners had consistently opposed both Great Western Bills and despite their eventual defeat, Brunel was well aware that any discussions with the Commissioners were likely to be difficult. Even before the second Great Western Bill had received the Royal Assent, Brunel appeared to have treated the Commissioners with disdain, ignoring their various requests, until virtually forced into replying upon the instructions of the Directors.

A bridge had first been constructed across the Thames near Maidenhead in 1775 and it was to be expected that the burgesses of the town would be concerned at the possible decrease in tolls once the railway was opened. The burgesses were initially protected by the insertion of a clause in the Great Western Bill should road traffic over the bridge decrease, but water-borne traffic on the Thames attracted no such protection. Consequently, the Thames Commissioners who had fairly recently invested heavily in improving the navigation on the river were, perhaps justifiably concerned at the almost certain loss of tolls once the railway began operating.

The preliminary arrangements for the construction of the bridge to carry the Great Western Railway over the Thames at Maidenhead had commenced in early 1836. Despite this, the Thames Commissioners were clearly being kept in the dark by Brunel and at a meeting of the Commissioners which took place at Henley-on-Thames on 17 May 1836, the General Clerk of the Navigation was instructed to write to:

'the agents of the 'Great Western' railway, for a plan & section of the bridge which they propose to erect over the river below Maidenhead and it is referred to Captain Gardiner and Thompson, and Mr. Venables to inspect and determine such plan, and take such steps regarding if they deem advisable'.

The Commissioners next met at Marlow on 24 June 1836 and it was confirmed that a reply had been received by the Directors of the Great Western Railway, which stated:

'the Directors had instructed their engineer to prepare and forward to Mr. Treacher [General Surveyor to the Thames Navigation], a plan of the bridge proposed to be constructed'.

The next meeting, which took place at Abingdon on 2 August 1836, learned that a plan of the bridge had been received and the Commissioners expressed concern that the barge channel and the towing channel did not pass under the same arch. The Commissioners' concerns over this aspect was passed back to the Directors, who eventually agreed to the necessary alteration being made to the navigation under the bridge. However, forever suspicious of Brunel's intentions, the Commissioners instructed the General Surveyor to:

'watch that the undertaking is, strictly adhered to'.

During this period, work on the construction of the bridge had not actually commenced, but materials had begun to be delivered to the site by river. Apparently the tow-path, the river itself and thus the passage of river traffic was becoming restricted, a fact quickly reported to the General Surveyor who immediately complained. Brunel - his feathers clearly ruffled - angrily defended himself on 29 August, writing:

'Sir, I have taken all due steps to ensure the security of the navigation during the construction of the bridge - and at considerable expense - and in a much more complete manner than I believe you yourselves would have provided had you been executing the work. I have designed the largest arch of any bridge above Southwark for the express purpose of including the whole of the present navigation channel and the wide towing path under the same arch. I have done that which I suspect I will be severely criticised for, namely, made a 2-arch bridge for the purpose of throwing the only pier required on an existing island. I believe this will be the only instance upon the entire river of a bridge being built without in the slightest degree altering, still less, injuring the navigation. After doing all this - far more than we could have been compelled to do - unasked - it is rather vexatious to be interfered with in the manner we have been.

I hope you will put it all right and restore the good feeling you seem disposed to cultivate. I have explained what I intend and cannot be responsible for the statements others may choose to make. The bridge has been designed peculiarly with regard to the navigation and without consideration of expense on the part of the railway. If the Commissioners are discontented and troublesome, there is still time for me to save £10,000 and still build a bridge as they can find no fault with - but it would by no means be as convenient as the one at present intended'.

Despite this final shot over the Commissioners' bows, they appeared unmoved, although the minutes of the meeting of the Thames Commissioners held on 29 September 1836 confirmed that the matter had certainly been contentious:

'*After much correspondence and preparation for obtaining an injunction to stop the progress of the Great Western Railway bridge over the river at Maidenhead, they had at length succeeded in obtaining a plan of the bridge whereupon the proposed towing path under the navigation arch is exhibited, and that upon such showing and a conference between Brunel & Mr. Treacher it does not appear that the bridge as proposed to be created will injuriously affect the navigation and it is now resolved that Mr. Brunel's offer to Mr. Treacher to make two of the arches on the eastern side into one, with a cut leading thereto is accepted*'.

Brunel eventually altered his original plan to allow the barge channel and towing channel to be accommodated using the semi-circular arch closest to the river on the eastern approaches to the bridge, this arch consisting of a 21-feet span compared to the three other small arches which had a span of 28-feet. However, still obviously without any great faith in Brunel, the Commissioners, resolved on 11 November 1836:

'*to recommend to the General Committee to exercise a watchful vigilence regarding the progress of the Great Western Railway*'.

What becomes evident is that Brunel had not discussed or sought the opinion of the Thames Commissioners or their surveyor regarding the three bridges which would eventually span the Thames. Nor, it would appear had he entered into any discussions regarding the design of these bridges or how the bridges' construction would effect the river-borne traffic.

Brunel's obvious dislike of the Commissioners would surface on numerous occasions during the construction of the Great Western Railway and his aloofness and disdain for them would continue, not only after the completion of the Great Western main line, but also with the construction of the Oxford branch in 1843-44. Once again, the Commissioners fought to prevent the construction of the railway as they considered the line a threat to the river's future. The Commissioners meeting on 16 February 1843 quickly resolved:

'*that the projected railway from Oxford to Didcot will be very injurious to the Navigation and to all interests connected with it and that the Petition against it now be adopted, signed and forthwith presented to the House of Lords*'.

But, despite these predictable statements, the Bill received the Royal Assent on 11 April 1843.

CHAPTER TWENTY-FOUR
RESIDENT ENGINEERS

In line with the decision to appoint a Bristol and London Committee for the general management of the railway, it was also decided that the construction of the railway would follow the same constraints. Consequently, the line was divided into Bristol and London Divisions and although all the contracts along the whole line of railway were ultimately Brunel's responsibility, the day-to-day monitoring of the progress and quality of the work and measurement of the work completed by the contractor for payment purposes, was undertaken by resident and assistant resident engineers. On 21 September 1835, Brunel had appointed George Frere as Resident Engineer for the works in the Bristol Division, while at the London end, John Hammond was placed in charge of the works, assisted by Robert Archibald.

For the first few years of the construction period, Brunel literally dealt with all the problems involved in the construction of the railway - and all the other projects he was involved with. His assistant engineers had little autonomy, their job being in the main to ensure that the Chief Engineer's instructions were carried out by the contractors. Any deviation from these instructions had to be reported back to Brunel who decided on any action that might be necessary. Brunel was particularly anxious that the brick viaducts and viaducts along the line of railway did not suffer from undue subsidence, writing to George Frere, shortly after his appointment as Resident Engineer for the Bristol Division in the following terms:

'Regarding the bridges along the line, in the first place I require a very accurate measurement taken of the sinking of all arches from the smallest to the largest. This is to be done by drawing a straight line across the arch as soon as you can after the mortar is set. Do this by means of a straight edge and after that by whipcord stretched to its utmost. From time to time - particularly after the centreing is struck - this line must be examined and any deviation noted. Until results are accurately obtained, we must allow for the 'probable' settling. Over arches, the brickwork courses of the spandrel walls and the string courses and coping stones must be set up out of their straight line, whether this be a straight or a curved one, by about 1/20th in. per foot span'.

As the number of contracts increased, the number of resident and assistant resident engineers increased, as Brunel - reluctantly - had concluded that he would not be able to supervise all the work, particularly as the contracts in the intermediate section i.e. between Reading and Bath were let. Consequently, on 20 September 1838, the Directors approved the appointment of additional engineers:

'To relieve the Engineer in Chief from the heavy and complicated detail of business which has hitherto engaged his attention'.

However, despite the subsequent increase in the number of resident engineers and assistants, Brunel continued to keep a critical eye on the progress of the works and the quality of workmanship, few details escaping his attention.

One such resident engineer on the works of the Great Western Railway was Michael Lane. Born on the 26 October 1802 in London, his professional career commenced working on the Thames Tunnel in 1825 when he joined the staff of Sir Marc Isambard Brunel as a foreman bricklayer. From 1832 to 1834, he was engaged at the Bristol Docks as Resident Engineer under Isambard Kingdom Brunel, from where he transferred to the Monkwearmouth Dock, Sunderland (north shore) which he also supervised for Brunel. Remaining in charge of the Monkwearmouth works until December 1840, he then became connected with the Great Western Railway, acting as assistant to G. E. Frere the Resident Engineer of the western division of the line. Two years later, he accepted the appointment of Resident Engineer to the Hull Docks where he remained until August 1845, when he rejoined the Great Western Railway, becoming Superintendent of permanent way for one of the Company's Divisions. He held this position for 14 years, eventually in 1860 becoming Chief Engineer of the Great Western Railway after the death of Brunel.

Every major contract along the line of railway would have its own resident engineer and sometimes an assistant resident engineer, as well as a surveyor. Brunel appeared to adopt a benevolent, but strict relationship with his assistants and 'sub-assistants', the latter being frequently very young men at the start of their careers. These young engineering apprentices, who were to eventually find themselves working under Brunel, could consider themselves privileged and their dedication to improving their own careers would be tested to the full. Brunel - in a letter dated 16 January 1836 - to a prospective employee, described the terms under which the young man could expect to be employed:

> *'... I must explain to you the terms upon which you or any other gentleman, must enter the service of the Great Western Railway. The sub-assistants must be considered as working entirely for promotion, their salaries and their continued employment depend entirely upon the degree of industry and ability I find they possess. Their salaries commence at £150p.a. and may be increased progressively up to £250 and perhaps in some cases to £350p.a. They must reside on such part of the line as required, consider their whole time, to any extent required, at the service of the Company and will be liable to instant dismissal should they appear to me to be inefficient from any cause whatsoever and, more particularly, to consider themselves as on trial only'.*

One such young assistant resident engineer who agreed to Brunel's terms was Thomas E. M. Marsh who was born at Biddestone, Wilts on 3 April 1818. The son of Major Henry Marsh of Grosvenor Place, Bath, Marsh trained as a civil engineer on the Great Western Railway during the period of construction and in the Autumn of 1837 was entrusted by Brunel with the recording and removal of the remains of the Roman villa at Newton St. Loe, which had been revealed during the excavation of a cutting. Entries in Marsh's surveyor's notebook - now preserved in the Bristol City Museum collection - shows that the young engineer worked intermittently on the site between 29 October and 24 December 1837. During this time, he produced plans and sections of the villa buildings and drawings of the mosaics, including a full-size tracing of the famous Orpheus pavement, later

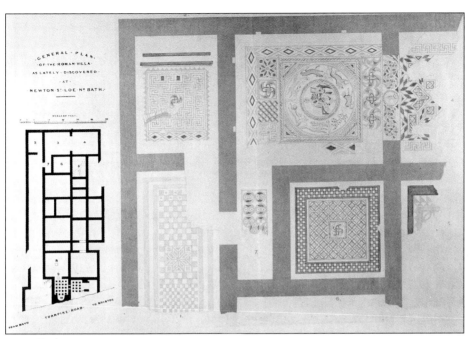

FIGURE 47. Above: General plan of the Roman villa discovered during the construction of the Great Western Railway at Newton St Loe, near Bath.

Left: Tessellated pavement from the Roman villa. This floor - which contained the central figure of Orpheus - was relaid in the Great Western Railway station at Keynsham, near Bristol until finally being donated to Bristol Museum in 1851.

Below: Drawings by Thomas E. M. Marsh of pillars found during excavation of the Roman villa.
(Department of Archaeology,
City of Bristol Museum & Art Gallery)

141

writing that he had:

> *'prepared as a precautionary measure in the case the falling apart of the tessera of that portion which would be difficult to restore with exactness'.*

He also successfully lifted and removed the Orpheus pavement and another geometric mosaic, which were displayed at the Great Western's Keynsham station near Bristol until 1851.

After 1837, Marsh continued his career as a railway engineer. He left the Great Western Railway in 1841 having risen to become resident engineer for the Bath section of the line and assisted with the construction of Box Tunnel. Thereafter, he worked in responsible positions for a number of British railway companies and was entrusted with several major projects by Brunel and his successor Sir John Hawkshaw. In the 1850s and 1860s, Marsh travelled widely abroad, constructing and inspecting new railway systems as far afield as Canada, Argentina, India, Mauritius and Australia.

Apart from his work at Newton St. Loe, Marsh does not appear to have taken any special interest in archaeology. He did, however, preserve his excavation records carefully. When Bristol City Museum was researching the Orpheus pavement in the early 1930s, the Curator of Archaeology & Anthropology at that time, was able to contact Marsh's daughter, who in 1936 deposited her father's notes and drawings, including the tracing of the Orpheus mosaic to the City Museum. Marsh died at Grosvenor Place, Bath on 19 December 1907 and is buried in Lansdown Cemetery.

The role of the resident engineers and their assistants during the construction of the Great Western Railway was extremely important. Without their diligence, Brunel's task would have proved virtually impossible and the line would never have been finished on time.

CHAPTER TWENTY-FIVE
DELAYS

The considerable delay in allocating the contracts for the Gatehampton and Moulsford bridges had already delayed the commencement of the construction longer than anticipated, but further problems would occur which was to delay even further the start of the bridge at Moulsford. This delay was due to a miscalculation, which proved that not even Brunel was infallible.

The earliest record of work commencing on the bridges over the Thames west of Pangbourne was a mention in a local journal of 14 July 1838, which stated:

'About a mile on the east side of Streatley [Gatehampton] piles are being driven to erect the bridges over the Thames'.

This statement confirms that the Gatehampton viaduct was the first to be commenced. While it might be expected that the labour force working on the bridges - skilled artisans compared to the men constructing the earthworks - would have completed the foundations on one bridge first, before moving to the second bridge, this did not account for the additional delays suffered by the Moulsford bridge.

Problems had quickly become apparent as the surveyors began to determine the exact line that the bridge at Moulsford would take. Brunel had originally intended that both bridges would be more-or-less identical and that the quantities and calculations for the Gatehampton bridge would be the same for both bridges. However, this proved not to be the case as Brunel appeared to have miscalculated the considerable wash of the river at Moulsford and on 13 September 1838, the engineer advised the Directors that the design of the bridge at Moulsford would need to be modified. The engineer also reported a revised figure of the estimated costs of Contract '2R', although he confirmed that even this revised figure could not be guaranteed to be correct. The original costs of both bridges had been estimated to be £24,241-10s-0d each. With deductions, the final estimate of Contract '1R' was eventually reduced to £23,053-10s-0d. However, Contract '2R' - because of the problems experienced with the wash of the river at Moulsford - was provisionally increased to £32,908. Brunel's report read:

'In Mr. Chadwick's original tender for No. 1 & 2R Contracts, the tender for No. 2R was made on the supposition of the quantities being the same as in No, 1R.

In setting out the work however it became necessary to increase their quantities and particular in consequence of the wash of the river through the channel passing the proposed site of the west abutment. Having determined their quantities exactly on the working drawings and have thought it better as the amount is large that it should all be included in the Contract instead of forming extras. The total amount in the ratio of the original contract will be £32,908 subject to some small reductions which have since been found practicable but which can be ascertained only as the work proceeds and must therefore be rated by the schedule of prices'.

FIGURE 48. The Gatehampton bridge - or 'Basildon Bridge' - incorrectly depicted by John Cooke Bourne. *(OPC/BR)*

FIGURE 49. Brunel's viaduct at Gatehampton today. During the 1892 quadrupling of the main line between Didcot and Paddington, the original structure was doubled in width, the original arches being faithfully copied on the west side. *(Author's collection)*

Chadwick (on the same day as Brunel reported to the Directors), requested that £5,000 be advanced to pay for the construction of coffer dams for the Moulsford bridge. However, the Directors rejected the contractor's request, only agreeing to an advance of £2,500.

The problem with the siting of the bridge at Moulsford being eventually resolved, the construction of the structure began. Although the exact date the bridge was commenced is not known, there is ample evidence to confirm that this was in the Autumn of 1838. By this time, the earthworks to the east and west of the bridge were well underway, as a report on 18 July 1838 confirms that the highest part of the Cholsey Common Field had been excavated and that:

'a chalk embankment had been thrown up'.

This was presumably the short embankment from the east of the Reading-Wallingford-Oxford turnpike to the west bank of the Thames at Moulsford, the site of the bridge which had yet to be started. The same situation prevailed in the east, where chalk cuttings were being excavated and embankments thrown up. At both bridge sites, temporary and very dangerous bridges - wooden walkways about 2-ft. 6-in. wide - were erected across the river. However, following an accident at Gatehampton on 24 November 1838 when a drunken labourer drowned, watchmen were stationed to ensure that a similar accident would not occur again.

The men who were building the bridges were in the main very skilled and S. M. Peto - the famous contractor - described them as:

'quiet, well-behaved men; we do not often find fault with them'.

The artisans constructing the bridges across the Thames were, perhaps, subject to even more risks than the labourers who were constructing the earthworks. They were also more exposed to the vagrancies of the weather, perched on their lofty scaffolding in high winds and above violently surging water. The River Thames in the early 19th-Century was not so deep or wide as the river is now, nonetheless, the river was as lethal then as it is today. The extremely precarious and exposed positions of the men working on the bridges was exacerbated at times by the weather conditions, particularly high winds.

January 1838 had begun with severe snow and frost in West Berkshire and ice 8-in. thick had been recorded on the Thames. This weather continued and on 21 April 1838 - about the time the labourers moved into the Parish of Cholsey to commence the works on Contract '4R' - snow was still falling. However, the arrival of May recorded thundery weather with a noon temperature of 70-deg. The summer of 1838 passed with no extremes of weather being recorded. However in the last week of October of the same year, a violent storm - described locally as a 'hurricane' - hit the area. The New Year again saw high winds and on 12 January 1839, it was reported that a bricklayer working on the bridge at Gatehampton had been blown off scaffolding into the water. The body was found almost a month later near Reading, with just the head and shoulders floating above the water. The spring of 1839 saw fair weather with a temperature of 73-deg recorded on 30 April. However, on 14-15 May heavy falls of snow blanketed west Berkshire. This sudden snap of cold weather was short-lived and a good summer followed, although further problems were to arise during the autumn of 1839. In October very wet weather was experienced and consequently, the Thames flooded. Late November saw sharp frosts and a further flood, together with a heavy fall of snow and by the beginning of December, the weather was very cold and foggy.

At this time, Brunel reported to the Directors on the state of the Moulsford bridge and some of the other works on the line. The engineer expressed his opinion that owing to the recent wet weather, the line could not be completed for opening to Faringdon until at least 1 May 1840. To make matters worse, another flood occurred on Christmas Eve 1839 and with the arrival of the New Year, there was little improvement in the weather. More high winds occurred in the third week of January and further floods occurred on the Thames, but this wet weather had changed by April to very dry and warm climatic conditions.

For the men working on the railway contracts west of Reading, the weather during the period 1838-40 had not been particularly kind and the initial delays in determining the site and specifications of the Moulsford bridge had already ensured that this particular contract would not be finished on time. Despite the delays with the Moulsford bridge, by the end of August 1839, most of the works west of Reading - including the viaduct at Gatehampton had been completed. Brunel anticipated that the 20½-miles from Reading to Steventon would eventually open to the public on Monday 1 June 1840. Although later than the engineer had originally planned - because of the delays caused by the weather and the consequent flooding of the river - this was the earliest date possible. In February 1840, Brunel reported that:

> *'Beyond Reading and up to Didcot, a distance of 17½ miles, the ballasting is completed with the exception of two short lengths, together about 2½ miles. The difficulty of procuring ballast for this part has been very great; the ground purchased for this purpose being under water, and it being necessary to resort to dredging the river to obtain gravel'.*

CHAPTER TWENTY-SIX
THE THAMES COMMISSIONERS AND THE TWO BRIDGES AT GATEHAMPTON AND MOULSFORD

Brunel, when giving evidence before the Parliamentary Committee in 1835, appeared not to have decided on a final specification for either of the two bridges over the Thames at Gatehampton or Moulsford. However, the actual sites of both bridges were well established well before this date and it appears that Brunel - as with the Maidenhead bridge - had not consulted the guardians of the river in any way about the effects the bridges would have on the river borne traffic.

At a meeting of the Commissioners held at Marlow on 30 June 1837, the General Surveyor was directed to obtain before the next meeting, plans of the projected railway bridges at 'Goring and Gatehampton'. The mention of Goring may give some indication of the lack of information available to the Commissioners at that time. It appears that once again Brunel had chosen to ignore the Commissioners and this apparent disdain on the part of Brunel may have been deliberate or may have been because the plans of the bridges simply were not available. However, at the next meeting of the Commissioners held at Abingdon on 7-9 August, the 'plan' of the projected railway bridge at Gatehampton was exhibited and approved by the General Surveyor. It is to be noted that only the plan of the Gatehampton bridge was exhibited, this being due to the fact that at this stage, Brunel had assumed that the two bridges would be more-or-less identical.

Once construction of the line of railway began, problems quickly arose with the navigation, bargemasters complaining of the encroachment of the railway works at several sites west of Reading. The main complaints involved the towing path at Purley - between Reading and Pangbourne - and the sites of the Gatehampton and Moulsford bridges. The Commissioners appointed a small committee to investigate the complaints and two officials quickly arranged to meet Chadwick - the contractor for both bridges - and Mr. Mitchell (the resident engineer for the Gatehampton bridge), however, Grainger, the resident engineer for the Moulsford bridge, did not attend. The meeting took place at the site of the Moulsford bridge on 10 November 1838, when it appears that confusion was the order of the day, both the contractor and resident engineer denying receiving any specific instructions regarding the construction of the towing path under the Gatehampton bridge. The two officials on reporting back to the Commissioners meeting at Wallingford on 8 November 1838, stated:

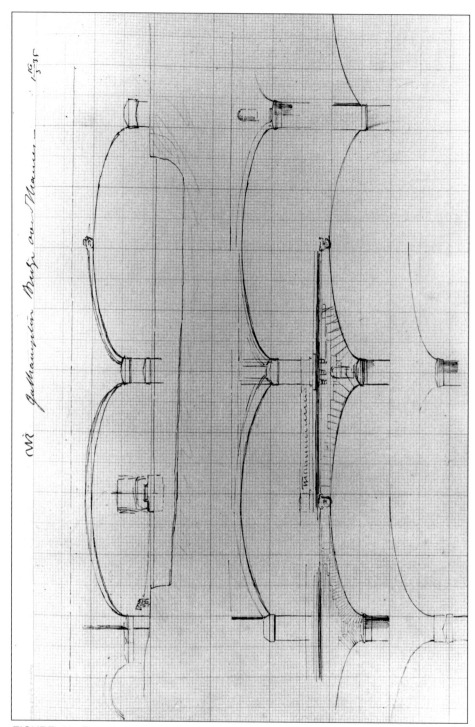

FIGURE 50. Brunel's original sketches for the Gatehampton railway bridge over the Thames. In the end, the lavish embellishments were rejected and the bridge was constructed almost entirely of locally made red bricks with minimal Bath stone dressings.
(Reproduced by kind permission of the Librarian of the University of Bristol)

'We stated the object of our coming, and shewed them the plan of the bridge sent to the Commissioners of the Thames Navigation by Mr. Brunel. & marked with his initials - Mr. Chadwick stated that his contract only extended to the formation of a temporary towing path - that Mr. Brunel had told him that the Company intended to make the permanent ones themselves - Mr. Mitchell said that he had received no instructions on the subject - the dam made for constructing the pier of the bridge, by the side of which the towing path is intended to pass as shewn on Mr. Brunel's plans, is formed entirely of buck piles, and it seems probable from this, coupled with the fact that the piles of the other dams, which will of course be drawn up when done with being of foreign timber, as well as from one or two statements by Mr. Mitchell that it is the intention of the Company to leave this dam for the future towing path. This the Company cannot allow for it is notorious that buck when exposed to the alternations of wet & dry would not last more than two or three years, consequently in the course of the period these piles, the only support of the towing path on the river side will give way with very serious inconvenience to the navigation & heavy expenditure must be incurred in a proper substantial towing path. We recommend therefore the General Clerk should immediately apply to the Secretary of the Great Western Railway to be furnished with a specification of the permanent towing path proposed to be made by the Company for the use of the Thames Navigation and an undertaking by him on the part of the Company that it shall be constructed to the approbation of the Commissioners and their surveyor'.*

On 13 October 1838, the General Clerk of the Navigation reported to the Commissioners meeting at Reading, that he had written to Brunel in the terms suggested. Brunel replied on 22 October 1838:

'Your letter of the 14 in reference to my assistant engineer and as I was out of town till the 18th not much time has been lost. The buck piles which you speak off will be cut off below water and the upper work necessary for the towing paths constructed of brick or other suitable materials'.*

The Commissioners concerns regarding the disruption to the towing paths were understandable, as they were justifiably proud of the system of towing paths which had been gradually been improved over the years. Originally, barges had been hauled along the navigation by teams of men, with sometimes as many as 80 men being needed to tow a fully laden barge upstream. In some locations, the towpath changed from one side of the river to the other and over the years territories developed, men from adjacent communities becoming responsible for towing barges along the towpath on their side of the river. These local hauliers - who had nearly as bad a reputation as the railway navvies - would haul a barge until the towpath ended on their side of the river, the tow then passing to a similar team on the opposite river bank. However, as the teams of men became more expensive to hire, horses began to be increasingly substituted and sometimes men and horses could be seen waiting on the towing paths waiting to take up a tow.

As can be seen, there were adequate reasons for the concern expressed by the Commissioners and their attempts to protect the towing paths. Brunel's letter of 22 October did nothing to reassure them and on 7 November the General Clerk was instructed to again write to the Great Western Railway. The clerk's tone in his letter attempted to convey the frustrations being experienced by the Commissioners:

'*require more premtarily than hereto before, the immediate removal of the frameworks, & the establishment of the towing path under the arch, the absence whereof has been the subject of great & reiterated complaints from the bargemasters. To also complain about the inconvenience arising to the trade about the want of headway at Moulsford Bridge, and also the bad state of the towing path there & Gatehampton*'.

The date when the centreings of both the Moulsford and Gatehampton bridges were eased and finally removed is not known, however, if previous experiences were anything to go by, it is doubtful whether Brunel would be hurried. A Minute, dated 7 November 1839 was the last reference to the Great Western Railway in the Thames Commissioner's records and it appears that the Commissioners were forced to accept that there was little they could do to force Brunel's compliance. It must be assumed that the officials of the river and railway begrudgingly settled their differences and that trade on the Thames eventually resumed some semblance of normality, albeit temporarily, with the railway gradually taking over most of the water-borne trade.

The Thames Commissioners and the Directors of the Great Western Railway do not appear to have crossed swords again until 1843-44, when the Oxford branchline was being constructed, when similar problems occurred with hindrance to the navigation.

FIGURE 51. The four graceful arches of Brunel's Moulsford bridge. The viaduct remains as originally constructed, except for the addition of 'refuges' in the parapets, introduced for safety reasons. *(Author's collection)*

CHAPTER TWENTY-SEVEN
THE CONSTRUCTION OF THE BRIDGES

The hindrance to the barge traffic on the Thames at Maidenhead, Gatehampton and Moulsford must have been considerable during the period of the construction of the Great Western Railway. The period was the start of the contest between river and railway for particularly goods traffic, a battle which the railway would inevitably win. The derisory attitude displayed by Brunel towards the Thames Commissioners was - perhaps - unfairly diverted to the barge masters, initially causing disturbance to their trade, but also ensuring that their livelihood was eventually almost totally destroyed.

At an earlier period in the history of the Thames, barges of 160-180 tons plied their trade with dimensions of 128ft length, 18ft 2in. beam and 4ft draught. Because of the huge sizes of these barges, much damage and inconvenience was caused on the river and before the end of the 18th-century, barges of 70 tons were more the norm. Brunel had to consider all these aspects when he designed the bridges which spanned the Thames and planned their construction. While the engineer would have had to make some arrangements for the continuing traffic on the river during the construction period and after, the evidence indicates that this aspect was of low priority. While accepting that gauging the various moods of the river over several years was an unpredictable exercise, it would appear that the considerable numbers of people employed directly or indirectly with the river-borne traffic were considered secondary by Brunel. In his mind, undoubtedly the railway always came first!

Perhaps some idea of the restrictions experienced by the river traffic at this period can be obtained by examining the procedures adopted for the widening of both viaducts at Gatehampton and Moulsford during the 1890s. The Great Western Railway had by now adopted a more conciliatory attitude to the river authorities, as by this time the traffic on the Thames had severally declined due to the effects of the railway. The Traffic Committee, meeting on 4 June 1890, approved plans for the quadrupling of the tracks, including the construction of new bridges at Moulsford and Gatehampton and plans dated 17 April 1890 give details of the likely restrictions at the two viaducts.

During the widening, the Moulsford bridge - built at a skew angle of 45 degrees - would be duplicated using Brunel's original design, except that brick would be substituted for the elegant Bath stone voussoirs. Again the river passage would be severely restricted, the new arches being constructed using centreings and staging that would block the passage of river traffic completely, except for a narrow opening 24ft wide under the eastern arch for the use of water-borne traffic. The two western arches were almost completely impeded by the construction of the

FIGURE 52. Laying the spandrel walls on a viaduct.

(Leicestershire Museums, Arts & Records Service)

supporting frameworks and staging.

Although a plan exists in the Bristol University Library of the centreing used on the original Moulsford viaduct, this is unsuitable for publication. Almost certainly, Brunel was responsible for the calculations and designs of these temporary and massive wooden constructions, evidenced by a sketch of the centreings used for the construction of the viaduct across the Brent Valley which appears in one of Brunel's early sketchbooks.

The design of the centreings would have been calculated at the same time as the the bridge specifications were completed and included with the final specification to the contractor. The frameworks had to be strong and stiff enough to ensure that they could absorb the total load that was likely to be placed upon them, without appreciably deflecting. Upon the completion of the construction of the piers of the viaduct, the centreings had to be used to form and carry the superstructure of the viaduct. These massive curved wooden structures were covered with substantial boards - called 'lagging' - onto which the superstructure of the bridge would be built. The centreings were normally supported on 'outer' props either securely founded on the stepped foundation of the piers constructed on the river bed, or by 'inner' props firmly embedded in the river bed. Between the props and the framework were 'folding wedges' or 'slack blocks', by which the centreings could be 'eased' following the completion of the superstructure of the viaduct.

As previously stated, a plan of the original centreings used for the Moulsford viaduct is still extant, although the specification of the centreings is unclear. However, a full set of plans used when the line was quadrupled and the bridges either widened or extended is still in existence, detailing the specifications of the centreings to be used. The wooden frameworks were to be supported on 12-in. x 12-in. props and to facilitate easier penetration of the riverbed, the props were pointed and faced with metal. The lagging consisted of 4-in. thick planks. The

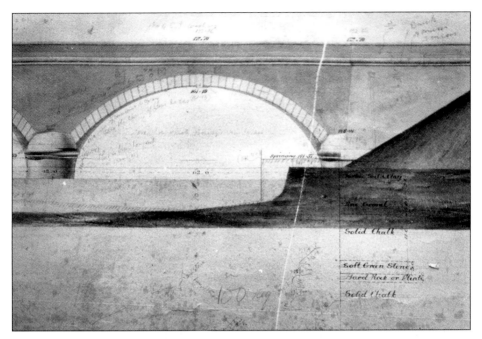

FIGURE 53. Plan of the original Moulsford bridge showing that the foundations for the structure were built on solid chalk some 29 feet below surface ground level.

(Author's Collection)

slack-blocks measured 2¹/₂-in. at the thinnest point and 5-in. at the widest. The easing of these wedges allowed for a maximum of 7¹/₂-in. compression when all the material in the viaduct settled (Brunel allowed for a maximum of 7in. compression in the design of the Thames railway bridges).

As any structure largely depends on a foundation for stability, such foundations have to carry an even load over their entire area. As it is essential that any faults in foundations are eliminated before the construction of the structure is begun, close examination of the ground on which it is intended to place a foundation is clearly necessary. In the case of the bridge at Moulsford, investigations by means of borings were carried out by Otto Heise which determined that a layer of hard chalk 29-ft below the surface would be suitable as a foundation.

The construction of the two bridges would inevitably disrupt the traffic on the river for a considerable period. At Moulsford, the towing path ran along the eastern side of the river bank and consequently it would be the eastern arch underneath which the towing path would eventually run. Under this eastern arch, the depth of the river was about 10-ft 6-in., while towards the west bank the water gradually shoaled, until finally no water would flow under the western arches unless the river was in flood. These 'dry' arches were essential, as it was imperative that the passage of the river - particular floodwater - was restricted as little as possible and failure to provide an escape route for excess flow could lead to scouring of the foundations of the bridge.

The foundations of all the Great Western Railway bridges over the Thames were constructed by the use of coffer dams. These dams were formed by first of all cutting to size huge baulks of timber to form 'piles'. The piles were rammed into the bed of the river in a continuous row to form a watertight barrier around the site of the foundation. Foundations in shallow waters could normally be excavated by the use of one row of piles. However, in deeper work or where the current was very strong, a double row of piles would be required, with a mixture of clay and sand mixed with water - known as 'puddling' - providing a watertight seal between the rows. The coffer dams would have severely restricted the river traffic and the later addition of the 'centreings' - or wooden frameworks - to facilitate the construction of the viaduct, plus additional staging would quickly cause further severe problems for the bargemasters. The timber piling was brought to the bridge sites by barge, then cut to size by hand, sawyers standing on top of the huge baulks, working in conjunction with other sawyers in pits below. The cost of cutting the timber for the coffer dams amounted to £250 for each bridge.

FIGURE 54. The view between the old and new viaducts across the Thames at Moulsford, with the original Brunel designed structure on the left. This bridge remains in its original form, apart from the brick arches which link it to the second viaduct, which was erected in the 1890s as part of the main-line quadrupling scheme and 'refuges' added in the mid-1970s.
(Author's collection)

CHAPTER TWENTY-EIGHT
CONSTRUCTION METHODS

Brunel's proposals for the unique bridge to carry the railway across the River Thames at Maidenhead gave rise to much anxiety among the Directors of the Great Western Railway, both during the construction and immediate post-construction period. Brunel himself appeared unperturbed and completely confident and he tried to calm the Directors' nerves by calmly informing them of the calculations he had used and the tolerances allowed for in the design of such a bridge. He confirmed that a total compression of all the material used in the construction of such a bridge could amount to as much as 7-in. - the amount he had allowed for in his designs. The Directors were advised that this maximum compression would have been caused by several factors:

'1. Sinking of the foundations.
2. Lateral motion in the abutments from the thrust of the arches.
3. The compression of the material forming the arches etc. which causes the settlement of the arches etc.
4. Alterations of form in the arches which might arise from the original form & dimensions of the arch being incorrect or from any excessive and unforseen movement in the first three points or from inequality in the third only, namely, the compressions from defective material. In the first striking of the centreings it is not unusual in stone bridges to see large spawls fly off, from the crushing of the material'.

Despite the knowledge that the Maidenhead bridge would set new records for the concept and design of brick built viaducts, Brunel appeared to have risked the whole project falling into disrepute by choosing a contractor for the construction of the bridge who was professionally inept. For the first major structure to be constructed in the London Division of the Great Western Railway - the Hanwell Viaduct - Brunel took no chances and chose the well-known contractors Grissell & Peto for the work. What is surprising is that Brunel placed the contract for the Maidenhead bridge - of equal status at least as the Hanwell Viaduct - in the hand of the contractor James Thomas Bedborough - a local builder! It was only because of the careful scrutiny of the resident engineer for the Maidenhead bridge who drew obvious discrepancies in the work to the attention of Brunel, that a major catastrophe was avoided.

Brunel's grand plans for both the bridges across the Thames west of Pangbourne appear to have been changed drastically for a variety of reasons. The engineer had originally assumed that the bridges at Gatehampton and Moulsford would be virtually identical, although as history records the end result was far from this! Partially through technical reasons, the Moulsford bridge became the most important, although an attempt by Brunel to appease the inhabitants of Wallingford and neighbourhood may be another important factor why the

Moulsford bridge became the most prominent.

The provisional tender price given by the contractor William Chadwick on 1 February 1838 for the construction of both the Gatehampton and Moulsford bridges was £45,000, although the final figure, as stated by Brunel on 1 September 1838 was '£24,241 10s 0d each'. However, due to adverse constructional difficulties, the Moulsford bridge finally cost £32,908.

The construction of the viaduct at Moulsford probably commenced in late 1838, as on 13 September 1838, Chadwick requested the Directors to authorise a payment of £5,000 for timber to construct the coffer dams. Belatedly, Chadwick had been informed on 1 February 1838 that his provisional tender for the two viaducts had been successful and it appears that little time was lost in commencing the viaduct at Gatehampton. The advertisement for Contract '3R', published on 24 February 1838, stated that the viaduct at Gatehampton was 'now building over the River Thames', although this statement might have a been little optimistic, as a report in a Reading journal on 14 July 1838, stated:

> *'About a mile east of Streatley piles are being driven to erect the bridges over the Thames'.*

There are, unfortunately, few details available about the actual construction of the two viaducts at Gatehampton and Moulsford. However, as it is unlikely that 19th-century bridge building techniques had altered little in this period, it is perhaps appropriate to give a description of the construction of a similar structure.

The canal age in Britain lasted roughly from 1760 to 1850. Probably the most interesting and attractive features of this bygone age were the aqueducts and these structures became to be regarded as the engineering triumphs of the eighteenth-century. Anthony Burton is his book 'The Canal Builders' gives this description of the construction of one such structure, the five-arch aqueduct - designed by John Rennie - which carried the Lancaster Canal over the River Lune. The scene is set from letters written by Archibald Millar the resident engineer to the Canal Committee in 1794.

The aqueduct when completed in 1796 cost the Canal Company a total of £48,000. Hundreds of workers had been involved in the construction and material had been brought from as far away as Italy - the 'pozzolana' - the waterproof mortar used in the foundations of the structure. Burton describes the scene at the site of the aqueduct and this probably differed little from the scenes at Maidenhead, Moulsford and Gatehampton when the bridges carrying the Great Western Railway over the river Thames were being completed:

> *The Lune aqueduct, like all the big aqueducts, took the canal across a river. This meant that the foundations had to go down into the river bed. The first stage was to build a coffer dam to keep the water out of the workings, and allow the navvies to begin the arduous job of pile driving for the foundations. Work on the Lune foundations began in January 1794 ... By March, they were beginning work in earnest, but things did not proceed with perfect smoothness. There were strikes and a number of hold-ups when the river flooded, overflowing the coffer dams, and in one case, carrying planks, piles and barrows away down-stream. Even when things were going well, the men who worked at the pile driving had to do so in the most atrocious*

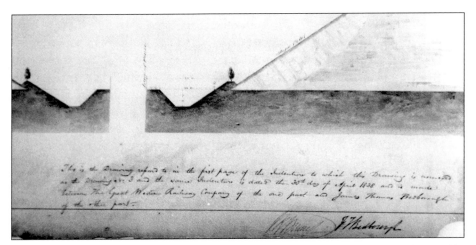

FIGURE 55. Section from drawing No. 3 from Contract '4R' with J. T. Bedborough's signature countersigned by Brunel and dated 30 April 1838. *(Author's collection)*

conditions, struggling in the mud behind the coffers in a pit which the pumps could never keep completely dry. The work of pile driving was hard and exhausting: as Millar reported to the Committee, 'it may be proper to give some small Sum dayly to the Pile Drivers in Drink'.

The job of cutting and sawing the massive piles was very little easier. The pile-driving engines, which had been constructed at the site, were crude, man-powered devices, and it is no surprise to find this entry for 6 May:

'a Labourer at the the Lune Aqueduct had the misfortune yesterday to have three of his Fingers on the right hand taken off by the Piling Ram falling upon them. I should recommend him to the attention of the Committee to give him a small sum to assist him in his present situation'.

The work on the aqueduct foundations ... continued at a reasonable pace into the Summer of 1794. By June, work on the coffer dam for the second pier had begun, and there were over 150 men at work - 127 labourers, 22 carpenters and 14 sawyers. ... The following month work on the second pier was so far advanced that there were eighty labourers at work in pile driving alone.

As the foundations were completed, so the next stage could be started. The masons came in and the scaffolding started to rise in readiness for the work on the arches. The area around the aqueduct was alive with activity. Hundreds of navvies were at work in cutting, banking and pile-driving. The steam engine was pumping night and day. The saw pits and carpenters shop was busy with the manufacture of piles and scaffolding. The masons were dressing stones for the piers. Carts passed continuously, bringing supplies of stone and timber'.

Similar scenes to the one described above were being repeated at numerous locations throughout Britain during the canal age and repeated during the later railway construction period, including the sites of Brunel's bridges across the Thames at Maidenhead, Moulsford and Gatehampton. Additionally at Moulsford, smoking brick kilns would have sent plumes of smoke into the pure and previously unpolluted air of the district, many thousands of bricks being hand-made adjacent to the site of the bridge.

At the bridge sites at Moulsford and Gatehampton an 'office' and an 'observatory' were constructed. At Gatehampton the office cost £23-6s-0d to construct, but at Moulsford a superior construction was built costing £33-7s-11d.

The function of the office is fairly self-explanatory, as here would have been kept the plans of the bridge and probably the artisans and labourers would have received their pay here. The definition of an 'observatory' - at a cost of £35 each - is more elusive, although one assumes this was probably a viewing platform, a lofty structure, built of wood which would allow the contractor or engineer to monitor the progress of the viaduct and the progress and lineation of the interconnecting embankments on either side.

The construction of the two bridges at Gatehampton and Moulsford would become part of the heritage left by Brunel. The viaducts - particularly at Moulsford - were elegant and in their original form were slender and aesthetically pleasing structures. The Moulsford viaduct - for whatever reason - appeared to have received special treatment and as this bridge is still in original form, it is an interesting experience to gaze upward between the gap between the original bridge and the later bridge which gives a perspective unobtainable at the sites of the two other Brunel bridges which still span the Thames.

FIGURE 56. Dimensions and inclinations of a standard Great Western Railway embankment. Note the hedge of 'Quicks' [hawthorn] and the drainage ditch.
(Reproduced by kind permission of the Librarian of the University of Bristol)

CHAPTER TWENTY-NINE
CONSTRUCTION MATERIALS

In the early days of railway construction, engineers such as Brunel were limited in the types of material they could use for the construction of structures. In later years, the success of the railway system enabled alternative materials to be used in locations where previously this had been impossible, the railway itself providing the mode of transport for the carriage of these new materials. A railway engineer - and particularly Brunel - would have been keenly aware of the intrusion of new buildings and other works in the previously rural scene along the line of railway. A successful designer could skillfully avoid aesthetic problems by blending the old with the new, using materials which were readily available in the neighbourhood. Further, the local people were already skilled in working these materials which would have been easy to come by, indeed some of the material would have been discovered as the works were excavated at virtually no cost to the railway company.

Brunel's natural inclination was to embellish the structures along the line of the Great Western Railway and evidence of this line of thought can be seen clearly today from Chippenham westwards. The engineer had originally intended that the whole line of railway should be similarly treated, but Brunel was frustrated in the London Division by the London Directors who frowned upon such frivolities. The London Directors had a reputation for their attitude towards superfluous embellishments, these being generally discouraged, while the Bristol Directors adopted a totally different attitude. Indeed, on several occasions the Bristol Directors were chided for their spendthrift attitude and George Henry Gibbs - one of the most prominent members of the London Committee - had discussions on several occasions with members of the Bristol Committee on the importance of keeping costs down. Consequently, it is noticeable that most of the architectural work in the eastern part of the railway and under the control of the London Committee is severely plain.

The parsimonious attitude of the London Committee was clearly at odds with the thoughts of the Bristol Committee and particularly when it applied to the proposed Bristol terminus. The following extract is from a letter dated 27 July 1839 from Thomas Osler, the Secretary of the Bristol Committee, to Saunders. The letter dealt with the anxieties of the Bristol Committee over the architectural features of the proposed station at Temple Meads, which the Committee felt should be in harmony with other notable buildings in the city, 'as far as motives of economy would permit':

'My dear Saunders, With regards to the Temple Meads Station and the great importance of its economical construction, the Directors here are persuaded it will be seen the [sic] every attention has been given to that essential object. So extreme was the anxiety felt on the first discussion of particulars that it was considered whether it would not be advisable to erect nothing more than

FIGURE 57 It was fitting that the City of Bristol - which played such a prominent part in the promotion of the Great Western Railway - should have found itself rewarded with such a handsome station, with the building occupying approximately one acre of land. Brunel put much care and thought into the planning and design of the original station in order to ensure that the building was in keeping with its surroundings. The building contained the booking hall and the magnificent train shed had an enormous mock hammerbeam roof which rested on arcades of Tudor style cast iron columns - a roof with a span of 72 feet - the widest single span of the age. The Boardroom of the Bristol Committee fronted onto Temple Gate and the building also housed the drawing offices, while beneath the platforms were extensive vaulted arches - in all over 72,000 feet of space.   *(OPC/BR)*

a mere wall in the line of the public road for the purpose, rather than any other, of concealing such plain buildings or sheds as would be indispensable to the temporary conduct of the business, leaving any erections of a more permanent character to be provided at a future period. On following out this idea, however, it was soon perceived that it would entail a long train of subsequent and considerable expense, as well as occasion a very serious amount of practical inconvenience which would be obviated by at once proceeding to erect Buildings that, as far as they went, would be of a permanent description. Brunel was instructed, therefore, to prepare plans of such offices only as were requisite and which were to be as devoid of ornament as was consistent with decent sightliness. In a week or two afterwards he submitted a couple of Elevations. The first of his sketches exhibited a plain specimen of what I believe is now called the 'Tudor' style; the second - with the exception of an open arch or gateway of the simplest kind at each end - consisted I think of as thoroughly naked an assemblage of walls and windows as could well be permitted to enclose any Union Poor House in the Country. A single glance at the two seemed to indicate that however agreeable the former might be to our tastes the latter was the thing for our pockets, but the Directors found, to their surprise, that the cost of the 'Tudor' front would exceed that of its Quaker companion by just £90. Now presuming the expense to be not materially different, many reasons presented themselves for preferring the Gothic facade. It harmonized not only with the character of the Bridges, Archways, etc., already built from Bath westward, but with the peculiar features of the better specimens of Bristol Architecture generally, it required less expenditure of ground room and it enabled the making of any subsequent additions that may be found necessary when the line is at work without involving such violation of symmetry in external outline as would be inevitable in an Italian design. The

Tudor style was therefore selected and the Bristol Directors are persuaded that their London Colleagues will approve the preference'.

Faced with such an argument, perhaps it is not surprising that the London Directors did not oppose this proposal. However, the question has to be posed, were the Bristol Directors in collusion with Brunel over the plans and estimates for the Bristol terminus, thus ensuring that the cost factor was not an overriding issue?

Brunel himself had very early on realised the potential of the use of Bath stone, which would be excavated in large quantities in the Bath area during the construction of the railway and Brunel stated in May 1836:

'In Dr. Fox's Wood the embankment is proceeding, the excavation at each end consists of very hard stone - from this part of it was always expected that we should obtain excellent materials for the construction of the Avon Bridge and the masonry generally and we have no cause to be disappointed - at the west end particularly a quarry of very fine stone has been opened and is now working and an ample supply of good stone for the smaller work may also be selected from the excavation at the eastern end'.

It could be expected that Bath stone would be used in profusion during the construction of the railway in the vicinity of Bath and Bristol, as the material was free and transport was minimal. However, Brunel's intentions to use Bath stone further east would involve transport costs and the question needs to be posed why did the engineer only succeed in obtaining the London Committee's permission to embellish only a few structures in the London Division?

Normally, the selection of stone for railway work required the source to be easily accessible and if possible, quarried close to the work to be completed. The material

FIGURE 58. A flint knapper preparing raw flints as a building material.
(Print supplied by the Rural History Centre, University of Reading)

needed to be easily and cheaply worked, durable, hard, strong and especially in large structures, capable of withstanding crushing through compression. Early on in the construction of the Great Western Railway, the Directors were approached by Cornish quarrymen anxious to sell their famous granite, an approach which was rejected, Brunel taking the more obvious course of action and using Bath stone which was readily available.

Building stone can be divided into four classes: granite and other igneous rocks, slate, sandstone and limestone. Of these categories, the last two would be used most successfully by Brunel for the construction of the Great Western Railway, particularly limestone. Oolitic limestone was one of the lightest building stones available, weighing 132-lb per cubic foot and this factor made the stone an ideal building material for transporting to distant locations by the primitive transport systems available in the 18-19th centuries. Prior to the opening of the Great Western Railway, Bath stone was used extensively in the Thames Valley and as far away as London, the opening of the Kennet & Avon Canal in 1810 allowing the stone to be transported from the Bath area by barge right through to London. Similarly, the Wilts & Berks Canal, although primarily used for the long distance transport of coal from the Somerset mines, was also used to carry stone from Bath and Bristol. The records of the Wilts & Berks Canal Company record that a considerable amount of Bath stone was carried for the construction of the locomotive works at Swindon, after the Directors of the Great Western Railway had decided in October 1840 to construct the locomotive works, ancillary buildings and 300 cottages for workmen at Swindon - all in Bath stone.

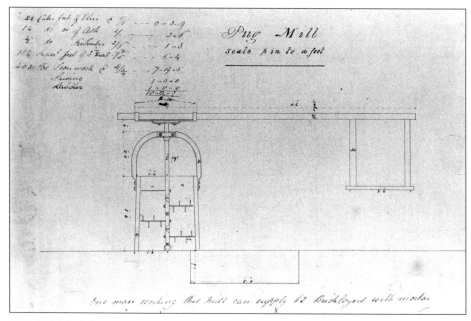

FIGURE 59. A Brunel designed 'Pug Mill' for making mortar. Note the legend 'one man working this mill can supply 12 bricklayers with mortar'.
(Reproduced by kind permission of the Librarian of the University of Bristol)

CHAPTER THIRTY
BRUNEL'S USE OF BATH STONE

The embellishing of bridges or other structures to pacify opposing or ambivalent landowners, was a practice which commenced during the canal building period. Many of the landowners - country squires - saw the canal as an irritating intrusion which would disturb their privacy and consequently they protested vociferously to Parliament:

'The Petitioners, being Owners or Occupiers of Houses and Lands near to or through which the Canal is intended to be cut, apprehend that great Injury will arise to them ... by the near Approach of the said intended Canal to the Houses and Pleasure Grounds of several of the Petitioners, which they have made at great Expence'.

The Kennet & Avon Canal, for construction and administration purposes had been divided into two parts. Rennie the Canal's engineer, had tried to ensure the smooth running of the construction by dividing the work into two sections and appointing a resident engineer to each part, a practice Brunel would later adopt. The decision of the embryonic Great Western Railway to adopt the Kennet & Avon's style of management with two separate committees of Directors, was a matter of some frustration for Brunel, the engineer once referring to the London Committee as 'a bunch of old women'.

The London Committee's attitude to frivolous expenditure is well recorded and Brunel's artistic and architectural traits were clearly inhibited by the dictates of the London Directors. In the Bristol Division, there were far less restrictions, Brunel's artistic abilities being used to their best advantage. Nevertheless, the London Committee did relent in some situations and the proposed Bath stone embellishments for the Moulsford station and the Moulsford and Gatehampton bridges are examples, although why such exceptions were permitted has not been clarified.

Therefore, the question has to be posed, were the Directors of the London Committee wrong in not allowing Brunel to use his considerable architectural and design talents to the full in the London Division? From the beginning, it had always been intended that the Great Western Railway would expand to the north and west of the kingdom by way of Oxford and Gloucester by 'probable' branches. If these plans came to fruition - as clearly was the intention - it would have been obvious to the hard-nosed businessmen who formed the London Committee that the whole infrastructure of the railway, particularly from Swindon eastwards, could soon be in a state of flux as the railway expanded and new and extra pressures were exerted on the original Brunellian line. What would be the benefit of unnecessary expenditure on permanent buildings which would probably need to be altered or torn down in the not too distant future? Where was the requirement for bridges and other structures to be ornamented, when almost certainly widening or other alteration would be required to cope with the needs of the expanding railway?

As history records this was certainly the case from Didcot eastwards, the line requiring urgent quadrupling to cope with the increased traffic from north to south and vice versa. With widening powers being authorised by Parliament in 1873, the line from Didcot to Paddington was completely quadrupled by 1899. The inevitable result was that the whole of this section of the line changed dramatically during this massive operation and most of the Brunellian features either disappeared, or were altered in some shape or form. By accident or design, the London Committee's frugality and their refusal to allow Brunel to run amok during the early construction period eliminated much unnecessary expenditure at an early and critical part of the Company's history and also enabled far-reaching changes to be carried out reasonably easy and cheaply when the line required essential expansion.

Brunel, by his decision to follow the Thames through the Goring Gap had reluctantly determined the necessity of bridges across the Thames at Gatehampton and Moulsford. The engineer had determined on this route during the first and second surveys and the sites of the viaducts decided at an early stage. The Second Great Western Bill passed through the House of Lords on 10 June 1835, the Bill then being referred to an investigating Committee. Brunel when giving evidence before this Committee, appears emphatic that both bridges would consist of two arches with spans of 75-feet each and four arches of 30-feet span each. Brunel's thoughts on the designs for the viaducts at Moulsford and Gatehampton are first captured in one of the engineer's sketchbooks dated 16 March 1835, in a drawing entitled 'GWR Gathampton Bridge over Thames'. The proposed bridge(s) are illustrated, but there is no suggestion in this drawing of the decorative voissours which would decorate the final design. However, Brunel does include a decorative keystone in one of the arches and one, perhaps, can ponder what motif the engineer have chosen to have decorated this important stone? Would it have the been the coat-of-arms of an important local person, similar to the Wharncliffe Viaduct across the Brent Valley at Hanwell, where Lord Wharncliffe had given his permission for his personal seal to be emblazoned on the centre of the south face of the structure?

Clearly illustrated in these drawings is Brunel's penchant for the decorative use of oolitic stone embellishments on both major and minor structures along the line of railway. Various suggestions for the voissours on bridge structures are tried and carved balustrades also appear, while designs for piers and cutwaters are explored. What also becomes evident is that Brunel intended to make the Gatehampton and Moulsford bridges more-or-less identical. This would be later confirmed by the known facts, that only one set of plans and specifications were drawn up. This is evidenced in a latter from William Chadwick - the contractor for both bridges - dated 1 February 1838 in which he states:

> *'Gentlemen, I am willing to undertake the works in erecting the two Thames bridges beyond Pangbourne for the sum of forty-five thousand pounds and to complete the works in twelve months from the date of the notice, with the undertaking that the extent of the work in the bridge*

FIGURE 60. The west portal of Box Tunnel in pristine condition in 1986 after a recent clean. Note the decorative 'acanthus' leaf keystone, a device Brunel used several times in the vicinity of Bath. Inset: a plaque erected in recent years.   *(Author's collection)*

beyond Streatley [Moulsford], is the same as the Gathampton Bridge (the plans of which I have inspected) which contains 7630 yards of brickwork and 12600 feet of stone'.

It becomes clear from this correspondence that Brunel intended to use Bath stone in considerable quantities for both viaducts.

Saunders authorised the Company's firm of solicitors on 10 April 1838 to forward the contracts for the construction of both bridges to Chadwick, stating:

'I see no objection to your sending the contracts to Mr. Chadwick for his signature if it be not an unusual course, but even then of course we must be subject to his suggesting alterations which would involve the necessity of reingrossment'.

There is perhaps, a hint here about the uncertainty of the final specifications for particularly the Moulsford bridge and to the delays which would take place in completing this particular structure.

It is also of interest that Brunel's earliest sketch of the Gatehampton Bridge shows a clearly defined towing path, complete with a single horse towing a barge, the horse being assisted by the vessel's own sail. Despite this early awareness that he would need to make arrangements for the towing path at Moulsford and Gatehampton, these facts appear to have been low on Brunel's list of priorities. Indeed, the engineer appeared to have gone out of his way to antagonise the Thames Commissioners and the users of the river by either totally ignoring them or by his condescending attitude when forced into having dealings with them.

Even when completed, Brunel's viaducts across the Thames at the two sites would attract controversy. The engineer, as soon as the necessity for the two bridges had become apparent, had decided to decorate both structures with handsome Bath stone embellishments. Brunel tried to ensure that the two viaducts were aesthetically compatible with the local scenery and that they matched the great river which they spanned.

The viaduct at Gatehampton would attract the attentions of artist John Cooke Bourne, who published in 1846 an engraving of the bridge - along with other Great Western Railway subjects - in his famous treatise the 'Illustrated History of the Great Western Railway'. Bourne shows the 'Bassildon Bridge' in its correct setting, as visible through the second arch of the viaduct is the 'Grotto', which was a white bowed building originally part of the nearby Basildon estate. This building is still *in situ* today forming an attractive part of the river landscape on the western bank of the Thames. Bourne's drawing of the bridge clearly shows the viaduct, with the eastern span totally on the river bank and the bridge arches, complete with Bath stone voissours forming an attractive edge to each span. However, an inspection of the Gatehampton bridge confirms that the viaduct was never built with Bath stone voissours! The original bridge was built almost entirely of red brick - from local brickworks - with only copings, cutwaters and a narrow band of stone forming a drip-rail of natural stone. Any suggestion that the Bath stone was covered during the quadrupling of the main line during the 1890s is not valid, as the viaduct was widened on one side only, the junction with the old and new work being clearly visible.

This disappointing discrepancy in Bourne's work begs the question why was the viaduct at Gatehampton not constructed as Brunel intended and why was this structure treated differently to the viaduct at Moulsford? The author can only assume that because of the tight rein on expenditure exerted by the Directors in the London Division some savings had to be made. At Gatehampton, hand-made bricks were readily available from brickyards at Basildon and Bradfield, the use of which would have saved the transport costs of bringing the Bath stone to the site. Another factor may have been the amount of Bath stone Brunel had planned to use in the construction of the two viaducts. For some reason, the amount of stone estimated required by Brunel for the Gatehampton bridge was considerably more than that estimated for the Moulsford bridge i.e. Gatehampton 16,152 cubic yards - Moulsford 12,000 cubic yards. As can be seen, using brick would have brought about a considerable saving. However, that still leaves the question, if the Directors were so determined to reduce costs, why did they sanction the use of Bath stone for the Moulsford bridge, but not at Gatehampton?

CHAPTER THIRTY-ONE
BRUNEL'S DESIGNS FOR THE GATEHAMPTON AND MOULSFORD BRIDGES

Brunel's natural inclination to design an individual structure for each location along the length of the Great Western Railway was generally stifled by the Directors in the London Division and there is clear evidence that the engineer originally did not give that much consideration to the 'standardisation' of structures for which he is so much credited today. This 'individuality' applied to all aspects along the line of railway, with the engineer attempting to give each location individual consideration. However, Brunel later developed 'standard' plans, which were adapted to meet local needs, this particularly applying to station buildings.

The difference in the aesthetic qualities of the two bridges across the Thames poses the question, why did the Great Western Railway Directors allow Brunel to transport Bath stone for use at the Moulsford site? The final design of the Moulsford bridge was clearly meant to impress, but the reasons for this are unfortunately lost in the mists of time! Many of the brick bridges on Britain's embryonic railway system had stone dressings of some description. This was not merely an aesthetic aid, but helped to protect the fabric of the bridge. Brick in certain circumstances decayed very quickly, particularly if the bricks were under-burnt when they were made. Stone could be used to advantage in those parts of the structures exposed to climatic conditions, such as parapets, tops of pillars, cutwaters and the like.

Brunel's famous bridge at Maidenhead, epitomised by Joseph Mallord William Turner (1775-1851) in his masterpiece 'Rain, Steam and Speed', published as an engraving by R. Brandard in 1859-61, earned the engineer acclaim for his daring use of brick, but nonetheless, the bridge also had dressings of Yorkshire stone. Another example was the turnpike road-bridge, 60-ft high, with three arches across the deep cutting at Sonning, to the east of Reading. This bridge was also constructed by the contractor William Chadwick and had stone copings.

The Gatehampton bridge - built to a skew of about 15 degrees - was in a particularly isolated location. The structure was only visible from the river or high vantage points on either side of the river valley, one of these being the turnpike road which passed some distance to the south of the bridge site. The Moulsford bridge was located much closer to the same turnpike road and was much easier to be seen by passing travellers. About three miles to the north of the spot where the railway crossed the river at Moulsford, was situated the Borough and market town of Wallingford. The town possessed many fine examples of architecture, including

FIGURE 61. With the Chiltern Hills as a background, a local stopping train passes over Brunel's Moulsford bridge. *(Author's collection)*

the Church of St Peter's with its square tower supporting an elegant spire of Portland stone, similar to Bath stone.

The citizens of Wallingford had been less than enthusiastic regarding the initial proposals to construct the railway between Bristol and London. The town would not be directly affected by the construction of the railway and rather belatedly and, perhaps impudently, the citizens of the Borough decided that their secluded town required preferential treatment regarding the provision of a railway station. On Thursday 7 June 1838, following a petition to the Mayor, a public meeting was held in the Town Hall to consider the propriety of sending a Memorial to the Directors of the Great Western Railway. The meeting concluded that the town deserved a 'first-class' station for the benefit of local citizens, as well as for the inhabitants of the nearby villages of Watlington, Benson, Dorchester and the like. However, there is no record of this Memorial either being sent by the town or being received by the Great Western Railway Company.

Brunel's sketchbooks record that his first intention for a station at Moulsford was an elegant two-story building. This proposal was later modified and the more familiar Brunellian single-storey building with all-round roof was eventually constructed to serve the area. Brunel's sketches appear to indicate that his design for the Moulsford station was the forerunner of many similar stations to be built along the line of railway. Thus, the fact that the Moulsford station appears to have been chosen in this way, highlights the importance the engineer and the Directors gave to this small station which would serve a relatively unimportant location along the line of railway. The fact that Brunel had originally considered a two-

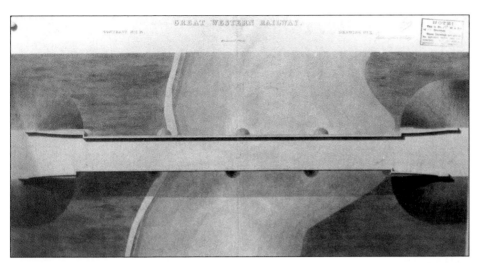

FIGURE 62. General plan of Gatehampton bridge. *(OPCBR)*

storey station necessary also reinforces the notion that the station at Moulsford had - for some reason - assumed an important role. The decision to relegate the station to a single-storey building, could be explained because of the cost savings rigidly enforced by the London Directors, or because they did not consider the town merited 'first-class' status. However, for whatever reason this relegation took place, it can only be assumed that Brunel considered the station buildings at Moulsford and the Moulsford viaduct still merited special attention.

One explanation for this may have been the fact, that located between the Moulsford bridge and the town of Wallingford, was Mongewell House. This house - complete with a large park - was situated close to the Oxfordshire bank of the Thames with good views towards Wallingford and to the south of the Berkshire Downs. Bourne in his 'Illustrated History of the Great Western Railway' states that Mongewell was observable from the Moulsford bridge. At the time of the Great Western Railway Parliamentary Bills, the estate was still the residence of the incumbent Bishop of Durham. However, due to the destruction of Parliamentary records, which occurred when the Houses of Parliament were virtually totally destroyed by fire in 1834, little is known about the Bishop's attitude to the railway proposals. However, it would appear that there was some opposition from the Bishop during the Committee stages of the First Bill, the vestiges of which still remained during the passing of the Second Bill through Parliament. Daniel Lousley, the Railway's land valuer was questioned about his knowledge of this property by the Parliamentary Committee prior to the passing of the Second Bill:

'... You have valued from Reading to Cholsey?
From Reading to Maidenhead and from Cholsey to the River Cole.
(By a Lord.) Is it Cholsey you mean?
Yes; it is below Shrivenham. I began at the River Thames.
(Mr. Serjeant Merewether.) Do you know where the Bridge is to go across the river?
It was pointed out to me.

Do you know how far that is from Mongewell House?
Not exactly.
Can you tell near about?
I am upon my Oath, and should not like to state a Falsehood.
Do you know so little about it, you cannot tell?
I cannot speak to it.
Shrivenham is at the other End of the line?
No, there are Two Lines.
Do you live near Mongewell?
Within Five or Six Miles.
It is the House I speak of?
I know the house, but should not like to speak to the Distance.
The House is low down on the River?
Yes, it may be Half a Mile or a Mile.
It is thereabout?
Yes, it may be.
(By a Lord.) From the River?
From where the Line is to cross the River to Mongewell House. ...'.

The innuendo contained in the cross-examination of Daniel Lousley during the investigation of the Parliamentary Committee, appears to suggest that there was opposition from the owner of the Mongewell estate. Brunel, from a very early date had decided upon a structure which would match the grandeur of the location and although the influence of Mongewell is unknown, an additional factor may have been the need to complement the aesthetic qualities of the house and estate, thus ensuring that the aspect from the house was pleasing to the eye. Any pressure which had been exerted on the railway officials by the Bishop relating to the presence of the bridge over the Thames at Moulsford, would ensure that some appeasement was necessary to remove any objections to the proposed railway. This course of action may account for the Directors agreeing to allow the Moulsford bridge to be completed with elegant Bath stone voissours, instead of the ubiquitous red-brick, which formed most of the other structures along this section of the Great Western Railway.

Similar reasons may have prompted Brunel to originally design the Gatehampton bridge with attractive Bath stone voissoirs. Situated 1 3/4 miles west of the site of the Pangbourne station and on the turnpike road from Reading to Wallingford, was Basildon Park. The great house, with its outbuildings and park was situated some three-quarters of a mile east of the proposed bridge site at Gatehampton. The estate was purchased by the Liberal MP James Morrison in 1838, with the Brunellian main line being constructed below the very gates of the estate. That Morrison was definitely for the railway is evidenced by the following quotation which he wrote shortly after moving to Basildon:

'We shall soon not want a Town House. In three years all the best Physicians will recommend a ride in a steam carriage before dinner as much better than a ride in the Park, and my cards will run thus; Train off at 6; dinner on table 7 precisely; return steam up at half past 10; carriages to Paddington at quarter past 11; Brunel and 50 miles an hour!'.

Morrison was clearly an admirer of Brunel and as the engineer would have passed close by this estate many times at this period, it appears unlikely that Brunel, who had a reputation as a designer and architect, would have not have made it his business to visit the house and its owner. Even if a visit had not taken place, Brunel must have been aware of this beautiful building built of Bath stone so close to his railway. The proposed bridge which would carry the railway over the Thames at Gatehampton was about three-quarters-of-a-mile from the house and the question has to be posed, was it the close proximity of the line of railway to such a grand building which determined Brunel to use Bath stone for the construction of the viaduct at this site, a proposal which was never carried out?

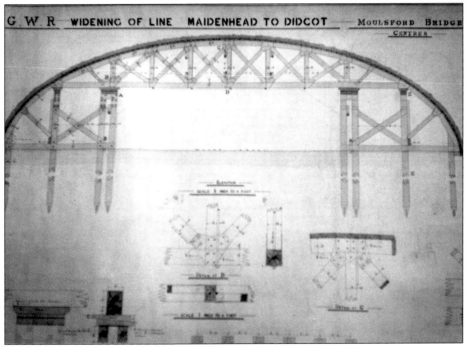

FIGURE 63. Plan of the centreing designed for the arch spanning the navigation channel of the Moulsford bridge and used for the construction of the new bridge when the main line between Didcot and Paddington was quadrupled in the late 1890s. *(OPC/BR)*

PART VII
BRUNEL'S PHILOSOPHY

'In conclusion, I must observe that no man can be more sensible than I am of the great advantage it would be to me as a civil engineer to be better acquainted with geology, as well as with many other branches of science, that I have endeavoured to inform myself on the subject, and that I have not altogether thrown away the many opportunities afforded me in my professional pursuits.'

June 1842

FIGURE 64. Plan of the Shrivenham station (the same plan was used for the Moulsford station. *(Author/The Institution of Civil Engineers)*

174

CHAPTER THIRTY-TWO
STATIONS

For mainly geological reasons, Brunel constructed the Great Western Railway through West Berkshire by crossing the Thames at Gatehampton and Moulsford. By taking this course of action, the engineer ensured that the difficulties which would have been encountered if the railway had taken the more southerly route with its more difficult terrain, were avoided. Further, by crossing the Thames in this way, this ensured that the line of railway was constructed in the best position to enable the site of the station at Moulsford to be located as close to the town of Wallingford as possible. At Moulsford, the railway would pass under the Reading-Wallingford-Oxford turnpike and the presence of this road was clearly another important factor when deciding to route the railway past this point. This is evidenced in a letter from Brunel - dated 1 February 1836 - to the Company's solicitors:

> 'With respect to Mr. Cundy [unidentified], enquiring about our proposed Depot [station] - he and many others would be glad to know our precise spot of these land improving stations - For the present tell him we have not yet fixed, but depend upon nature of our purchases, &c. but that the existence of a Turnpike Road to Wallingford would command our attention and require a depot'.

Despite this consideration, the Moulsford station was still located some three miles from Wallingford and it was this isolation which would ensure that the town's dependency on the Thames continued in this locality long after the opening of the railway.

The Great Western Railway - as first conceived - was primarily a fast trade artery between the west of England and the metropolis. Consequently, Brunel when forging his railway appeared to deliberately neglect some areas of heavy population, instead concentrating on constructing a railway which enabled traffic to pass as quickly as possible between the two terminii. He was, of course, criticised in some quarters for this philosophy and particularly for apparently ignoring the fact that between Reading and Bath there was no large centre of trade. At that time, this observation was certainly true and Brunel is rumoured to have answered these attacks by stating that the Great Western 'was a gentleman's railway'. As history records, Brunel had been instructed before beginning his surveys, to concentrate on providing a communication with the areas around Gloucestershire and South Wales, as well as a direct line to Bristol. Brunel after due deliberation, rejected a route south of the Berkshire Downs which would have have provided more intermediate traffic, but which would have made expansion to the north almost impossible.

Brunel's disarming statement in the previous paragraph was no jest. The engineer deliberately set out to exploit the potential of the route he had chosen and the comfort his broad-gauge was able to provide. Bourne (1846) compounds Brunel's argument, when he compares the Great Western Railway with the London & Birmingham Railway. On the latter, according to Bourne:

'Comparatively few passengers join ... at its [L&BR] intermediate stations, and but few carriages are taken up or set down upon the road, consequently the stations are small, often only a shed; ... But on the Great Western, private carriages are taken up and set down, not only at Slough, Reading, Steventon, Swindon and Bath, but also at such stations as Maidenhead, Twyford, Pangbourne, Faringdon, Shrivenham and Chippenham, some of them not even first class stations. The consequence is a necessity for large, roomy and comfortable stations and waiting rooms, a covering over the rails to keep off the weather, an easy approach to the stations and arrangements for the addition or removal of a private carriage with as little delay as possible to the train'.

Bourne continues:

'The stations upon this railway [GWR] are in some respects peculiar. The great proportion of first class intermediate traffic, and of general persons travelling upon the line with their private carriages, requires more attention to the general accommodation than in under other circumstances, considered necessary. At the principal stations of London, Slough, Reading, Swindon, Bath and Bristol, the trains stand wholly under cover, and the stations themselves are roomy, constructed with reference to the comfort of passengers of all classes who may be waiting at them, and approached by broad roads. Both at these stations and at those of the next class, including the whole, arrangements are made for the addition or removal of private carriages or horseboxes to the train, without the delay occasioned by the ordinary method'.

Bourne, in the latter part of his statement, is referring to the small turntables provided by Brunel at nearly all the stations. These made the transhipment of road-carriages a relatively simple matter, compared to the arrangements on other railways where road-carriages were sometimes craned on to carriage-trucks.

Brunel and the Directors were painfully aware of the financial vulnerability of their railway, particularly before the line was completely open between Bristol and London. The Great Western Railway would not have the advantages of some of the early railway schemes, despite being the longest line of railway so far built. For instance, George Stephenson's Stockton & Darlington Railway was built to transport coal from mines to the west and north of Shildon via Darlington for transhipment on the Tees at Stockton. The Liverpool & Manchester would provide the catalyst for the expansion of the Port of Liverpool and for the growth of industry in and around Manchester. Of course, similar possibilities existed in the long term for the Great Western Railway, but in the short term, the carriage of 'gentlefolk' along the line of railway would provide the main source of income.

Consequently, Brunel paid great attention to the requirements of this class of person, with the broad-gauge lending itself to the kind of luxury travel Brunel envisaged, with both locomotives and rolling stock allowing the engineer to develop this theme to its full potential. The stations and ancillary fittings would come out of the same mould and each would be unique to suit a particular location. Although, Bourne (1846) uses the classifications 'Principal' and 'Minor', this categorisation is, perhaps, an injustice to Brunel's great design skills. The

FIGURE 65. Above: Maidenhead ('Dumb-bell' bridge) station, the temporary terminus constructed of timber to which the first Great Western Railway train from Paddington ran on 4 June 1838.

(Author's collection)

FIGURE 66. Left: An existing relic of 1838. Still to be seen today in the south-eastern abutment of the 'Dumb-bell' bridge is the entrance to the staircase which led to the platforms of the original terminus of the Great Western Railway at Maidenhead. *(Author)*

stations erected at locations such as Pangbourne and Moulsford, although categorised by Bourne as 'Minor', far outweighed some of the rudimentary structures erected at other locations and termed 'Principal'.

It becomes evident from observations made by early railway commentators that Brunel used many different designs and materials for the construction of the stations along the line of railway between Bristol and London. A study of George Measom's 'The Illustrated Guide to the Great Western Railway 1852' reveals some of the different designs chosen by Brunel for the wayside stations. However, many of these were later additions to the original number of stations built for the complete opening of the railway between the Bristol and London. The hypothesis that Brunel used standard designs for his early stations appears to be incorrect. That the engineer later used certain standard basis design concepts cannot be denied, these being used to design an individual station, tailor-made for a particular location. Such requirements would depend on the number of passengers likely to be carried, the status of the town nearest to the station site and perhaps, whether a gentleman's country-seat was situated nearby.

As the modern-day rail traveller quickly learns to recognise local features which enables them to recognise their 'home' station, so Brunel designed his stations with individual features which told the early rail traveller that 'home' had been reached. Even in today's era of 'rationalisation', the regular traveller is still able to recognise the local station very quickly and Brunel tried to make the passengers on his railway feel at home. Despite the stringencies exerted by the London Committee, the engineer was able to use various methods to assist the passengers on the embryonic Great Western Railway. A train travelling along the Brunellian main line would have passed a succession of different and interesting wayside stations and although a few of them would have been very similar, subtle differences would ensure that the rail passenger would quickly recognise them.

Railways which had been constructed up to the 1850s were generally constructed using local and more traditional materials. To do otherwise and import large quantities of 'foreign' materials from other areas would have been time-consuming and expensive. At the same time, the use of traditional materials ensured that the infrastructure of the new railways and particularly new buildings did not impinge on the aesthetic backdrop of many station environments. In other words, the use of the traditional materials ensured that the visual impact of the new railways on a particular environment was reduced to the minimum, as local people were used to seeing buildings constructed of local materials. However, as the railways themselves grew, they would provide the means by which bricks, iron and other materials could be transported to be used in any location. This ensured that eventually many local and traditional materials were superseded by the use of 'imported' materials. One benefit of this process would be the 'standardisation' of particularly railway stations and ancillary buildings, with uniform designs being complemented by standard materials.

During the construction of the Great Western Railway, the London Directors' attitude to unnecessary spending had ensured that Brunel had to develop the concept of using local and traditional materials to their full potential. Brunel, with his mastery of design, ensured that traditional materials were used to their best advantage and some of Brunel's original station buildings quickly developed an atmosphere of 'belonging'. At the time of the construction of the Great Western Railway, the navvies had altered the face of the countryside along the line of railway in a way probably never before envisaged by local people. Admittedly, the raw earth soon healed - with nature aiding full recovery - but how would the many new buildings and structures along the line of railway fare and would they blend into the scene in the same fashion? By using local traditional materials, Brunel ensured that the impact was lessened as much as possible. The local people were used to seeing buildings made of local materials and Brunel did his best to ensure that his buildings proved equally as acceptable and 'belonging'.

CHAPTER THIRTY-THREE
THE MOULSFORD STATION

Through the Thames Valley and the more distant Vale of White Horse, Brunel chose to construct his stations of either flint - complemented by dressings of either limestone or red brick - or more cheaply of wood. East of Reading, the red brick gave way to the grey brick of the London area, with some stations being constructed entirely of wood, while to the west Brunel chose to use limestone in profusion. This attractive stone - cut from the Company's own quarries or direct from the railway works - was a relatively easy material to cut and shape and the engineer, with the blessing of the Bristol Directors, used these assets to the full.

One method of building with flint was the use of squared and coursed flint blocks. With this method, each flint was painstakingly 'knapped' to form blocks. The hand-finished flints would vary, of course, some examples being almost perfectly squared blocks, others less symmetric. Each course of flint blocks, as with bricks, would be laid overlapping each other, each succeeding course strengthening the preceding layers. This style of building was very labour-intensive and was rarely used, however when completed, squared and coursed flints were extremely attractive and it is not surprising that Brunel chose to use this style for the Moulsford and Shrivenham stations.

The same specification and contract was used for the Moulsford and Shrivenham stations and the instructions contained in the contract document were very carefully worded to ensure the squared blocks of flint were used to their best advantage:

'... the flint facings are to be of a Uniform colour and properly squared - the mortar to be composed wholly of Dorking or strong grey stone lime or lime equal in quality and clean sharp sand well washed and to be in the proportion of one Bushel of lime to three bushels of sand and to be well mixed - the whole of the flint work to be carried up to and far as shewn by the Drawing well flushed up with Mortar & Grouted with hot Limes ... The external face of the flint is to be properly squared and pointed in between with fine putty and well bonded together with the stone work ...'.

Brunel's decision to use flint for the main part of the station buildings at Pangbourne, Moulsford and further west at Shrivenham is not surprising and to the average citizen of the Thames Valley and the Vale of White Horse today, flint needs no introduction. Flint has been utilised for many uses over thousands of years and Prehistoric man found flint ideal for making stone tools because of its durability and the ease at which a sharp edge could be formed. Later uses included road construction and as a building material. Calcined flint during the mid-1700s was mixed with the body material as a whitener in the manufacture of pottery in the Midlands. Flints were also used from early times for lighting fires, and when used in conjunction with steel, pyrite sparks were generated, the sparks being tiny slivers of white-hot metal - the harder flint remaining unchanged. This process also enabled the development of the flintlock gun to take place. Today, the main demand for flint is as gravel, vast quantities being consumed in the mixing of concrete for which flint is the perfect aggregate. Flint as a building material can be seen in many areas of England and the Thames Valley is no exception. However, as the common brick began to gain popularity and the encroaching railways allowed the import of alternative materials, the awkward flint began to wane in its use.

Locally, flints are found in the chalk - almost all in the Upper Chalk - which forms the main mass of the Chilterns and the Berkshire Downs. Chalk is made up of grains of the mineral calcite (carbonate of lime) and scientists consider that for chalk to be precipitated, the water would have had to been warm - such as a clear, sunlit sea. Flints are very commonly found in deposits of chalk and it is thought flints are formed from sponges which dissolved and then solidified again along lines of weaknesses in the chalk. Flints are very irregular shaped masses of silica and consist of a multitude of needle-like quartz crystals, much too small to be seen with the naked eye. The spaces between the crystals contain about 1% of water and a small amount of glassy, non-crystalline silica.

During the construction of the Great Western Railway west of Reading, deposits of flints were found in several locations. East of Pangbourne - near Purley - a few flints had been found about 20-ft below the surface, but it was to the area west of Pangbourne that layers of flints in profusion were unearthed. The local archaeologist - Richard Allnatt of Wallingford - reported excitedly in late 1838 about the fine examples of chalk flints found as the railway was excavated west of Pangbourne:

> '*splendid specimens of silicious deposits, many of them embracing large and perfect branches of white coral indeed of such frequent occurrence is this peculiar structure in the flint, as to encourage the belief that the chalk deposited in this bed of the ancient sea might have been originally derived from the detritus of a coral reef*'.

From these deposits of flints, the squared flints used to constructed the Moulsford station were obtained, the rubble left after the flint-knappers had completed their work being used to construct the Pangbourne station. On 17 October 1838, the Great Western Railway Finance Committee sanctioned payment of £182-11s-3d for 'stacking flints' at Pangbourne.

Flint is a cheap material to find and excavate, but unless the flint is used in a more-or-less natural state, the advantages begin to disappear. As a modern building material flint has largely been neglected, the problems experienced working the material and even obtaining supplies proving detrimental. Apart from the hazards of working with flint, builders using the material are handicapped in other ways. A flint - unlike brick or most natural stone - has no absorption properties (suction), to absorb some of the water used in the mortar mix. Consequently, a builder constructing a flint wall can only build a few feet at a time, the mortar having to dry naturally before the wall can be extended with a another few layers of flint. This can be a fairly protracted process and even if great care is taken, it is not unknown for a builder to return to the site the next day, to find - frustratingly - that the heavy flints have proved too much for the mortar mix and both flints and mortar lie in a disorderly pile at the base of the construction!

J. C. Bourne in his 'Illustrated History of the Great Western Railway' describes the station buildings at both Pangbourne and Moulsford and Brunel's alternative use of flint is adequately described:

'The Pangbourne station has been selected as an example of the second class or minor stations upon the railway. The station, as is usual with those of this class, is composed of a house, placed on the side of the railway most accessible to the public, and which here happens to be the north, a covered platform being placed on the opposite side. At a short distance are the turntable and other arrangements for the speedy putting on or removing carriages and cattle. The station-house is constructed of flint rubble, neatly pointed, with quoins, door- and window cases, and dressings of red brick. The general style is Elizabethan. It consists of one story only, and is divided into a booking office with a bow, looking upon the railway, and two waiting rooms. The eaves of the building are produced so as to form a complete covering all round the house, and extending over the platform towards the railway'.

Bourne then describes the Moulsford [Wallingford Road] station:

'The Wallingford-road Station stands upon the Berkshire bank of the river, 47½ miles from London, and about three from Wallingford; the station-house is placed upon the northern side, it is of one story [sic], and constructed of flints squared and coursed, with quoins and dressings of Bath stone; near it is a large goods shed, and in the court yard stands a very pretty inn, recently erected. The road from Reading to Oxford, through Wallingford, passes close to the station and crosses over the railway. The buildings of the station are sheltered by a hill of grey chalk, but the country generally is unenclosed and without timber, and much exposed to the wind; the land is for the most part arable ...'.

These descriptions, apart from containing a wealth of detail about the location of the stations, also emphasise the different nature of the construction of these two wayside stations.

At Pangbourne, Brunel considered it suffice to use flint rubble with brick dressings, which aesthetically would have given a very pleasing effect. However, could this compare to the aesthetic qualities of the Moulsford station? Here, despite the problems associated with this method of construction, Brunel chose to use the more expensive, squared and coursed flint blocks. The flint blocks were complemented with pale Bath stone and the whole must have presented a very pleasing sight.

Brunel's decision to use the more expensive flint 'squared and coursed' for the construction of the Moulsford station, gives added evidence to the argument that the station and the river bridge at Moulsford received special attention. The economic measures dictated by the London Committee ruled out unnecessary embellishments and the flint blocks used at the Moulsford station could easily have been replaced with a cheaper material. A pessimist might conclude that

Brunel was simply being thrifty by using the remains of the Bath stone used for the nearby river bridge at Moulsford, to provide the dressings for the Moulsford station buildings? Conversely, an optimist might conclude that the plea from the citizens of Wallingford and district for a 'First-class' station had not been ignored?

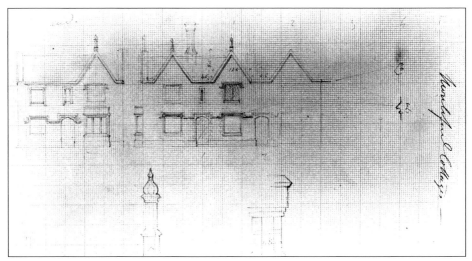

FIGURE 67. Brunel's designs for railwaymens' cottages at the Moulsford (Wallingford Road) station site.
(Reproduced by kind permission of the Librarian of the University of Bristol)

FIGURE 68. The Brunel-designed railwaymens' accommodation still extant today at the site of the original Great Western Railway station at Moulsford. *(Author's collection)*

CHAPTER THIRTY-FOUR
STATION FACILITIES

Supremely confident that the Great Western Bill would receive Parliamentary approval, Brunel at an early stage was putting his fertile mind to many of the technical details connected with the unique railway he was about to engineer. His sketchbooks reveal in the pencil drawings, the minutia the engineer was considering for this the the 'finest work in England'. Surprisingly, few of the stations planned by Brunel appear in these preliminary sketches and this particularly applies to the 'minor' stations. One exception is the station at Moulsford which Brunel planned in detail, lending further evidence to the argument that the construction of the railway in this location was considered of primary importance. Brunel's early sketches of the Moulsford station buildings were to be used as the blueprint for some of the other stations to be constructed on the Brunellian main line and would become the bench-mark for that Brunel hallmark, the small wayside station, with pitched roof and all-round awning or 'verandah' (to use Brunel's own description).

The engineer originally proposed for the station house at Moulsford a two-storied structure with two chimneys, the two storeys being divided by an all-round awning. The building would be an elegant, tall construction of some 26-feet height from ground-level to the top of the chimneys. The roof would be graced with elegant, carved wooden barge-boards decorating each gable - one large and one smaller gable on the north and south elevations and one large gable on the east and west elevations. The upper storey had square-headed windows to match the lower storey and all windows were protected by moulded stone drip-rails. Short, square chimneys were planned, instead of the more familiar diamond-shaped type which Brunel later favoured.

The reasons why the engineer decided upon such an imposing structure at Moulsford can only be speculated on. The station site was virtually invisible from the north and the west and possibly Brunel, by designing such a lofty structure, was trying to ensure that the station house was visible from as many directions as possible. In any event, the plan of the upper storey was at some later date crossed through on Brunel's sketch and the station house constructed as a single storey building.

From the beginning, Brunel had decided that whenever possible and in all aspects of railway operation, first-class passengers should be segregated from the more lowly second-class travellers. Indeed at first, third-class passengers appear not to have been catered for at all, probably being discreetly loaded or unloaded when the platforms were empty of 'gentlefolk'. This separation of the first- and second-class passengers certainly took place at the principal stations, although the arrangements at the minor stations are more obscure. However, it does appear from Brunel's sketch of the Moulsford station that this principal was clearly to the fore in the design of the station building.

Brunel's original proposal for a two-storied station house at Moulsford required an oblong building with exterior dimensions of 40-feet x 16-feet (interior: 38-feet x 14-feet). From ground level to the height of the first floor ceiling was 10-feet and the height of the second-floor rooms would be 8-feet. From ground level to the bottom of the all-round awning or 'verandah' would be 11-feet. The awning would overhang slightly more on the rail side to give passengers the protection they would need as they boarded or alighted, illustrating Brunel's consideration for the comfort of the passengers using the Company's trains and stations. Brunel's plans show that the station house was divided into three rooms: a central booking hall with two smaller rooms - one on each side. The booking hall measured 21-feet x 14-feet and included the Booking Clerk's counter.

The western room, completely separated from the Booking Hall by a wall and doorway, was the 'First Class' ladies' room. 'First Class' gentlemen, although not provided with a separate room, were separated from more lowly passengers by the Booking Clerk's counter. The eastern room - not separated by a wall, but only by the Booking Clerk's counter - was a combined Booking Hall and Waiting Room for 'Second Class' passengers of both sexes.

Passengers would normally have to share their brief sojourn in the station house with the incumbent railway official. His responsibilities - apart from issuing tickets and making up the weigh-bill - would have included enforcing the Company's Bye-laws regarding smoking and to ensure that this obnoxious habit was excluded totally from the Company's property. To be caught smoking in any of the Company's trains or premises carried the risk of being ejected forthwith or even being hauled before a local magistrate!

A further indication of the consideration that Brunel took of 'First Class' passengers is revealed in his sketches. On many railway stations - right up to the present day - ablution and toilet facilities are constructed outside of the station building itself, entry being obtained by leaving the main station building and walking - in all winds and weathers - to the outside toilets. Once safely ensconced, protection is normally offered from the weather by the station awning above and prying eyes are diverted by the familiar strategically placed screen in front of the entrance. Brunel originally proposed such arrangements for both men and women passengers, but apparently eventually concluded that 'First Class' ladies could not be allowed to suffer such indignities. On the engineer's early sketch of the station, the toilet facilities for both men and women were placed outside the main station building, but this was changed with a small room for 'First Class' females with a 'Bramahs Patient Valve Water Closet' and a '1-in. [thick] Mahogany Moulded Seat & Riser [cover]' contained in a mahogany frame being finally included in the western part of the station house. The toilet flushing facilities were of impressive proportions with:

'a Cistern over the water closet 6 feet long 3 feet wide & 2 feet depth with proper bearers from partition to wall to carry the same'.

FIGURE 69. A rare photograph of the Moulsford (Wallingford Road) station c.1856.
(Mrs. M. Wyatt)

The men were less fortunate, only urinals being provided, although a degree of privacy was provided by:

'two rubbed Yorkshire partitions in Watering Place Five feet six inches high and three inches thick securely fixed to the wall'.

One can only imagine what the toilet arrangements were for the more lowly classes of passengers, although some alternatives are described in the following passage:

'When the old night expresses halted at dawn, the station lavatories were often hopelessly inadequate in the short time allowed; men sought platform ends or, most dangerously, got down on the off-side of the carriages; women more modestly stretched their invisible legs in their substantial travelling costumes, while they commended to one another the beauty of the mountain sunrise. Few people cared to buy, and wear, an appliance designed for the infirm. Coarser persons resorted to beastly expedients inside the train ...'.

Brunel, similarly gave serious consideration to the well-being of the Company's employees. A familiar feature of Brunel's smaller stations was the bay window protruding on to the platform. This arrangement ensured that the Booking Clerk or other railway officials had the facility to observe the traffic arrangements without leaving the station building. Many a railway employee must have praised the engineer for his consideration for including such a vantage point, particularly during severe weather. However, this may not have been a Brunellian innovation, as lock keepers' cottages on the Caledonian Canal, south of Inverness in Scotland had from a much earlier date been equipped with large bay-windows, which provided for the observation of the canal's traffic without leaving the comfort of the cottage.

Brunel's plans allowed the Booking Clerk to perform his duties from a 'Wainscotted' [wood panelled] enclosed counter located in the main room of the station house, this central hall measuring some 21-feet x 14-feet. The engineer proposed that a continuous counter - 'with one end of each hung as a Flap' - enclosing a space some 10-feet x 14-feet be located in the eastern side of the booking hall, effectively forming an enclosed well in which the clerk performed his duties. One side of the counter would contain 'a nest of drawers ... the centre drawer to be a money drawer', the opposite counter to 'have one money drawer and one 1½ inch shelf the whole width of the counter'. In addition, the clerk had available the space created by the bay-window. Brunel also planned for one fireplace, with a 'York hearth in one stone' to warm the building, this strategically sited in the wall separating the 'First Class' ladies' room from the booking hall.

Close study of the final plans for the station house at Moulsford reveal few differences from Brunel's original proposals. The end result was the sturdy wayside station that would, perhaps, characterise Brunel's work more than any other aspect of his work. The hand-knapped flint, laid in courses and complemented with pale-yellow dressings of Bath stone, would have almost sparkled on a sunlight day and gleamed on wet days. During inclement weather, the overall station awning would provide adequate cover and the square-headed casement and sash windows - glazed with 'the best second Newcastle Glass' with mullions - were graced with moulded Bath stone drip-rails for further protection. All doors were similarly protected and passengers entered or left the station through half-doors set in square-headed apertures with stone steps. There were two diamond-shaped chimneys shafts - the western taller than the eastern - again constructed from Bath stone, but with a Portland stone chimney. The short, but steeply pitched roof was weatherproofed with 1½-in. thick 'yellow deal' covered by sheet zinc and secured by flat-sided round-topped wooden battens. The canopy or 'verandah' consisted of 6in. x 4in. rafters and purlins of 7in x 2½in. laid on the main structure of the building and which extended beyond the walls. Over the track, the awning extended 10-feet from the walls of the main structure, but on the other three sides of the building, the overhang was 6-feet. Cast brackets on each corner provided additional support, with weatherproofing of the awning being by lead-sheeting, but with a sill above and below the edge of the awning preventing seepage from the apparently flat-topped awning surface. The now familiar valance did not appear in these very early designs.

The interior walls of the station building were covered with:

'Deal wainscotting round the whole of the Rooms 4 feet 3 inches high from the floor with proper backing'.

The whole of the interior received four coats of paint - the walls with 'good lead and oil colour' - and the:

'Doors, Wainscotting round Walls, Window Frames inside and out varnished with two coats of the best Copal varnish'.

186

Another distinctive feature of Brunel's stations, were the raised platforms. Brunel referred to his original stations as the 'High Stations', the engineer referring, of course, to the raised platforms which enabled passengers to virtually walk into the railway carriages. This was a practice not previously seen on Britain's embryonic railway system, with passengers embarking and disembarking from ground level, with the consequent inconvenience and danger this posed. However, in Brunel's eyes and bearing in mind the 'First-class' traffic the railway was seeking to attract, such inconveniences could not be tolerated. Brunel, in his sketchbooks refers to the platforms at the Moulsford station as 'raised terraces', with the length of the 'terraces' or platforms being given as 180-feet. Also included, is Brunel's proposed track layout for this station.

On the Down platform, a waiting shed - of matching design - was provided for intending passengers. Although no plans of the original waiting sheds provided at the smaller wayside stations have been traced, it would appear from illustrations from the period that they were all of the same basic sign. Open on the rail side only, a less ambitious awning than that incorporated in the main station building protected passengers as they waited for their train. Chimneys are also evident which illustrates that a stove or fire was provided to ensure that travellers were protected as far as possible from the cold and wet. Illumination at night was by means of a lantern suspended from the awning.

Although a copy of the contract document and the plans for the station building at Moulsford are in existence today, the contractor responsible for the construction of the Moulsford station buildings has not been established. However, the superior style of construction required by Brunel would need a contractor who would be capable of completing the station in the specified time of three months, with a penalty of £25 for each week the buildings were behind time. The probable contractor for the station buildings at Moulsford appears to be Messrs. J. & C. Rigby of Millbank, London who were responsible for the building of the stations between Steventon and Corsham, as well as the station at Slough. Estimates presented to a Great Western Railway sub-committee on 3 August 1839 confirm that £600 was allowed for the construction of the buildings at Moulsford plus another £400 for roads and fences. A sum of £383 13s 0d was paid to Messrs. Rigby on September 24 1840 for work undertaken at Moulsford, making the firm the likely contender for the station contract.

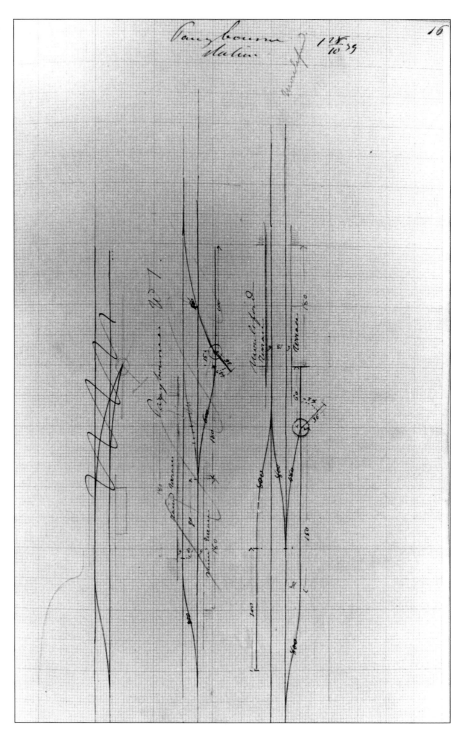

FIGURE 70. Brunel's early sketches of the proposed track layouts for the Pangbourne and Moulsford stations. Note Brunel's use of the word 'Terrace' instead of 'Platform'.

(Reproduced by kind permission of the Librarian of the University of Bristol)

CHAPTER THIRTY-FIVE
OCCUPATION BRIDGES

From Bristol to London, the line would pass through areas of Common land composed of smallholdings under the tillage of small groups of local farmers. This would necessitate either the Company paying compensation for severance of access, or building occupation bridges or crossings to enable the farmers to maintain access to their severed lands. It has been stated by contemporary railway historians that the early railway companies deliberately tried to promote their lines through Common lands, as apparently the smallholders gave much less trouble than the influential landowners, with the former usually content to settle for less compensation. However, there are no indications that Brunel, when setting out the line of the Great Western Railway even considered this aspect and even if he did do so, the small farmers in the Parish of Cholsey were no walk-over and caused Brunel and the Directors considerable problems.

The Enclosure of Common lands in England began in the 15th-century. At that time, large land estates prevailed after many small landowners - vassals of the great lords - had been driven off their lands. The distinguished historian, the late Lord Max Beloff, states that between 1600 and 1800, there were 2,000 Parliamentary Enclosure Acts, pasture being turned into arable land 'to give the peasants work', but immediately denying them the right to graze their cattle or gather wood for their fuel. Violent disturbances are recorded from 1612 to 1696 and the great riot at Windsor Forest led to the Black Act of 1723 under which a range of offences attracted the death penalty or transportation for life.

In the 18th-century and due to different causes, the enclosure of Common lands recommenced. Many districts which had escaped the earlier enclosures would in turn be legally enclosed and some of these would be areas through which the Great Western Railway would eventually pass. From 1809 onwards, there were approximately 100 enclosures a year in England, the Government having quickened the process due to its interest in agriculture in the 18th-century. The Government founded in 1793 an important institution - the Board of Agriculture - which enabled landlords to deliberate together upon their common interests and one act of the Board was to bring about the simplification of legal formalities for Enclosure Acts. Waste and Common lands were described as:

'land lying continually fallow on which everyone had the right to pasture his cow, to cut a little wood, and dig some turf'.

this land - by enclosure - became the private property of an individual owner.

The Cholsey Common Field - through which the Great Western Railway would pass, prior to Enclosure, was an open field which was cultivated every year by the smallholders to whom belonged one or more of the narrow strips of land into which the field had been divided. The crops on these smallholdings were part of a common plan, the produce being divided among the small farmers in proportion to the size and value of their allotments. By Enclosure, these allotments would probably be grouped and redistributed and the cultivation, as well as the ownership would be henceforth 'individual'.

Despite the small amount of land involved, persons entitled to rights over Common or Waste lands had the same rights as the large landowners. Clauses XVII and XVIII of the Great Western Railway Bill dealt with the rights of Commoners and on the 'Enlarged Plan of Cholsey Common Field' deposited in Parliament at the time of the Second Great Western Bill, the complicated formation of these small strips of land is shown, with the railway passing through in excess of 50 separate strips of land. The procedures, as laid down in the Act, were quite clear. Because there were in excess of 12 farmers whose land would be required through the Cholsey Common Field, a meeting had to be convened by the Company to 'treat for Compensation'. The Company were obliged to insert on two occasions in a newspaper circulating in the county where the land was situated, notices announcing the meeting. At least eight of the farmers had to attend before the meeting became legally effective and a Committee, not exceeding five of the farmers, would be chosen by the farmers themselves to negotiate with the Company for the compensation to be paid for the extinguishment of Common rights.

James Thomas Bedborough - the contractor for Contract '4R' - had quickly moved into the Cholsey Common Field and the cutting through the field had been commenced before negotiations with the farmers had even been instigated. Because of this, several months after the navvies had started work, Saunders was forced to write to the Company's solicitors stating:

> *'Mr. Lousley [land valuer] is very anxious that the requisite advertisements should be given for the appointment of Committees to settle the Common Rights of Hagborne & Cholsey properties & I shall feel particularly obliged by your immediate attention to it, as the land is already in the Contractor's hands & the parties are threatening some proceedings against the Company'.*

For some unknown reason, Saunders' request was not complied with until almost 11 months later and it was not until 3 August 1839 that the *Berkshire Chronicle* ran the first of the statutory notices announcing the convening of the meetings to appoint Committees of farmers.

All the allotment holders in the Parish of Cholsey, Cholsey Moor and Hagborne Marsh were invited to attend separate meetings to elect committees. These would be held on Thursday 8 August 1839 at the Crown Inn situated at South Moreton. The first of the meetings - for the farmers of Hagborne Marsh - was scheduled to commence at 11 a.m. The next - for the farmers of the Parish of Cholsey - at 11.30 a.m., with the final meeting for the farmers of Cholsey Moor being held at noon. The area around this small village inn would for a few hours have probably been a scene of intense activity. The farmers - particularly on Cholsey Common - would insist on protecting their interests and the Company, who it appeared had envisaged little opposition, would be eventually and belatedly forced to agree to the wishes of these smallholders. Similar meetings had been held for the farmers of the South Stoke Common in early 1838.

The error in deferring the formation of the farmers' committee for the Cholsey Common Field would have some far-reaching consequences. The occupation bridge across the railway at 47-miles 79-chains (from Paddington), would become almost a 'folly', with the bridge quickly becoming known locally as 'Silly Bridge'. The construction of this bridge was not included in the original Contract '4R' specifications, nor was it included as an extra in the 'General Statement of Land and Compensation' dated 3 August 1838. Almost certainly, the Directors even at this late stage, had not the slightest idea that a bridge would be required. After all, approximately 130-yards to the east, a perfectly adequate bridge spanned the railway carrying the Reading-Wallingford-Oxford turnpike.

The meetings duly took place - Daniel Lousley representing the Great Western Railway - with the representatives of the small-holdings:

> *'to treat and agree with the said Company for the compensation to be paid by the said Company for the extinguishment of such Commonable or other Rights, and for the Purchase of their estates and interests in such land'.*

The farmers were represented by a Wallingford solicitor, who at one period threatened the Company with an injunction unless the matter was resolved. A Cholsey magistrate was also involved representing the interests of the small farmers of Cholsey Moor. There is little written correspondence and this may be due to the urgency of the situation with much of the detail being agreed verbally.

It is known that in the middle of 1838, the Cholsey Common Moor was being excavated as part of Great Western Contract '4R' and this this would have entailed interference and temporary severance of the small holdings which criss-crossed the field. The farmers had mostly assented to the construction of the railway, their agreements being recorded in the submission to Parliament. Probably, it was this general agreement which misled the Directors and resulted in a tardy response to the allotment holders' legal rights, as it would not be until the middle of 1839 that the committee of farmers to negotiate with the Company was formed.

The sequence of events after the forming of this committee appears to be as follows: As was their right, the farmers initially decided to opt for an occupation bridge to facilitate continued communication to their now divided small holdings. Although not unique, such a response was unusual, with most smallholders normally accepting increased compensation to cover any inconveniences suffered. Early in June 1840, the firm of Hedges & Sons, solicitors of Wallingford, had written to Saunders - on behalf of the farmers - threatening legal action unless the farm crossing was started. Saunders had checked with Hammond - the Resident Engineer whose responsibility included Contract 'R4' - and had been assured that the occupation bridge had been commenced.

Despite this reassurance, Saunders further impressed on the engineer the urgency of the situation, this instruction being emphasised in the Secretary's reply to the solicitor:

FIGURE 71. A typical London Division occupation bridge, constructed of local red brick, with a limited amount of Bath stone dressings. This example, situated in the long cutting to the west of the Moulsford (Wallingford Road) station and nick-named 'Silly' bridge - was constructed belatedly by the Great Western Railway for the use of smallholders whose land had been severed by the construction of the railway through the Cholsey Common Field. The original bridge is to the left, the later right-hand arch was constructed in the same form. *(Author's collection)*

> *'I am informed by Mr. Hammond that the works are actually in active progress with the Bridge at Cholsey. I have begged that it may proceed without intermission'.*

However, some of the farmers were still ambivalent about the benefits of having a bridge, instead preferring extra compensation. The result was that Brunel issued new instructions halting work on the bridge and at this point, J. Arnould (a Cholsey magistrate) became involved in the dispute, appearing to act as an intermediary. Saunders wrote to Arnould on 30 June 1840, stating:

> *'It was intimated to the Company that some of the Farmers at Cholsey would prefer receiving a compensation in money, instead of altering the Bridge & Road in the manner which had been determined when I first had the pleasure of seeing you.*
>
> *It was in consequence of this that Mr. Brunel stopped the works, and the Directors ordered Messrs. Swain Stevens & Co, to ascertain what sum would be required collectively by the parties interested.*
>
> *I had hoped ere this to know the result either to pay the money or go on with the works as might seem necessary'.*

The final conclusion must be that a majority of the farmers eventually rejected compensation, because the bridge was completed, although the whole business must have been a totally frustrating experience for Brunel and the Directors. The line from Reading to Steventon had opened to traffic on 1 June and in one of the deepest cuttings was all the paraphernalia of a bridge under construction. No wonder the bridge quickly earned the local nickname of 'Silly' bridge and one can imagine the local populace shaking their heads in total disbelieve at the goings on!

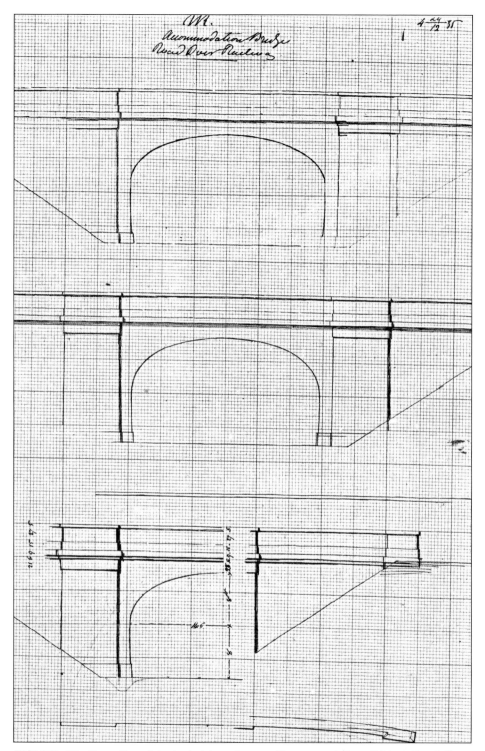

FIGURE 72. Brunel's original sketches for an 'Accommodation Bridge Road Over Railway'. *(Reproduced by kind permission of the Librarian of the University of Bristol)*

Once the farmers had finally made up their minds, work on the occupation bridge recommenced with all haste. While in this case it appears that little attention was given to the normal rules on Sunday working which had applied to the main contracts, it could safely be left to the Reverend Lloyd, the Vicar of Cholsey to draw this desecration to the notice of the Company. The London directors promptly discussed the complaint, with the result that Saunders wrote to the Rev. Lloyd on 3 September 1840, confirming that he had been ordered:

> *'to instruct Resident Engineer their regret that any work should have been permitted on the Sabbath at the Cholsey Bridge - with order to prevent the recurrence of it'.*

The date when the occupation bridge was completed has not been clarified, although on 14 July 1841 the Directors sanctioned a payment of £477-11s-4d for 'brickwork' on Contract '4R'. This belated payment - over 12 months after the railway had opened to Steventon - may give a clue as to the final date of the completion of this insignificant bridge.

'Silly' bridge remains today as a memorial to the small farmers who in earlier times cultivated the difficult soils of the Berkshire Downs. The bridge - used little today - is a place of solitude, despite being only a short distance from the Reading-Wallingford main road. From the bridge, the views of the railway are superb and the walk either from Cholsey or from the main road along the top of the railway cutting is an area where a quiet and observant traveller will be rewarded by many different aspects of wildlife. Little altered, the bridge itself has many stories to tell. Underneath these arches has passed much of the history and legend which the Great Western Railway left to posterity, with today's railway continuing the same theme. Well over 150 years ago, mesmerised passengers were carried for the first time east and west at speeds unheard of only a short time previously, while today, the passengers on today's railways have little time to look around them as they are whisked at 125mph under this simple farmers' crossing.

FIGURE 73. Despite the restrictions placed on Brunel by the London Directors, the engineer's designs for structures in the London Division still remained aesthetically pleasing. This simple bridge near Cholsey, constructed of local red brick with minimal stone dressings, still remains architecturally attractive.   *(Author's collection)*

CHAPTER THIRTY-SIX
LAYING THE RAILS

The construction of the railway from the west bank of the Thames at Moulsford to the western outskirts of Didcot, appeared to have been completed with no serious delays. The chalky soil through which the works were cut presented no serious problems to the navvies and the few disputes recorded with local landowners were soon resolved. Brunel himself appears to have been satisfied with James Thomas Bedborough, the main contractor for Contract '4R' and his style of working, with the engineer sanctioning regular payments as the work progressed:

1839	£
March 14	1,232-1s-4d
March 28	1,679-10s-8d
April 25	1,420-4s-6d
May 9	1,009-13s-4d
May 23	1,222-7d-10d
June 6	1,259-14s-10d
June 20	2,851-12d-4d
July 4	1,413-19s-4d

The extraordinary wet weather of the autumn and winter of 1839-40 delayed the eventual opening of the railway to Faringdon, but Contract '4R' does not appear to have been seriously affected by delays caused by the elements. By July 1839, at least one of the brick structures - the archway at Hagborne - had been completed and the materials, horses and stables which had been purpose-built, put up for sale by auction. The river bridge at Gatehampton had been completed at about the same time, while the Moulsford bridge and the line east of Pangbourne were expected to be ready by Christmas. In February 1840, Brunel reported:

> *'Beyond Reading and up to Didcot, a distance of 17½ miles, the ballasting is completed with the exception of two short lengths, together about 2½ miles. The difficulty of procuring ballast for this part has been very great; the ground purchased for this purpose being under water, and it being necessary to resort to dredging the river to obtain gravel. The laying of permanent rails is in a forward state, a single line being laid for fifteen miles, upon which the materials for the second line are carried and distributed at all parts so that this work will proceed rapidly'.*

It is interesting to note Brunel's admission on the question of dredging, as there is no mention in the Minute Books of the Thames Commissioners of the period recording a request by the engineer or the contractor to obtain gravel from the bed of the river.

Gravel was the material used almost exclusively on Britain's earliest railways for ballast, providing a firm and dry foundation on which the timbers supporting the rails could be laid. The cost of ballasting the 6-miles 10-chains or 61,300-yards of Contract '4R' at two-shillings a yard amounted to £6,130. The Company had intended to obtain the ballast for this section of the works from nine-acres of land purchased especially for the purpose from J. W Morrison - the Lord of the Manor of Cholsey. This land was situated in a long strip almost directly adjacent to the west bank of the Thames at Moulsford and close to the river bridge which was nearing completion. Being close to the river, the 'ballast hole' (gravel pit) was susceptible to flooding and was very vulnerable especially during the winter. Because of the ballast hole being flooded during the construction period, dredging the river had to be resorted to obtain adequate supplies of ballast. However, the ballast hole was eventually put to good use, the Company continuing to obtain gravel obtained from this land for a number of years after the line of railway had been completed..

The disappointing results obtained with Brunel's original permanent way resulted in a different method being used for the rest of the line. When the permanent way was first laid, the longitudinal sleepers were held together by transverse beams, bolted to long wooden piles previously driven into the ground. The engineer when initially deciding on the use of beech piles, had realised that this method was not feasible through the chalky ground to the west of Reading and he stated in August 1838 in a report to the Board of Directors, that:

> 'upon the portion of the line where the permanent way must next be formed piling could not be resorted to, the ground being a solid hard chalk for many miles. I had intended, however, recommending the same principle, but in a different form, holding down the longitudinals by small iron rods driven into the chalk'.

As history records, Brunel eventually abandoned the piling completely, instead increasing the scantling of the timber and substituting a heavier rail. Despite these changes, Brunel continued to experiment and on 29 May 1839, he proposed to the Directors that:

> 'Opportunity now offers itself of making this investigation without any expense and I think without any inconvenience - we have the rails and I propose that about ½-mile of the line somewhere between the Boyne Hill [near Maidenhead] Bridge should be laid with the old rails. Being on a sound platform of chalk there can be no question of their sufficiency so far as to prevent any inconvenience resulting from their use. And if the experiment should only prove that in a similar situation - for instance all through Purley, Pangbourne, Goring & Cholsey chalk cuttings ... a rail of 55-pounds should be ample, a very considerable economy would be offered'.

There is no record to indicate where this experiment ever took place.

The laying of the permanent rails in the London Division would be put out to tender under three separate contracts. The first contract involved laying the rails from London to Twyford; the second for the section between Twyford and Didcot and the third contract, from Didcot, to the termination of the London Division at Uffington. From London to Didcot the separate contracts for the two sections were

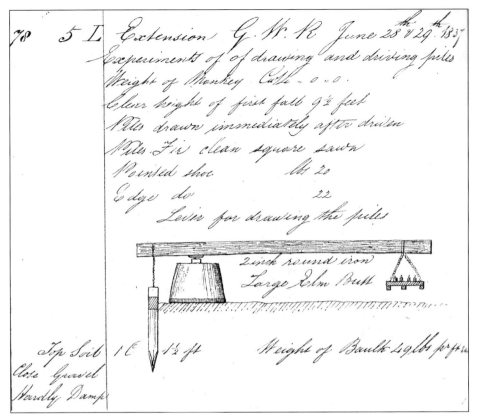

FIGURE 74. A drawing of a device for drawing and driving piles used for securing Brunel's baulk road. Tests were conducted in various types of soil in both the eastern and western Divisions of the railway and during these experiments, it was reported that the device withdrew the piles 'in perfect order'.
(Reproduced by kind permission of the Librarian of the University of Bristol)

let to a John Shedlock, his tender being first considered by the London Directors on 20 June 1839. For the final contract - that between Didcot and Uffington - a John Pritchard of Wallingford successful tendered. Using the auspices of the Wallingford bankers Wells, Allnatt & Clark for a surety, Pritchard tendered a price of £380 per mile. He was also contracted to maintain this section of permanent way for a period of 12 months after the completion of the work at a rate of £5 per mile.

The Company had established depots in both the Bristol and London Divisions for the receipt of the rails and timber required for the permanent way. Yards were established at Temple Meads and Keynsham in the Bristol Division and at Bull's Bridge [Hayes] and Maidenhead in the London Division, the former being the chief depot, being served by the adjacent Grand Union Canal. The depot at Bull's Bridge consisted of a yard and station, with sawpits, derricks, tanks and reservoir plus ancillary offices and storerooms. Eight wooden tanks had been constructed by Messrs. Grissell & Peto, with the Company themselves constructing four more tanks at Maidenhead. The baulks of American pine had been brought by ship to

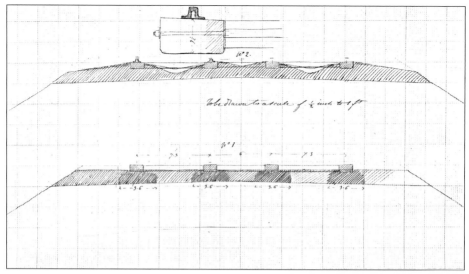

FIGURE 75. Early sketches by Brunel, illustrating the formation and ballasting to be used for his controversial baulk road on embankments.
(Reproduced by kind permission of the Librarian of the University of Bristol)

the docks at London initially, then loaded on barges for transhipment by canal. The timber, after being unloaded from the barges was then stacked ready for the sawyers. Brunel's specification for these timbers stated that the 'average' should be 15-in. x 7.5-in. and about 'thirty-four feet long'. All the timber before being used on the railway would be previously 'kyanized'. This was a process, recently invented by a Dr. Kyan, for preserving wood by saturating it with a solution of corrosive sublimate, otherwise known as bichloride of mercury. The timber after being cut to size, was placed in the wooden tanks, submerged in the sublimate and protected from the weather for at least eight days. The baulks would then be removed from the tanks and marked in red paint, indicating the length and gauge of each piece.

The rails were received at the upper yard at Bull's Bridge, the earlier and lighter 'Bridge' rails - to Brunel's own design - needing delicate handling to avoid damage. The rails after being unloaded, were sorted, weighed and stacked according to each individual rail length. Any rails which were found to be the 'least bent or Bruised', were to be immediately 'straightened'. The novel design of Brunel's permanent way required much care when laying down the rails and the amount of materials required was prodigious. Brunel had himself estimated these amounts in March 1838:

'Estimate of One Mile of Permanent Way
[Load equalled 50 cubic feet of timber]
Timber Loads 430 @ 105/- per load or £2,257-10s-d. per mile
Hardwood Loads 50 @ 130/- per load or £325 per mile
Piles 650 @ 13/- each
Rails 14 tons @ £12 per ton plus freight and Carriage to line 14/- per ton £1,778 mile
Screws 26,000 £350
Bolts and Washers 6 tons £100
Felt £100

Tar and Grease £10
Nails 40,000 £66'.

The method of laying the longitudinal track was a complicated business and consisted of:

'Trenching the ballast 12/- per chain or £50 per mile
Driving the piles 5/- each
Fixing the transomes 9/- per chain or £40 per mile
Fixing the longitudinals 20/- per chain £80 per mile
Hardwood adzed, planed etc. 41/- per chain or £176 per mile
Tarring timber £20 per mile
Laying rails, felting and screwing 5/- per yard or £440 per mile
Packing, repacking, etc. £160 per mile
Sundries £64 per mile
Trimming ballast & Carrying it about 5/- per yard or £440 per mile
Draining £270 per mile'.

Of course, by the time the contractor came to lay the permanent way west of Maidenhead Bridge, Brunel had completely abandoned the concept of piling, using instead Bridge rails weighing 62-lb. to the yard on longitudinal timbers 14-in. wide by 7-in. deep with transomes and strap bolts.

Brunel - apart from designing his unique baulk road - was also responsible for the design of the tools and gauges which would be required to lay down the broad-gauge rails. A modern addition to the Brunel Collection held by the University of Bristol Library is an album of fine drawings prepared by the Great Western Railway drawing office between 1837-1840, showing a variety of tools used in the construction of the line. These include tools for laying and straightening the rails, together with a machine for measuring their deflection; two cranes used by the contractor William Ranger on the River Kennet bridge; pile drivers; a pug mill and a putty mill; a diving bell; a moveable horse-gin; trucks and wheelbarrows and humbler items, such as screwdrivers, hammers and spanners. Many of the drawings have notes or captions - some in Brunel's hand - while a few bear a detailed breakdown of manufacturing costs.

The Company had initially proposed the establishing of a temporary railway for carrying the timber from the various depots to serve the whole line of railway and for this purpose, 12 wooden wagons were ordered for the carriage of the baulks of timber. As the railway progressed westwards and eastwards, the materials were transported first by establishing one line of permanent way, this then being used to transport the materials for the second line of railway. However, some of the materials used for Contract 'R4' - rails and timber - were delivered by river.

The section of railway from Reading to Steventon opened to the public on Monday 1 June 1840. The embankments would have had little time to settle before being pressed into service and it is not surprising that for a time, slips - some very persistent - were experienced. As most of the embankments were formed by the material being excavated from adjacent cuttings, it was necessary to allow for settlement and shrinkage, the nature of the material being tipped determining the amount allowed for settlement. In later railway engineering practice, when forming chalk embankments, about 1-in. extra per foot height was allowed for settlement.

The subsidence of the embankments caused Brunel some anxieties, particularly Embankment No. 2 at Cholsey (now the site of Cholsey main line station). This particular embankment - built to a maximum height of 16-ft 6-in - started to subside some few months after the railway was opened to Steventon. By the start of October 1840, James Bedborough - the contractor - was busily engaged in preventing further slippage, with the embankment eventually stabilising at the beginning of November the same year. Other less persistent examples of subsidence occurred with embankments at Moreton and Pangbourne, but these appear to have stabilised quickly. Brunel used 'Permanent Ballast' or gravel tipped on to the areas of the embankment which were causing problems, to bring about stabilisation.

FIGURE 76. Drawings of the components of a broad-gauge roller truck.
(Reproduced by kind permission of the Librarian of the University of Bristol)

CHAPTER THIRTY-SEVEN
NEARING COMPLETION

The Directors of the Great Western Railway on 30 March 1830 extended their broad-gauge line with the opening of the section between Twyford and Reading. The troubles experienced in the excavation of the Sonning Hill caused many incidents and delays, with contractors failing and the Company having virtually to take charge in order that the opening was not further delayed. The original intention had been to open the entire line from Twyford to Faringdon (32½-miles) in the spring of 1840, however, the severe weather of the previous autumn and winter dashed any hopes of this.

Brunel was still hopeful that the line could be opened between Reading and Faringdon at the same time, but this was not to be and the line eventually opened from Reading to Steventon, some 10 miles from Oxford on Monday 1 June 1840, with intermediate stations at Pangbourne, Goring and Moulsford. Despite being of a cheap wooden construction, the Steventon station would continue to be the nearest access point to the Great Western Railway for the population of Oxford and country to the north until the Oxford Railway Company received the Royal Assent for the construction of the branch line to Oxford on 11 April 1843.

The main impetus in constructing the railway through Berkshire was nearly over and the line was already earning revenue. Rapidly, as each section was completed, the plant and materials used by the contractors was either auctioned or moved to another contract should the individual contractor have been successful in securing a new contract further to the west. On the banks of the River Thames at Pangbourne, the plant used to construct this part of the line was assembled for auction on Wednesday 3 June 1840, with the auction taking place at:

'Eleven in the Forenoon', under the auspices of Allnatt and Bracket, 'Estate Agents &c, Wallingford, In consequence of the completion of that part of the works of the Great Western Railway. ... The materials of numerous labourers cottages, stables and other buildings, about 80 two-and-a-half-yard strong railroad earth wagons in thorough repair with coupling chains and shackles complete ... metal rails, beech sleepers and other railway plant'.

The first part of Contract '4R' between Moulsford to Didcot to be completed was the arch which would carry the railway over the Wallingford-Faringdon turnpike and the sale of the plant used on this contract took place on Tuesday 23 July 1839, under the auspices of Mr. Owen an auctioneer of Wallingford. At Hagborne, a thatched stable about 70-feet long, especially constructed for Mr. Pritchard (the contractor) amongst other effects, including '245 useful railway horses' were put up for sale. Beyond Didcot, at Baulking near Faringdon, another sale took place on 5 February 1841. Here the contractor - Mr. Cogswell - had for sale:

'14 active young cart horses, 20 sets of stout harness, timber carriage and chains, several stout

wagons, and carts, about 300 wheelbarrows, about 10,000 strong elm sleepers, 6,000 feet of deal plank, several pieces of American timber, a carpenter and blacksmith's shop, a long range of stabling, 4 pumps, 4 pairs of smiths bellows, 4 anvils, 3 pairs of vices, a large quantity of iron, tools, and various effects'.

From the above descriptions, some idea of the materials and structures involved in the construction of the line of railway can be gathered. It is notable that at Pangbourne, labourers' accommodation was specially constructed. However, this is not too surprising, as the main contractors for the 'Pangbourne' contract were Messrs. Grissell & Peto who had a reputation for looking after the welfare of their employees.

Accidents, however, continued to occur even during the dismantling of the works. One of the most serious occurred in late May 1840, a Robert Bailey - who was employed in pulling down a temporary engine house at Basildon - being crushed when a board fell on him, it being reported that:

'He was conveyed to hospital and is doing well'

Despite the completion of the railway through Berkshire, problems continued to occur with the nefarious activities of the navvies, even more so now that many of the men had lost their employment. The Chairman of the Berkshire Midsummer Assizes, held at Abingdon on Tuesday 30 June 1840 stated that:

'He regretted to observe that the calendar was a heavy one'.

The majority of the offences took place along the line of recently completed railway and the offenders - in the main - came from Steventon, Wallingford, Shrivenham, Sunning-Hill [Sonning] and Maidenhead. Sentencing was severe. Two young boys - originally from Wandsworth, London - had offered several hoes for sale. Both boys were found guilty and were sentenced to one calendar months imprisonment as well as being:

'whipped privately four times before the expiration of their period of imprisonment'.

Some of the men and boys who had been attracted to the temporary security of employment working on the construction of the line of railway, would be retained to work on the next contract their particular contractor had successfully tendered for. However, others would prove less successful, some ending up in local workhouses.

As the railway continued to progress westwards, the presence of large numbers of men working on the various contracts continued to effect the ordinary citizens of Berkshire. At the Reading Michaelmas Fair, a severe shortage of cheese was experienced. This was due to all the local cheeses not being sent to market, the producers of the cheeses - mainly small farmers - choosing a more lucrative market, supplying the railway labourers direct. As the presence of the railway labourers gradually dissipated, the supply of cheeses to the market in Reading gradually recovered, the only difference being that most of the cheeses were now being transported by the new railway. This caused other problems, as the *Berkshire*

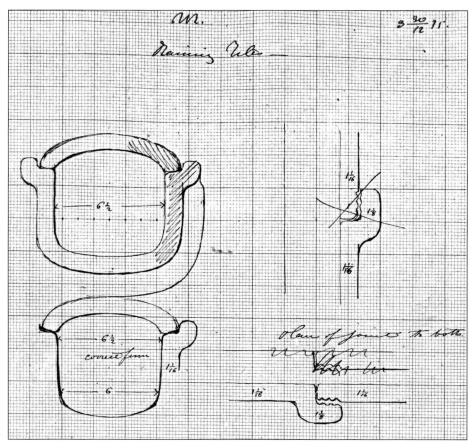

FIGURE 77. Brunel's design for clay draining tiles, which were essential in ensuring that water drained from embankments as quickly as possible, thus reducing the risk of surplus water causing the embankment to become unstable.
(Reproduced by kind permission of the Librarian of the University of Bristol).

Chronicle reported:

> *'The heath and birch-broom trade, which used to be of a very considerable extent at Reading Michaelmas Fair, and from which many of the industrious poor profited, has fallen away to a mere nothing. When the dairyman had their cheese brought up the old road they used to load the wagons home with brooms; but now, since the mode of conveyance is changed to the railway, it does not answer the purpose of the dealers to pay the carriage for them by that mode of transit'.*

The Great Western Railway between Bristol and London was finally opened completely on 30 June 1841, many of the labourers who had constructed the line now facing an uncertain future. However, as Britain's embryonic railway network continued to expand, their skills were required in other parts of the country and advertisements began to appear in Berkshire journals, such as:

> *'Northern & Eastern Railway - To Navigators - Wanted 800 good able-bodied men. Apply Mr. McKeone at Roydon Burnt Mill, Harlow or Sawbridgeworth'.*

At the same time as the men who had built the Great Western Railway transferred to other railway construction sites, the predictions of the anti-Great Western brigade were proving well founded. As the railway neared completion through Berkshire, one correspondent forecast:

> *'Few, save the pedestrian, can properly appreciate the important addition to a road constituted by the rapid and ever changing traffic of stagecoaches and omnibuses. We must not, however, descant too fondly upon the subject, as it is probable, that within a few months, the completion of our very fine line of railway will totally annihilate the agreeable variety, and the hanging woods of Englefield and Beenham will no longer echo back the nocturnal challenge of the mail-guard's horn'.*

However, there were to be far more serious consequences, some of which are vividly described in the following passage:

> *'We put up for the night at a good commercial posting house, but when we entered the travellers' room, where all had so recently been activity and high spirits, we were truly horrified at the desolation which prevailed ... and the gloom and melancholy which depicted themselves on every countenance. 'What cold meat have you in the house?' we enquired. 'None, Sir', was the reply. 'What, not in such a house as this? Well, then, can't you get us a chop?' 'We don't know where to get such a thing', was their answer. 'Nobody kills any meat now, for we have no company; they all go by the railway'.*
>
> *'We called for the landlord, who, though he plainly showed that he had been a man of business, was now all that was hopeless and despairing. 'I had a flourishing trade', he said. 'One hundred horses stood in my stables, at a guinea a year each, where now only two remain. Fifty coaches stopped here daily; not above one in ten now comes their road. I kept eight or ten ostlers; a boy is now employed about half his time; I had ten or twelve maidservants, and now but one ...'.*

In a very short time, the worst predictions were indeed coming true. The roads would become silent, except for the slow rumble of carts and wagons and even these - except for local traffic - would eventually disappear, with the railway slowly but inexorably eroding the long-distance trade conducted by these carriers. The disappearance of most of the private carriages and stagecoaches also ensured that many of the famous and large inns in the area would be forced to close.

Also hit hard were the manufacturers of the coaches themselves and the ancillary trades, such as wheelwrights and harness makers. Similarly, the posting houses and stables which supplied the horses. It would only be those trades willing to embrace the new railway that would survive, one such case being an Oxford coach manufacturer. - William Shackleford - with works also at nearby Benson, who quickly diversified into making railway coach bodies for the Great Western Railway. While Shackleford's entrepreneurial ability ensured that much distress was alleviated in the Benson area, nonetheless this would not prevent two large posting inns in the locality being forced to close by 1842. Appeals in local journals for relief by the friends and old customers of bankrupt innkeepers and coach proprietors began to appear. One such appeal was to the inhabitants of Reading and the surrounding neighbourhood:

'An appeal on behalf of the wife and family of Thomas Williams, is most humbly made. Having been well known for 35 years in this town, as a coach proprietor, he is now utterly ruined - partly by heavy losses in business and ultimately by the operation of the railroad'.

The turnpike trusts would also suffer as less traffic ensured less revenue was received in tolls and within 10 years some of the trusts were bankrupt. The roads gradually fell into disuse and eventual decay as the highway improvements began in the days of MacAdam and Telford were abandoned.

The situation on the waterways was as equally critical, advertisements for the sale of Thames barges appearing increasingly frequently in local journals. There was clearly no hope of riverborne traffic maintaining any superiority, it being rapidly undermined by the efficiency and regularity of the railway. The deficiencies of the waterways continued to be exacerbated by the weather and as the Great Western Railway was being completed, a correspondent reported on 21 October 1840 that:

'the Thames was very low and that the navigation was nearly closed. The trade on many canals was stopped for want of water'.

There were other disadvantages connected with the opening of the railway. Correspondence began to appear in Berkshire journals, complaining about the close proximity of the line of railway to the turnpike road between Reading and Wallingford. This was particularly so in the vicinity of Tilehurst and Streatley and the detrimental effects on horses and their passengers, scared by passing trains began to attract attention. Consequently, John A. Hedges - Clerk to the Turnpike Trust - published a notice on 12 November 1839 stating:

'Representations having been made that in many parts of the road, particularly in the Parish of Tilehurst, travelling will be rendered dangerous, by reason of the proximity thereto of the Great Western Railway. Notice is hereby given - that a meeting of the Trustees will be held at the Angel Inn Reading, on Tuesday 26 November at 11 a.m. to take the subject into consideration, when a full attendance is requested'.

There is no record of the conclusions reached by the Trustees, but it is difficult to see what could have been suggested at that late stage to alter the situation. Clearly, the earlier fears were justified, as shortly after the opening of the railway from Reading to Steventon, a Reading correspondent in a Berkshire journal stated on 13 June 1840:

'Railways have their disadvantages, as well as benefits. We may state as an instance of the former, that so great is the danger apprehended from the contiguity of the Great Western Railway, to the road between this town and Streatley, that we have known instances of travellers going some miles out of their direct route rather than risk frightening of the horses, by the sudden and close approach of the trains'.

Brunel, when commissioned to make the first surveys of the proposed line between Bristol and London, soon laid before the sub-Committee what was to prove virtually a new concept in railway construction. The proposed line was, at that time, the longest to date proposed in the kingdom and Brunel's versatility as a trained engineer clearly and quickly exhibited a new approach to the construction and operation of a railway. Brunel, convinced that the potentialities of high-speed running should be fully exploited, stated:

> *'I shall not attempt to argue with those who consider any increase in speed unnecessary. The public will always prefer that conveyance which is the most perfect, and speed within reasonable limits is a material ingredient in perfection in travelling'.*

Despite the restrictions imposed on the earlier section of the line, caused in part by the imperfections in Brunel's controversial permanent way, there appears to have been no serious problems apparent on the newly opened section of line between Reading and Steventon. A correspondent noted:

> *'I was a few days since on the Great Western Railway, between Steventon and Reading, we started with a remarkably light load, and as we seemed to be going at much more than customary speed, I had the curiosity to note the time for a considerable distance. One mile performed in 70 seconds (or 50 miles per hour) and for a quarter of a minute we attained the speed of 60 miles per hour'.*

Such observations became the start of a new pastime; the timing of trains for generations of railway observers now being made possible by using the mileposts situated every quarter of a mile along the line of railway. Other new and lasting hobbies quickly developed, Brunel's massive railway, its magnificent locomotives and rolling stock, proving an awe-inspiring sight for both young and old. Right from the start, the custom of the Directors of the Great Western Railway to name their locomotives proved extremely popular and another new phenomena soon developed, that of train-spotting and recording the names of individual locomotives. On 7 May 1840, a young Berkshire diarist records:

> *'In the evening went up to the railway [Sonning]. Saw a new engine started today, the Tiger. I have seen altogether nine engines, running on the railway. The Morning Star, Evening Star, Dog Star, Ajax, Atlas, Planet, Mars, Firefly, & Tiger'.*

In June the same year, amongst youthful activities which included shooting two wild swans; fishing for perch and eels and paying 'six-shillings to have a kingfisher stuffed', the same young man records:

> *'7 June - Saw the Fireking. 8 June - Saw the Leopard'.*

However, along the new line of railway through Berkshire other more harmful activities quickly developed. Shortly after the opening of the railway from Reading to Steventon, a passenger was injured in the mouth after a large stone was thrown from a railway bridge. A similar incident later in the year resulted in three boys - all under 17 years of age - being brought before magistrates at Little Stoke. The boys were stated to have:

> *'in the evening wantonly cast and thrown a quantity of stones and missiles upon the Great Western Railway, to the danger and inconvenience of passengers'.*

Being found guilty, all three were given two alternatives - a fine of £5 or six weeks in the Castle Gaol, Oxford. Their individual choices are not recorded!

Further advantages associated with the opening of the railway included bringing prosperity to locations which had previously been backwaters prior to the railway explosion. Swindon quickly began to prosper and by September 1840, considerable changes were noticeable in the town. Where previously only a few coaches served the area, now 12 coaches a day ran to or from the town, mainly carrying passengers who had used or who intended to use the Great Western Railway.

The arrival of the railway would also dramatically improve the distribution of Fleet Street newspapers along the line of railway. By September 1841, newspaper agents were able to advertise with total confidence the delivery at all Great Western Railway stations of newspapers from the metropolis by the first train each morning. In some instances, this would be little more than one hour after the newspaper had been published in the metropolis.

FIGURE 78. The horse-bridge erected adjacent to the 60 feet span brick arch - with four 18 feet side arches - by the Great Western Railway over the mouth of the River Kennet at Reading to enable barges towed by horses to continue their way unimpeded.

(Author's collection)

PART VIII
COMPLETION

'If ever I go mad, I shall have the ghost of the opening of the railway walking before me, or rather standing in front of me, holding out his hand, and when it steps forward, a little swarm of devils in the shape of leaky pickle-tanks, uncut timber, half-finished station houses, sinking embankments, broken screws, absent guard plates, unfinished drawings and sketches, will, quietly and quite as a matter of course and as if I ought to have expected it, lift up my ghost and put him a little further off than before' [to Saunders].

3 December 1837

GREAT WESTERN RAILWAY.

LONDON to MAIDENHEAD.

Private Carriages will now be conveyed upon this Railway, between London and Maidenhead, by the several Trains, previous notice being given at the Company's Stations to secure a Truck, and the Carriage being ready at the Station a quarter of an hour before the departure of the Trains.

FROM PADDINGTON AND FROM MAIDENHEAD.

TRAINS.

8 o'Clock . . . . . . Morning, *(excepting on Mondays from Maidenhead, when it will leave at Half-past 7.)*	**5 o'Clock** . . . . Evening.
9 ,, ... Morning.	**6** ,, ... ditto.
12 ,, ... ditto.	**7** ,, ... ditto.

The Eight o'Clock Morning Train from LONDON, and the Seven o'Clock Evening Train from MAIDENHEAD, will *not* call at West Drayton.

Fares of Passengers.

			First Class.		Second Class.	
			Posting Carr.	Passenger Coach.	Coach.	Open Carr.
PADDINGTON STATION.	To or from	WEST DRAYTON . . .	4 0	3 6	2 0	1 6
	,,	SLOUGH	5 6	4 6	3 0	2 6
	,,	MAIDENHEAD	6 6	5 6	4 0	3 6
MAIDENHEAD.	To or from SLOUGH		2 0	1 6	1 0	1 0
	,, WEST DRAYTON . . .		3 0	2 6	2 0	1 6
	,, PADDINGTON . . .		6 6	5 6	4 0	3 6

The same Fares will be charged between West Drayton and Slough, as between Maidenhead and Slough.

ON SUNDAYS

The Trains will leave Paddington and Maidenhead at the undermentioned hours only :

at 8 o'Clock . . . . Morning.	at 5 o'Clock . . . . . Evening.
Half-past 8 ,, ... ditto.	6 ,, ... ditto.
9 ,, ... ditto.	7 ,, ... ditto.

The Eight o'Clock Morning Train from London, and the Six o'Clock Evening Train from Maidenhead will call at Slough ONLY.

Omnibuses and Coaches run from Princes Street, Bank ; Spread Eagle, Gracechurch Street ; Angel Inn, Islington ; Bull Inn, Holborn ; Moore's Green Man and Still, Oxford Street ; Golden Cross, Charing Cross ; Chaplin's Universal Office, Regent Circus ; and Gloucester Warehouse, Oxford Street, to the Paddington Station for each Train.

Post Horses are kept in readiness both at *Paddington* and *Maidenhead*, and upon sufficient notice being given, would be sent to bring Carriages from any part of London to the Paddington Station, at a moderate charge.

1st AUGUST, 1838.

W. SNELL, PRINTER, NEWCASTLE PLACE, EDGWARE ROAD.

FIGURE 79. Fare list and timetable of the Great Western Railway dated 1 August 1838.
(BR and successors)

CHAPTER THIRTY-EIGHT
PREPARATIONS FOR THE OPENING OF THE RAILWAY BETWEEN READING AND STEVENTON

The attempts by the Directors to seek Parliamentary authorisation to construct the two extremities of the railway emphasised the importance placed upon the likely traffic between the Bristol-Bath and London-Reading sections. At that time, however, even the Directors were not convinced that the line would be profitable if Parliament only authorised the construction of the two ends of the scheme. George Henry Gibbs reported that:

'To my mind, it is quite clear that the paying part of the line will be from London to Maidenhead. ... I remember when the question of confining the work to the two ends was so much discussed at our Committee, before I left it, we could not make out that the line from Bristol to Bath would pay'.

It was possibly this apprehension which made the Directors extremely reluctant to embark upon or to finance any frivolous expenditure and Gibbs again expresses this concern in a letter dated 8-9 April 1837, when he stated:

'what advantage can the Great Western line derive from the road from Reading to Box commensurate with the expense of making it, at any time previous to the whole line being completed? A country less fertile in traffic than that which this line passes through is not to be met with, I should think'.

The Directors knew that the success of the intermediate section between Reading and Bath would depend to a great extent on the completion of railway schemes to serve Cheltenham, Oxford and areas to the north of these places. As early as the Autumn of 1833 and soon after the issue of the Great Western Railway Prospectus, enterprising residents in Cheltenham and neighbourhood projected a railway from that town by way of Gloucester and Stroud. This would connect with the Great Western main line at Swindon and afford a communication with the metropolis and Bristol. Brunel himself surveyed the proposed line. The proposal was opposed by the London & Birmingham Company, who would subsequently promote a rival line from Tring, by Oxford to Cheltenham. The Cheltenham & Great Western Union Company obtained their Act in 1836 and would connect with the Brunellian main line with a junction at Swindon. Similarly, a branch to Oxford with a continuation of the line to Worcester was also encouraged by the Directors of the Great Western Railway as early as August 1836. A 'probable branch' of 12 miles to Oxford was shown on the map of the original Great Western Prospectus of 1833, but no steps were taken to promote such a branch until three years later. Despite several attempts to encourage the promotion of a line to Oxford, the city was left undisturbed, with its station 10 miles away at Steventon and it was not until 11 April 1843 that the Oxford Railway Bill had an uneventful passage through Parliament.

As both these projects were essential to the long-term success of the Great Western Railway, because of the uncertainty of these two schemes, it was even suggested that contracts already entered into for the construction of the Great Western main line between Reading and Bath be withdrawn. Gibbs recorded these anxious moments:

> 'Robert [assumed to be Robert Bright the Deputy Chairman] won't hear of with drawing contracts.
> Robert says that withdrawing the contracts would be sure to throw them [shares] down. Of course it must be done with caution, but surely the seeing an immense and immediate outlay upon such a barren road as that I have alluded to must upon thinking people have a much more unfavourable effect than the knowledge that you are confining your operations to the parts of the line best fitted to return an early income. Who that knows anything about these matters will think it possible for the Oxford or Cheltenham to make much progress in these times? . . . '.

Despite these pessimistic predictions, the construction of the intermediate section of the line between Reading and Bath was eventually undertaken. It would appear, however, that the caution felt by the Directors and particularly Gibbs regarding the success of the enterprise delayed certain decisions being made. These misgivings may explain the tardiness to issue the contracts for the two river bridges over the Thames at Gatehampton and Moulsford. It will be recalled that the contracts for these two bridges were first advertised in March 1837 with Chadwick's successful tender not being accepted until nearly a year later!

However, following the success of the Cheltenham Bill and most apprehensions overcome, the construction of the Great Western line continued unabated. Early in 1839, Gibbs and some of his fellow Directors visited the works through Berkshire and on the morning of 5 February, they travelled as far as Cholsey. They returned to London on 6 February apparently satisfied with what they had seen. They were also confident that the line would be opened to the public as far as Didcot by the end of the year. Later in the same year, Gibbs following a further visit to west Berkshire, stated:

> 'Went onto Didcot, where we met the clergy, farmers, road commissioners and lawyers of the neighbouring country and had a long talk with them about roads, drainage, bridges, etc., etc., Got home to dinner at half-past seven. I was satisfied on the whole with the state of the work and have no doubt that we shall open to Twyford on 1 July and to Steventon very possibly on 1 February, or 1 March 1840'.

As further sections of the line were opened, Brunel and the Directors quickly gained confidence, learning from experience regarding the forward planning required for their unique enterprise. Earlier sections had been opened with a confidence which had been quickly shattered due to problems associated with the unpredictability of the locomotives, Brunel's controversial permanent way and other vicissitudes. As the railway pushed beyond Reading, Brunel's confidence had been reinforced by the knowledge that the Company was now in a position to more-or-less guarantee a punctual service to the public.

Despite this confidence, there were still some anxious moments. Messrs. T. & C. Rigby [MacDermot records this as J. & C. Rigby] of Millbank, Westminster had been employed by the Company to build all the stations between Steventon and Corsham, as well as the the station at Slough. Later, the company would be responsible for the construction of the locomotive works and 300 cottages for workmen which would form the nucleus of the town of New Swindon. The temporary terminus at Steventon was to remain the main station for Oxford, until the Oxford Railway received the Royal Assent on 11 April 1843.

The station buildings at Steventon were constructed of wood and it is, perhaps surprising that Steventon, as the main station for the City of Oxford, could only boast a cheap wooden structure. As early as 1837, in a Bill promoting the branch to Oxford, it was proposed that Oxford would be reached from a junction starting from Didcot. Perhaps, for this reason Brunel (or more probably the London Committee) anticipating the possibility of the branch to Oxford from Didcot, decided on the wooden buildings at Steventon. This temporary structure would have been cheap to construct (which would have pleased the Directors) and could easily be altered or demolished to suit any future requirements. Brunel also had constructed at Steventon - adjacent to the railway - two fine stone houses and a row of 11 terraced cottages in brick after the Tudor style for the accommodation of the Company's servants. Similar accommodation for the railwaymen who would work the stations along the route was also designed by Brunel and the engineer shows his consideration for his more lowly railway colleagues in a letter addressed to the resident engineer at Faringdon - J. H. Gandell:

> *'My Dear Sir, I have sent Mr. Saunders my certificate of the completion of the cottages & stabling. You must undertake however that fires shall be burned in them daily untill they are dry as it would not be safe for the men to come into them in their present state'.*

At a meeting of the Directors in London on 20 April 1840, they heard to their horror that the contractors had made no attempt to start the construction of the station buildings at Steventon. Saunders was hurriedly instructed to write to Messrs. Rigby emphasising:

> *'it being the intention of the Directors to open the line on 2nd June, I have to acquaint you that they rely upon your putting on such force as will complete it for the use of the traffic by that time'.*

As already stated, Messrs. T. & C. Rigby had also successfully tendered for the construction of Brunel's one-sided station at Slough which would open to the public in June 1840. However, the contractor's labour force was over-stretched at

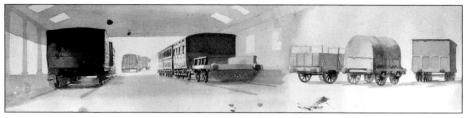

FIGURE 80. Above and opposite page: Wash drawings of early locomotives and rolling stock used on the Great Western Railway by John Cooke Bourne.
(Elton Collection: Ironbridge Gorge Museum Trust)

this period and Saunders had to write to the company again on 12 May, insisting that the stations at Steventon and Slough be ready for the planned opening.

The preparations for the opening to Steventon progressed and on 26 May 1840, some of the Directors visited Steventon to appoint staff. Prior to this visit, a Minute of the Great Western Railway London Appointments Committee dated 18 May 1840, records that six men were appointed as porters and five men as policemen. Three of the men named in this Minute were recorded as being appointed to work at the Moulsford station. One was Edwin Clewitt of Cholsey and in the 1841 Census, Clewitt is recorded as being a 'Switchman on the GWR'. Also appointed was a Mr. Stevens, who had been appointed 'Principal Station Clerk at a salary of £100' and finally, John Parson who was appointed as porter. It would appear, therefore, that these three men comprised the total staff at the Moulsford station at its inception.

The custom latterly was for the Directors to personally inspect each new section of line before it was officially opened to public traffic. Consequently, on 4 May 1840, the Directors decided that they would inspect the line to Steventon the following Monday. This inspection probably almost certainly adopted the same procedure as used for the previous extension of the line some seven weeks later, when the line was extended to the next temporary terminus at Faringdon. On this occasion, it is recorded that the Directors and Brunel left the Steventon station at six in the morning, travelling the 7¼-miles to the Faringdon Road station. The object of this trial was:

'for the purpose of trying the solidity of the ground'

with in excess of 70 tons of ballast being placed in luggage trucks for the purpose of the experiment.

Some of the earlier openings necessitated the original timetables having to be altered because of the dictates of the postal authorities. In the early stages and as the Great Western Railway gradually extended the line both east and west, the postal authorities were able to stipulate in their contract with the railway company that the trains had to either collect mail from the road mail coaches at the various temporary termini, or even carry the mail coach by means of a carriage truck on the train. Because of the financial vulnerability of the embryonic railway, the Directors agreed in the early stages for the trains to connect with the mail coaches. However, as the financial vulnerability of the railway decreased, the Directors prior to the opening to Steventon, decided that to save inconvenience to the public because of having to alter the timetables, as well as the cost of publishing revised timings, the mail arrangements would have to fit into the railway's timings and not vice versa. Consequently, Saunders on 2 May 1840 wrote to George Stowe of the General Post Office, requesting confirmation that the mails would be carried when the line was opened to Steventon and then consequently to Faringdon. Saunders suggested:

'If the arrangement for doing so could be simultaneous with the opening of the line for general traffic, both on account of the public inconvenience in the arrangement of the trains, with as little change as possible, and also to avoid additional expense in advertising, printing etc. of bills and notices'.

Saunders also proposed the following timetable:

From Steventon	From Paddington
UP	DOWN
3.15am (Mail)	8.00am
8.15	9.00
9.15	10.00
11.15	12.00
1.15pm	2.00pm
3.15	4.00
5.15	7.00
7.15	9.05 (Mail)
Goods	Goods
4.15am	4.00am
9.40pm	9.00pm

These proposals appear to have been mutually acceptable by both the railway and postal authorities as they remained in force when the railway was extended beyond

Steventon to the Faringdon Road station, although an extra 15 minutes was allowed for the 7¹/₂-miles between Steventon and Faringdon, except for the Down mail which was accelerated to 10 minutes. A month later and prior to the opening to Steventon, the London Directors on 4 May 1940:

> *'Ordered that the ticket books be forthwith prepared'.*

Following the Great Western Railway Bill receiving the Royal Assent, road coach proprietors and associated trades and professions were filled with foreboding over their future. Prior to the first section of the line opening to Maidenhead, it must have been with some surprise that coach proprietors received a circular from Saunders. The Secretary had been instructed by the Directors on the 3 April 1838 to circularise:

> *'... Proprietors of Coaches, Wagons, etc., now employed on the line of road to Oxford, Cheltenham, etc. and also to the West of England'.*

The Circular explained:

> *'they [the Directors] have desired me to indicate to you, as proprietors of a coach likely to be affected by the railway that they are quite disposed to make any arrangement with you that may be mutually serviceable to connecting your present coach with the trains of the Company at Maidenhead'.*

However, this proposal was not a altruistic gesture by the Directors! In the short term - and particularly until the whole line was opened - the revenue generated by the connecting road coach services was essential for the financial survival of the railway. In the long term, the long distance coach trade would be completely annihilated by the success of Brunel's great enterprise. As the railway neared completion, any co-operation gradually evaporated, restrictions were imposed and facilities withdrawn at the Company's premises for coach proprietors and inevitably the coach trade became a thing of the past.

The road coach traffic was a necessary evil tolerated by the Great Western Directors during the early construction stages of the railway, but as little assistance as possible - in practice - would be extended to the coach proprietors. The railway opened from London to Maidenhead on Monday 4 June 1838, although the conveyance of horses was postponed until 4 August and coaches were not carried until the following month. Despite the fact that particularly at Maidenhead the connecting road coach services would bring a large proportion of the passengers to the temporary terminus at Taplow, the only provision the Directors would agree to was that 'a stable shed of the cheapest construction' be built.

As the railway opened in stages to the various temporary terminii, the coach traffic quickly adapted itself: either by connecting with the new train service; being carried by the railway, or by closing down. The site of the Steventon station being some 10 miles from the City of Oxford would clearly provide a good source of income for the coach proprietors and one enterprising carrier - Costar & Waddell of Oxford - wrote to the Directors on 24 September 1839, requesting:

'information when the line would be open to Steventon'.

On the 30 May 1840, *Jackson's Oxford Journal* announced on the following Monday when the line opened to Steventon:

'Messrs. Costar and Waddell beg to inform the publick [sic] that they have made arrangements with the Directors to send conveyances to Steventon and Moulsford stations to meet every Up and Down. ... there will be eight trains each day'.

For the anticipated opening to Steventon and then on to Faringdon, the Directors had quickly realised that extra rolling stock would be required. They had decided on 4 November 1839 that 15 extra carriage trucks, eight horse boxes and 21 Open Second-class carriages be ordered. All the vehicles ordered had to be delivered in February 1840. The early rolling stock for the Great Western Railway was supplied by 10 different firms. Two of these specialist firms were local - Dells of Reading and William Shackleford of Oxford and also at nearby Benson. Both of these firms had quickly switched from making road-coaches to building railway vehicles, a practice apparently despised by many traditional coach-builders of the period. Of the new vehicles ordered for the opening through to Faringdon, a good proportion would be built by Dells and Shackleford. The Directors decided to place an order with Shackleford to build the eight horse boxes and between four and six of the Second-class carriages. Dells would build the same number of Second-class carriages - if the order could be completed on time. Shackleford appears to have established a good relationship with the Great Western Railway and the Company continued to order rolling stock from this former road coach builder for some considerable years.

Towards the end of April 1840, the Chairman and several of the Directors travelled to Didcot by train and they found:

'the works on the line progressing so rapidly towards completion that they have little doubt of opening it for public traffic to the above place by the 1st of June'.

The official Directors' inspection of the works to Steventon took place on 11 May with the first advertisement appearing in local journals of the opening of the railway to the public on 16 May. On 30 May, the timetable of the new service to Steventon was published. As with all the early Great Western Train Bills, this only showed the time the train commenced its journey from the terminus and it would not be until December 1840 that the first true time-table was issued, when the time the train left each station along the line of railway was confidently published.

So the scene was set. The railway was completed three-quarters of the way through Berkshire. Some seven weeks later, the line would be opened to Faringdon Road station. The responsibility of the London Committee terminated at Shrivenham, a few miles from the west Berkshire boundary and on 17 December the line would open completely between Swindon and Wootton Bassett.

CHAPTER THIRTY-NINE
THE RAILWAY OPENS BETWEEN READING AND STEVENTON

When each of the sections of the Great Western Railway was opened, it was the practice of the Directors to travel by train to the latest temporary terminus. This would be the 'official' opening and would take place on the Sunday preceding the 'public' opening. This procedure was adopted for the opening to Steventon on Sunday 31 May 1840, when the Directors 'and a large party of ladies' arrived by train at the new terminus at Steventon at 12.30 a.m. The journey had taken one hour 10 minutes to cover the distance between London and Steventon. The train consisted of first-class carriages, hauled by a brand new locomotive *Charon*, the first of a batch of 20 locomotives of the 'Fire Fly' class, designed by Daniel Gooch and ordered from the Leeds Company Murray & Jackson. The official party - amongst others - consisted of Charles Russell (Chairman of the Great Western Railway), Viscount Barrington MP and Lady Barrington, H. Simonds, Riversdale Grenfell, F. Gower, Brunel and Saunders. The party inspected the new works and had a 'cold collation' before returning to London. Thus, the line from London to Steventon was ready for the public opening the following day.

Monday 1 June 1840 dawned. At Steventon there was much celebration and a carnival atmosphere was evident. An extensive fair had been set up and many gypsies were in evidence with 'vast numbers of booths'. The first scheduled train arrived at the wooden station at 10.30 a.m. having been timed to leave the London terminus at 8 a.m. The train had been unavoidably delayed by the large numbers of passengers who wished to avail themselves of this unique occasion, eventually arriving at the new terminus in a little under two hours. The train on this occasion having been hauled by the newly arrived locomotive *Leopard*, which was the second of a batch of 10 engines of Gooch's 'Fire Fly' class ordered from the Manchester company of Sharp, Roberts & Co. The locomotive had been delivered sometime during May and just before the opening to Steventon. Almost certainly, for the rest of the day the remainder of the scheduled trains would be very heavily loaded, many local people using the trains to view the new railway works and stations along the extension. Most - after taking part in the festivities - would return to their homes full of admiration for Brunel and his great enterprise.

But, how had the Moulsford station fared in the opening festivities? First of all, the decision to name the station intended for passengers from Wallingford and district 'Moulsford' raised some steam amongst the citizens of Wallingford! As the station was located close to the small hamlet of Moulsford, the decision to name the station in this way is, perhaps, not that surprising. However, for the railway traveller with business in Wallingford or district, the name was perceived by some as confusing. Whatever the reasons for naming the station Moulsford, the citizens of Wallingford objected most strongly, with the result that the Directors decided on 6 October 1840:

'That in compliance with the wishes of the inhabitants of Wallingford the Moulsford Station be called the 'Wallingford Road Station''.

The station at Moulsford retained this name until 1866 when the Wallingford branch line was constructed, the station then reverting to the original name 'Moulsford'.

Despite this apparent rebuff, the citizens of Wallingford and neighbourhood made arrangements to celebrate the arrival of the Great Western Railway. A few of the more wealthy amongst the populace took the opportunity to visit the metropolis, now only 1¾-hours away. Others made the shorter journey to Steventon, which could now be reached in 15 minutes to experience for themselves first-hand travel by railway and to partake in the festivities which were taking place there. Some simply went to the railway works which now split the Parish and also to the Moulsford station, to see and marvel at Brunel's magnificent venture. There were many vantage points along the new section of line and both young and old could not have been but impressed with the railway which had now come to their community.

Despite this general interest, the population of Wallingford - even on the opening day - perhaps showed the ambivalence which had been so pronounced when the first proposals for a railway between Bristol and London had been made. The *Berkshire Chronicle* records the event:

'GREAT WESTERN RAILWAY - In consequence of the opening of the line from Reading to Steventon, on Monday last, vehicles of all descriptions and pedestrians were observed at an early hour, in all directions progressing towards the station in Cholsey Field [Moulsford], and we are happy to say that we have not heard of any accident having taken place to mar the pleasure of the holiday. At five o'clock in the afternoon, a respectable gathering sat down to the opening dinner provided by Mr. Sherwood, the new landlord of the Feathers Inn. Thomas Wells Esq. presided on the occasion, and ably sustained the duties of Chairman. The dinner was served up in excellent style, and glee and sound humour prevailed until the separation of the party, the only feeling of regret being that more were not present to partake of the ample viands'.

So, the Great Western Railway had arrived. At first, the Moulsford station was not able to accept either horses or carriages for conveyance by the trains due to incomplete facilities, but this was quickly remedied and by the time the line opened to Faringdon, both were being accepted. Problems soon developed with the train service and the Directors quickly took appropriate action. The Moulsford station was serviced every day - except Sundays - by four trains both Up and Down, plus both Up and Down mail trains. On Sundays, the service was reduced to two trains each way, plus both Up and Down mails. Shortly after the line opened to Steventon, several requests were made that more trains stop at the Moulsford station. This was rejected outright by the Directors and Saunders replied to one of the correspondents on 10 June 1840 in the following terms:

> *'In reply to your letter of yesterday I am sorry that I cannot offer you any hope that the Directors will cause additional trains to stop at Moulsford.*
>
> *On the contrary they find that there are already more stoppages for the Long trains that is consistent with their requisite speed and if an alteration takes place it will rather be to reduce than to increase the number of stoppages'.*

A similar request was received a few days later and on 13 June Saunders again expressed the Directors thoughts on the subject:

> *'The opening to Faringdon will take place on 6 July [eventually 20 July] and the Directors have it in contemplation then to reduce the number of intermediate stoppages both at Moulsford and Pangbourne'.*

The problem appeared to be the increasing and unavoidable delays which occurred at the intermediate stations when passengers, carriages, luggage and horses had to be unloaded. As the trains stopped at each station along the route, the timing grew progressively worse. Saunders explained:

> *'Our recent experience shews how much unavoidable detention there is in the frequent stoppage of a train, more especially when coach luggage has to be removed either into or out of the railway trucks'.*

When the railway was first opened, some of the luggage carried was conveyed on the roofs of the railway carriages in much the same way as luggage was carried by the road coaches. This practice was soon abandoned and by October 1840, separate luggage wagons with tarpaulin coverings were running in passenger trains. Even this did not totally solve the problem and the Directors decided that the only solution to these delays was to split the trains. Again Saunders explains:

> *'Already to meet this difficulty the Directors have divided the 3.15 train into two by sending separate engines forward from Reading and in like manner the 10 o'clock Down is also divided, in order to ensure greater speed and punctuality'.*

In the six months ending 31 December 1840, passengers carried on the two sections of the railway so far open, amounted to 648,000. The London Division, now open to Hay Lane, had carried 492,000 passengers and in the Bristol Division (the line was now open between Bristol and Bath) 156,000 passengers had been carried. On 13 April 1841, the London Directors were informed of the number of passengers carried by the railway during the previous year. The section between Reading and Steventon had been open to the public for just over 45 weeks. The railway's own figures confirmed that during this period, 5,820 passengers had either embarked or disembarked at the Moulsford station. This indicated that approximately 130 passengers a week or 18 each day had used the station. Despite the prediction made in their Parliamentary submission that it was possible to:

> *'more than double the ordinary traffic of the Road'*

clearly, the traffic so far was not up the Directors' earlier predictions. However, they were not too downhearted, as they had high hopes that the numbers would increase when the line was fully opened to Bristol.

The situation at the Pangbourne station was little better. During the same period, 3,320 passengers had been carried or approximately 74 per week (10 a day). At the small station at Goring the situation was critical, although no passenger returns are available to give the true picture. The London Directors had been originally presented with a Memorial from the inhabitants of Goring on 12 August 1839, requesting the establishment of a 'Minor' station close to the village for the convenience of local people. Despite some pessimism from the Directors, a station was erected close by, albeit of a very simple nature, being constructed of wood and officially described as a 'booking shed'. Initially, only three trains in each direction stopped at Goring on weekdays and Saturdays and neither the mail or goods trains stopped at this diminutive station. Also, there were no facilities for the unloading or horses or carriages. On a Sunday, the only service was one Down train and two Up trains. This timing remained the same until a new timetable was published on 30 July 1841, when the service at Goring was cut back to two trains each way per day. However, the Down and Up Day Mail train stopped now, but there were still no other facilities. Indeed, the Directors at one time, seriously considered withdrawing the service to this small community completely and requests for more trains were consistently refused. On 5 October 1840, Saunders answered one such request, stating:

> *'In fact, it is really a serious question whether it be quite consistent with the general interests of the Company and the Public to have the Goring Station continued at all'.*

A further request was received the following year and again Saunders spoke of the quandary facing the Directors:

> *'The fact is that the station affords so very little traffic lying within so short a distance from Wallingford [Moulsford] & Pangbourne that the public are pressing upon the Directors to abandon it altogether'.*

Despite this pessimism, the small booking office would survive until the 10 February 1865 when the structure was reduced to ashes after a fire.

The first 'recorded' accident on the Great Western Railway did not occur until 25 October 1840, when the locomotive *Fire King* - hauling the night goods train - ran unchecked through the Faringdon Road station and through the closed doors of the engine house. The driver was killed and four people injured in this accident. However, as the line gradually opened throughout, other situations arose with the operation of the railway which would have been a new phenomenon at the time for the local people.

A hazard which had quickly become apparent on the earlier sections of the railway was the danger of fire caused by hot cinders from the locomotives. Coke was the fuel in use on all the early railways during this period and would not be superseded by coal until 1857 after many years of experiment. There were many

FIGURE 81. A lovely scene in the vicinity of Bath shortly after the opening of the Great Western Railway. The artist - Thomas Francis Dicksee - captures the evocative scene during the period 1840-1845, as a small child waves at a passing train.
(Elton Collection: Ironbridge Gorge Museum Trust)

instances on the early Great Western Railway of fires from such causes, the first on the section of line to Steventon occurring on 20 June 1840, when a goods truck caught fire. To try to prevent such occurrences, the goods trucks were covered with large and heavy tarpaulins, which were secured tightly over the arched ribs which formed the top of the truck. The ends and sides of the truck were effectively covered by the tarpaulin with the intention of making them fireproof as well as waterproof. This method was not always effective, however and a large conflagration occurred on 22 July 1840 at Acton near London, when 29 trucks filled with valuable merchandise were involved in a fire. Luckily, only two of the trucks and their contents were lost.

Another kind of incident - which unfortunately would escalate in frequency - occurred at South Stoke near Moulsford on 21 August 1840. This was the first recorded fatality on this newly opened section of line and in the accident Joseph Pearce - aged 54 - a postman from London, was killed by the locomotive *Tiger*. Pearce, after visiting a cousin at South Stoke, had started to walk along the line to the Steventon station. He had an umbrella held over his head and had not heard - or seen - the train approach. This would be the first of many such incidents and death - particularly to the families of the men who worked on the early Great Western Railway - would be a frequent visitor throughout the following years. The *Berkshire Chronicle* poignantly describes this incident:

'Fatal Railway Accident - On Monday morning as the 'Tiger' was bringing down the 9 o'clock train from Paddington, on approaching the Moulsford station, the engine man discovered a person <u>walking on the same line of rails</u>; He blew his whistle so loudly that it attracted the attention of several persons who were nearly a mile off, but it did not appear to alarm the person

it was intended for, and who was most unfortunately knocked down before the train could be stopped. The wheels passing over his legs, severed them from his body; his arms were both broken ... so that he was at once pronounced a dead man, although his pulse continued to beat for several minutes ...'.

The same day as this dreadful accident occurred, a much more happier event was taking place at the western extremity of the line. The line between the Bristol terminus at Temple Meads and the Great Western Railway station at Bath was almost ready for opening to the public and - as usual - an official party made the first journey over the section. The event is recorded by a local journal:

'The party consisted of five of the Directors: Messrs. R. Bright, W. Tothill, T. R. Guppy, C. B. Fripp and R. Scott, attended by Mr. Brunel, Mr. Clarke, the Superintendent, and some other officers of the Company. In consequence of the rails not being quite finished at the station in Temple Meads, it was not easy to get a carriage upon the line at the Engine-house, and the party were therefore content 'to take their places' on the engine and tender. The engine selected for the first part of the journey was the 'Arrow', the first Bristol made locomotive, and a very creditable specimen it is of the skill of the manufacturers, Messrs. Stothert & Co., of this City. The start was made from a point nearly opposite to the engine-house at 20 minutes after 4 O'clock, and after threading the darksome passage of Tunnels Nos. 1, 2 and 3, and skimming over the new embankment at Fox's Wood the engine was stopped at the Keynsham Station at 4h. 30m. Here the Directors alighted and after a delay of 8 minutes they started again, on the other line of rails, with the 'Meridian', a fine engine from the manufactory of Messrs. Hawthorn & Co., of Newcastle. As the engine flew onwards, the party were greeted with hearty cheers from bands of workmen and spectators at different points, and after making a short stoppage near the Cross Posts Bridge, to take up the assistant engineer, Mr. Frere (who we regret to hear has lately met with a serious accident from a fall), the Directors completed their trip to Bath, arriving at the Oak Street Viaduct at 4h. 53m. After staying some time to inspect the bridge over the Avon the party again took their places on the engine and the start was made at 32 minutes after 5. A short stoppage was again made at the Cross Posts Bridge and then the Keynsham station was reached at 5h 45m. Here the Directors again 'took flight' by the 'Arrow', which landed them safely at the engine house in St. Philips in 10½ minutes. In consequence of the numerous workmen still at work on the line it was not thought prudent to make any trial of speed, but our readers will see that the trip was performed to Bath in 33 minutes including two stoppages, one of these 8 minutes. Such a run as this must be quite sufficient to secure an abundant traffic as soon as the line is opened to the public'.

This section of the line opened to the public 10 days later, on 31 August 1840.

At the Bristol Temple Meads terminus of the railway, intending passengers gained entry to Brunel's magnificent 220-ft Great Train Shed, with its 72-ft single roof span, through the Gothic stone facade by what became known as the 'Clock Gate'. This was the 'in' gateway for departures and had a large clock surmounted in the recess between the dripmoulds. There was a separate 'out' gateway for arrivals.

CHAPTER FORTY
THE ROYAL CONNECTION

The Great Western Railway from Reading to Steventon - a distance of 20¹/₂ miles - was opened to the public on Monday 1 June 1840. The Moulsford station, with the other intermediate stations at Pangbourne and Goring, appeared to play little part in the opening celebrations and there are no records of the special train carrying the Directors and their important guests either stopping or even slowing as it passed through the intermediate stations. However, the Moulsford station shortly after opening to the public, received a visit which would ensure the station's place in Britain's railway history.

Main line railways ran from the metropolis to the Midlands and the North and to Southampton and soon the Great Western Railway would connect Bristol to the capital. All the existing main line railway companies were anticipating Royal patronage, not least being the Great Western Railway with Windsor Castle prominently visible from the Company's line near Slough. Despite the violent opposition from Eton College which ensured that:

'No diversion, branch, or station was to be made within three miles of Eton College'

this did not deter the Directors and they had decided that Royal patronage would be a lucrative, as well as honoured business. Consequently, orders had been given for a Royal Carriage to be constructed.

In appearance, the first Great Western Railway broad-gauge Royal saloon would not be unlike an elegant, well fitted, roomy road coach, on an underframe with four wheels. The *Reading Mercury* on 25 July 1840, described the carriage as being 21-feet in length, 9-feet wide and 6-feet 6-inches high with a clerestory roof and formed of three compartments. Smaller compartments at each end measured 4-feet 6-inches in length, while a 'noble' saloon in the centre, measured 12-feet long. A rosewood table was situated in the centre of each compartment and the floors of the three compartments were covered in chequered India matting. The coach was painted brown externally, in line with the rest of the Company's fleet of carriages.

The Directors did not have long to wait for the patronage they craved, the *Reading Mercury* commenting:

'It [the coach] has been rather hastily finished on account of Her Majesty the Queen Dowager [Queen Adelaide] having expressed her intention of proceeding on the 11 August as far as the Moulsford station on her way to Nuneham, on a visit to His Grace the Archbishop of York, but which journey was postponed on account of the alarming illness of the Princess Augusta'.

Princess Augusta Sophia (1768-1840) was the sixth child and second daughter of King George III. The princess eventually died at 9.17 p.m. on 22 September 1840 at Clarence House. The princess had been ill for some months and immediately prior to her death, His Royal Highness Prince Albert had been rushed by a Great

Western Railway train from Slough to the Company's terminus at Paddington. On the Prince's return to Paddington from Clarence House and before commencing his sad return journey to the Slough station, he was reported to have said:

'You travel very fast on this line; not so fast, back, if you please'.

Because of the Princess Augusta's illness, Queen Adelaide - the widow of King William IV - changed her plans to travel by train from Slough to the Moulsford station.

Each railway company during this period vied with each other for Royal patronage and each tried to out do each other. For instance, on Monday 10 August 1840, Queen Adelaide travelled from the north of the country using the L&NWR station at Wolverton in Buckinghamshire, where the Directors of that Company had made extensive arrangements for the reception of the much revered Queen. These included an immense 'triumphal arch of oak and evergreen' which the Royal train had to pass through before stopping at the station.

Following the announcement of the intention of Queen Adelaide to travel from the Slough station to Moulsford, the Directors of the Great Western Railway immediately contacted a Mr. Benjamin Edgington, the proprietor of a tent and marquee warehouse at 2 Duke Street, Southwark (Brunel had offices at 18 Duke Street). It was arranged that Edgington, accompanied by the Company Secretary, would visit the Moulsford station to give his opinion regarding the decorations required for the Dowager Queen's impending visit.

On 2 July 1840, a letter was sent from the Directors to Edgington stating:

'Mr Saunders, having mentioned to the Chairman that he proposed employing Mr. Edgington to fit up the station at Moulsford, for the occasion of the Queen Dowager travelling to it by the railway has been desired to ascertain from Mr. Edgington what will be the expense of it in the way suggested to him when he was at Moulsford. The Chairman as soon as he knows the expense will determine whether the order shall be given, and this will perhaps induce Mr. Edgington to favour Saunders, with an early answer in order that no time may be lost'.

Edgington replied promptly, for on 4 July, Saunders again corresponded with him:

'The Directors will be happy to give him the order for fitting up the Moulsford station on the terms mentioned. Mr. Saunders wishes however that Mr. Edgington should do as little as he can to the station room itself before the day as it must be used as a public booking office up to the morning of the thirteenth. The two inner rooms can be fitted up previously'

Several days notice having been given of the postponement of the Queen's journey, Saunders wrote to Brunel on 9 July 1840, who was at Bristol advising:

'My Dear Brunel, The Queen's visit is postponed and without any other day being yet fixed - I write this at once, as I suppose you were coming up almost expressly for Monday'.

This is ample evidence of the early importance given to the conveyance by train of Royal personages. This would have been the first official Royal train on the Great Western Railway and the procedures being set in motion for this Royal visit would establish a pattern for future journeys, it becoming standard practice for high-ranking Company officers to accompany future Royal trains. On this very first occasion, Brunel had been prepared to travel a considerable distance to assist in the safe passage of his Royal passenger, but he was probably not too dismayed at the cancellation, as he was well aware that it would be only a matter of time before a similar event would occur.

Queen Adelaide had, in fact, paid a series of visits to the Northern and Midland counties in July and August 1840 and on 20 July 1840, Queen Adelaide wrote to Queen Victoria from Belton House, Leicestershire:

> 'We had a most prosperous and quick journey and were only ten hours on the road from Bushy to this place. We left home at half past eight o'clock and stoppt [sic] half an hour at Leicester on leaving the Railroad from which place we posted on with horses instead of steam to this most comfortable and beautifully furnished house ... My sister [Duchess Ida of Saxe-Weimar-Eisenach] did not feel quite well after the Railroad Expedition, it made her almost sea sick'.

On Saturday 1 August 1840, the *Reading Chronicle* reported:

> 'Her Majesty having passed through the Midland Counties, arrived at Lancaster on Tuesday, having made a tour of the lakes. The Queen then proceeded by railway to Stafford, and Uttoxeter, to Alton Towers, the Seat of the Earl of Shrewsbury. Her Majesty to leave on Friday for Matlock Bath, in Derbyshire, and on the following to Gopsall Hall on a visit to Earl Howe, where she will stay for a couple of days'.

Queen Adelaide wrote to Queen Victoria again about her travels on 31 July 1840, when she wrote from Matlock:

> 'I have been wandering about so much that I could not write sooner again, and hasten now to give you an account of my journey which has been most prosperous and very agreeable, favoured by very fine weather. From Belton we passed through Nottingham, Derby, Leeds, Harewood and slept at Bolton Bridge ... Thence we went to Kirkby Lonsdale, Bowness and Lancaster ... On Wednesday we embarked on the Railroad again, went through Preston to Stafford where we left the rapid Railway again to travel onto Alton Towers ... This afternoon we arrived at this lovely place ...'.

The Dowager Queen also wrote to her niece Queen Victoria in an undated letter:

> 'I am setting off directly for Gopsall and hope the Duchess of Gloucester will get on well on the Railroad. I fear she will be alarmed at first'.

On 8 August 1840, *Jackson's Oxford Journal* recorded:

> 'On Wednesday last, when the Queen returned from Lancaster a special train was provided for the conveyance of Her Majesty and suite from Lancaster to Parkside by Lancaster & Preston & North Union Railway Companies. Thence to Stafford, being the nearest point to Alton Towers, the seat of the Earl of Shrewsbury, which was Her Majesty's destination by the Grand Junction Railway Company. The train consisting of three railway carriages, one of which had been handsomely fitted up by the London & Birmingham Company and five private carriages on trucks, making eight in all'.

On 6 August, Queen Adelaide wrote from Gopsall, saying that she was to leave there on the 10 August to visit the Duke and Duchess of Buckingham at Stowe. On 11 August she wrote from Stowe, where she had arrived the previous evening, indicating that she would be leaving on 13 August to stay with the Archbishop of York at Nuneham, Oxfordshire. On Saturday 15 August, the *Reading Chronicle* reported:

> 'On Thursday, the Queen Dowager passed through Oxford from Stowe, where she had been visiting the Duke of Buckingham for the last three days. Proceeding to Nuneham the seat of the Archbishop of York, escorted by a party of Lord Norrey's Troop of Oxfordshire Yeomanry'.

Queen Adelaide stayed as the guest of the Archbishop at Nuneham until Saturday 15 August 1840, then travelling through Wallingford on her way to the Moulsford station before entraining to the Company's Slough station.

As with the previous abortive Royal journey on the Great Western Railway, the Directors had plenty of notice regarding the Queen's travelling arrangements. The General Traffic Committee, meeting on 10 August, agreed that:

> 'The arrangements at Moulsford and at Slough for the reception of the Queen Dowager upon her intended journey on the railway on the 15 inst. were considered and made. The Secretary was ordered to carry them into effect'.

There is no record to confirm what these arrangements were or whether Edgington was employed to decorate the station. What is known is that the Company treated this journey of Queen Adelaide - the first official journey by a Royal Personage on the Great Western Railway - as a very important occasion and the culmination of all the hopes of Brunel and the Directors.

The occasion was treated accordingly. The Queen's journey had been planned for the late afternoon and the Royal party after leaving Nuneham, took the turnpike road. All tolls were suspended and the gates kept open to allow the entourage unimpeded passage through Dorchester-on-Thames, then crossing Shillingford bridge to Wallingford. At Wallingford, the only acknowledgement of the passage of the Queen through the town was the ringing of bells, the ringers being especially employed for the occasion. The procession passed through the town and continued its journey to the Moulsford station.

Only a few weeks prior to the opening of the station at Moulsford, the Directors had appointed the railway officials who would staff the station. These consisted of a Mr. Stevens (Principal Station Clerk), John Parsons (porter) and Edwin Clewitt (policeman/switchman). Although it is likely that Mr. Stevens had some previous managerial experience of some sort or another, the other inexperienced members of staff had barely settled into their new posts, with all the rigorous routines involved in operating the recently opened railway, when the Royal visit took place. Their experience was unique on the Great Western. Although Royalty had used Brunel's broad-gauge railway before, these journeys had been unofficial and the probability is that the railway staff on these odd occasions may not even have realised the importance of their passengers. As early as 1839, the Great Western

FIGURE 82. A contemporary illustration depicting the Royal family travelling in a Royal railway carriage, with Windsor Castle in the background. *(OPC/BR)*

Railway had attracted the attentions of the Princes Ernest and Albert of Saxe-Coburg-Gotha. Both were co-suitors of Queen Victoria, although as history records it was Albert that won the Queen's hand. On 14 November 1839, the two Princes, after travelling to Windsor by conventional methods, returned to Paddington via the railway.

For the occasion of the Dowager Queen's journey by rail, the ranks of the regular station staff had been swollen - albeit temporarily - by the railway hierarchy. In attendance were Seymour Clarke (Traffic Superintendent), Charles Russell (Chairman) and Brunel who was acting as engineer in the place of Daniel Gooch who is not recorded as being present. Gooch, later in 1841, would comment in his diary:

> *'The Queen [Victoria] had given up travelling by road between London and Windsor & had gone by us. While I held the office of locomotive engineer I nearly in all cases took charge of the engine myself when the Queen travelled & have been so fortunate as never to have a single delay with her & she travelled under my care a great many miles. I was the first who had such a charge & it was some time before she had occasion to travel on any line but the Great Western'.*

Meanwhile, at the Moulsford station, the Dowager Queen and her party were welcomed by Charles Russell. This, the first official journey on the Great Western Railway by any member of the Royal Family, perhaps also interested the Dowager Queen. The recently completed station buildings, probably bedecked with bunting and flags, would have made a pleasing sight and one must wonder what were the Queen's impressions of Brunel's great enterprise? How would Brunel's massive locomotives and rolling stock compare with the other railways the Queen has thus far experienced? Was the Queen pleased with the spaciousness and fittings of the new Royal carriage? Unfortunately, there are no records in the Royal Archives to supply the answers to such questions.

From the arrangements made for the abortive visit on Monday 13 July 1840, it is known that the Queen and her party would have access to all three rooms in the station building. The Queen's party had earlier been reported as consisting of five road carriages. The constituent members of the Royal party are nebulous, but it is confirmed that the Queen was accompanied by her sister. The rest of the party would have consisted of servants and the luggage required for such an extended tour as the one now almost completed. It is also possible that the Queen entered the impressive and recently completed 'Wallingford Road Station Hotel' - sited adjacent to the station complex at Moulsford - while the Royal equipage was loaded onto carriage trucks. In local records of the period, the building sometimes bore the name 'The Royal Hotel' a frequent pointer to the fact that a member of the Royal family had used a particular building.

Although speculation, the composition of the Royal train can be perhaps envisaged. The locomotive, resplendent, would have stood simmering quietly, awaiting the arrival of the Royal party. The station staff would have been waiting to load the road carriages onto the carriage trucks and would have swung into action as soon as the Queen and her party had left their carriages. Although the working arrangements can only be guessed at, there was no turntable at Moulsford large enough to turn the locomotive, so probably the engine would have had to travel to Steventon to make use of the facilities there, before returning to Moulsford.

The first journey by Queen Victoria on the Great Western Railway - or any railway - would not take place until 13 June 1842, by which time the Company had more experience of such journeys and the arrangements for this journey were reported as having been completed in less than 48 hours. The arrangements of Queen Victoria's train is described thus:

> *'The train must have adequate braking, so the next vehicle [after the locomotive] was one of the Great Western's extremely spartan second-class carriages, with open sides above the waist, wherein the brakeman normally sat with his vertical-screw hand brake column amid the usual second-class passengers. After this came a posting carriage, for part of the Royal Suite, and next the Royal Saloon. Fourth came another posting carriage, and then three carriage trucks for such vehicles as the Party might be taking with them'.*

It is known that the Dowager Queen's party were using posting horses, which ensured that the horses would be changed at inns and stables at regular intervals during the journey by road. The horses used for the last stage of the journey to the Moulsford station would probably have been left at the stables attached to the station hotel, new horses, probably from the Royal stables, waiting at the Slough station to enable the Queen to complete her journey. Normally, prior notice had to be given to the Company if the use of a carriage truck was required and road carriages could not be loaded or discharged at all the Company's stations. Road carriages had in normal circumstances to be at the departure station 15-minutes prior to the departure of the train intended to be used. The early practice on the Great Western Railway was that the horses used to convey the carriage to the station were used to load the carriage onto the carriage truck. This practice was discontinued at an early date, following an accident when compensation had to be paid by the Directors for the death of a horse. From that time, men only were used to load and unload road carriages from carriage trucks.

At Moulsford, there was only one small turntable, situated in a well between the station building and the goods shed on the Up side of the line. Each carriage had to be loaded and secured separately before the carriage truck was manhandled clear, to enable a similar operation to be conducted with the next road carriage and almost certainly, the Dowager Queen would have been kept waiting for some time while this operation was completed.

The locomotive chosen to haul the Royal train was rather sombrely named and one wonders whether Queen Adelaide had sight of the nameplate? If so, what were her thoughts on the subject? Most of the original Great Western Railway locomotives had failed miserably, apart from two untrammelled by Brunel's earlier ideas. Based on the success with Stephenson's two 'Stars', 10 more had been ordered. In the meantime, Gooch had been instructed to prepare drawings for future locomotives. One result of Gooch's investigations was the ordering of 62 engines of the 'Fire Fly' class. These were built between March 1840 and December 1842 by seven different manufacturers. All the broad-gauge engines built by and for the Great Western Railway had names, but no numbers. The classical and other names of the engines of the 1840-42 period, were probably selected by Russell, Brunel or Saunders and all appear most appropriate.

The firm of Fenton, Murray & Jackson of Leeds had been contracted to supply 20 of Gooch's 'Fire Fly' class of locomotives, which had a wheel arrangement of 2-2-2 and 7-ft. driving wheels and Gooch reported that the batch supplied by this manufacturer were the best of the class. All these locomotives bore names associated with Greek mythology, the first locomotive to be delivered being the funereally named *Charon*. In Etruscan sepulchral art, a terrible god with this name was the slayer and in Greek mythology, Charon was the ferryman who conveyed souls across Styx to Hades. *Charon* was the pride of the Great Western Railway and it had been this locomotive which had conveyed the Directors to Steventon when the line opened between Reading and Steventon on Monday 1 June 1840.

Charon, waiting at the Moulsford station, must have been an impressive sight. The makers had been given little latitude when constructing these locomotives, as standardisation and interchangeability had been one of Gooch's main aims. The makers were also responsible for both materials and workmanship until each locomotive had ran 1,000 miles with normal loads. The specification for the 'Fire Fly' class of 1840, stipulated that parts 'not bright' had to have three coats of lead colour prior to delivery and afterwards finished on the line according to patterns furnished by the Company. There is no record of the livery of *Charon*, although a later engine *Acheron* - again from the original batch produced by Fenton, Murray & Jackson - was reported to have had:

> *'Frames chocolate brown, and frame ties, steps, life guards, axle boxes, and springs black. Buffer beam vermilion and buffers of leather. Wheels had dark green rims and spokes, and the faces of the tyres were black. The boiler and firebox were lagged with wood strips, painted dark green, and bound with brass bands, and the top of the haycock firebox, the safety valve cover, the spring balance, and the whistles were of brass. The boiler brackets, smokebox, and the chimney were painted black. Splashers and handrails were brass, the latter supported on steel columns. There is no record of lining or of the painting of the tender ...'.*

The delay between the arrival of the Queen and her entourage and the departure of the Royal train would have been as brief as possible. But, however long the Royal party were kept waiting, they would have been either safely deposited in the station building or possibly the adjacent hotel. Perhaps, the Queen might have inspected the line and the Royal Saloon, or even enquired about the arrangements as her niece Queen Victoria would do when she first travelled on the Great Western Railway.

One can only imagine the Dowager Queen's thoughts when being shown the brand new Royal Saloon. Was she impressed by the spaciousness and after all, the carriage had been fitted up by a Mr. Webb, an upholsterer of Bond Street. The larger central saloon had hanging sofas of carved wood in the style of Louis XIV and the walls panelled in the same elegant manner of rich crimson and silk. Surely, the Queen could not fail to have been impressed when comparing the wide-bodied broad-gauge saloon against that of the other railway companies she had recently used whose vehicles were of the narrow-gauge.

Eventually, the last road carriage would have been loaded and the formation of the train completed. The train was now ready to leave the Moulsford station. Probably, spectators lined the turnpike bridge which overlooked the station, a perfect vantage point to view the arrangements for this splendid Royal occasion. Clewitt the station policeman - or a superior - perhaps, Inspector Joseph Collard the Great Western Railway Superintendent of Police, whose responsibilities covered the whole of the London Division - made sure it was safe for the Royal train to proceed before signalling the right away.

Although no official Great Western Railway records have been traced recording this journey, the *Berkshire Chronicle* describes the event in some detail:

> *'Her Majesty the Queen Dowager passed the Reading station of the Great Western Railway on Saturday last, at four o'clock, being the time that was at first intended. The engine 'Charon' was attached to the Royal railway carriages, which are of the most splendid description, and the train 'flashed' along at a rate exceeding sixty miles per hour. The distance between Moulsford and Slough about 30 miles, was traversed in 38½ minutes. Her Majesty was right royally attended, the chairman of the company, Charles Russell, Esq., directing the arrangements, the principal engineer, I. Brunel, Esq., acting as engineer on the trip, and the principal*

superintendent Seymour Clark Esq., taking the part of conductor for this occasion. The engine and tender were polished up to the highest brightness, the servants of the company in their best appearance to the establishment, and to pay fitting tribute to the illustrious traveller ...'.

This first official Royal journey on the Great Western Railway was an important milestone in the Company's history, but despite the uniqueness of the event, it would never attract the acclaim devoted to the first journey on any railway by Queen Victoria which took place on 11 June 1842.

In January 1842, the probability of the original Great Western Railway Royal saloon being required for the service of the King of Prussia during his stay in England, led to an examination of the carriage in an effort to improve its running qualities. Brunel reported that because the saloon ran on four wheels, the carriage was less easy and not so safe as the Company's first-class carriages which ran on six wheels. As a consequence, a new frame carrying eight wheels was substituted and the saloon in that form was used for Royalty until 1848, when a new Royal carriage was introduced. In 1851, the old Royal saloon was altered and made available for passenger traffic during the Great Exhibition of that year when it was decreed that 'every carriage will be probably required for constant use'. In fact, the saloon continued to be used as an ordinary carriage until 1879 when it was condemned and broken up.

FIGURE 83. An HST powers past the site of Moulsford (Wallingford Road) station, the former Station Hotel a memorial to the first Royal journey on the Great Western Railway.
(Author's collection)

FINALE

Following the opening of the section of the Great Western Railway main line between Reading and Steventon on 1 June, the remainder of 1840 saw the opening of the 7 mile 29 chain section between Steventon and Faringdon Road (63½ miles from Paddington); the 11 mile 43 chain section between the Bristol terminus and Bath and the Faringdon Road to Hay Lane (Wootton Bassett Road) section, consisting of 16 miles 29 chains. The commencement of 1841 saw only two sections left to be completed, the first being the 13 mile 57 chain section between Hay Lane and Chippenham and the Chippenham-Bath section, which included the 12 mile 73 chain Box Tunnel. The former opened to traffic on 31 May and the latter on 30 June, which was also the official date for the opening of the complete line between Bristol and London.

As the various sections of the railway opened, not all the stations were ready for use and others would be added later. When the railway opened between Paddington and Maidenhead on 4 June 1838, the trains stopped at West Drayton and Slough, despite the fact that at Slough no station could be built at that time. The Slough station eventually opened in June 1840, although the stations at Ealing and Hanwell did not open to the public until December the same year. In May 1839, the station at Southall was completed and opened. East of Didcot, stations were added at Langley (1845), Hayes (1864), Acton (1868), Taplow (1872), Westbourne Park and Castle Hill (1871) (the latter renamed West Ealing in 1889), Taplow (1872), Tilehurst (1882) and Burnham Beeches (1899). Iver was not added until 1924. West of the junction station at Didcot - opened in 1844 - stations were added at Wantage Road (1846), Bathampton (1857), Uffington (1864), Dauntsey (1868) and St. Annes Park (1898).

On the same day that the Great Western Railway opened between Hay Lane and Chippenham - 31 May 1841 - the Cheltenham & Great Western Union Railway opened its broad-gauge line between a new junction station at Wootton Bassett (Wootton Bassett Road station then closing) and Cirencester. A few weeks prior to the complete line opening between Bristol and Paddington - on 14 June 1841 - the Bristol & Exeter Railway opened to Bridgwater. Branch lines from the Brunellian main line were opened to the following towns: Windsor (1849), Bradford-on- Avon (1857), High Wycombe (1854), Henley-on-Thames (1857), Calne (1863) and Faringdon (1864). The first narrow-gauge branch line from the main line - the 3-miles 20-chains Wallingford & Watlington Railway - opened in 1866, running from the original Brunellian station at Moulsford, to a 'temporary' terminus at Wallingford (the Wallingford Road station then reverting to its earlier name 'Moulsford').

APPENDIX ONE

THE DEMISE OF THE MOULSFORD (WALLINGFORD ROAD) STATION

Quickly renamed 'Wallingford Road' shortly after the opening of the Great Western Railway, the little station at Moulsford would have a relatively short life. Despite this, the proud little station, singled out by Brunel for special attention and built to his aesthetically high standards, would have its moments. The first of these was the first official Royal train on the line, when the Dowager Queen travelled from the station to Slough on 15 August 1840.

The station at Moulsford's second claim to fame was the opening of the branch line to Wallingford in 1866. The branch, originally planned to extend to Watlington, was constructed by the Wallingford & Watlington Railway Company and opened on 2 July 1866, the line being operated from the beginning by the Great Western Railway. On the opening of the branch line, the Wallingford Road station immediately reverted back to its original name 'Moulsford'. Although the rails never pushed beyond Wallingford, this tenacious little offshoot of the GWR - 3 miles 30 chains in length - survived until 13 June 1959. Today, the line continues in existence, the Cholsey & Wallingford Railway Preservation Society being determined to return the line to its former Great Western glory.

The station at Moulsford would also play its part in the so-called 'Battle of the Gauges', which was according to E. T. MacDermot 'really a long war, lasting some ten years from the first meeting of the two gauges at Gloucester in 1844' and which would result in mixed-gauge rails being laid down between Oxford and Basingstoke. The laying of this third rail to form a narrow-gauge connection from north to south of the GWR main line would eventually cost the Company over £138,000, which was solely for the accommodation of other railway companies.

Due to the serious interruption of railway traffic due to the break of gauges, a Royal Commission was appointed on 9 July 1845:

> 'to inquire whether in future private Acts for the construction of railways, provision ought to be made for securing an uniform Gauge'.

Starting on 6 August 1845, the Commissioners heard evidence from a total of 48 witnesses of various skills and interests. Brunel, who was convinced of the total superiority of his Broad-Gauge, eventually suggested experiments to test the power of the locomotives of both factions. Reluctantly, the narrow-gauge camp agreed to Brunel's proposition.

The eventual routes for these high-speed tests would be from Paddington to Didcot (53 miles) and York to Darlington (44 miles). For these tests, Gooch - as he had done for many of the prestigious events in the brief history of Brunel's railway - chose a member of the 'Fire Fly' Class, 72 of these locomotives then running on the Great Western Railway at that time. *Ixion* was one of a batch of 20 engines built by Fenton, Murray & Jackson, with a wheel arrangement of 2-2-2 and 7-feet driving wheels . Thus, in the winter of 1845, the men on the Great Western awaited these tests with some considerable interest. *Ixion* on the 16 and 17 December would thunder through the Wallingford Road station with trains of 80, 70 and 60 tons respectively. Three separate trips to and from Didcot took place, the maximum speed reached being 60-mph. In the New Year, further trials took place with a 6-coupled goods engine over the same section of track.

Brunel's confidence was vindicated, as the general result was much in favour of the Broad-Gauge engines, both for speed and power. However, disappointingly, the Report of the Gauge Commission which was laid before Parliament at the beginning of the 1846 Session was not in favour of the Broad-Gauge. The Report stated:

'That, in order to complete the general chain of Narrow Gauge communication from the North of England to the Southern Coast, any suitable measure should be promoted to form a Narrow Gauge link from Oxford to Reading, and thence to Basingstoke or by any any other route connecting the proposed Oxford and Rugby Line with the South Western Railway'.

The mixed-gauge already existed from Oxford (Millstream Junction 63 miles from Paddington) for a total of 66 miles 24 chains to Birmingham. Now, the mixed-gauge would be extended from Oxford (Isis Bridge) through Didcot, through the Wallingford Road station and thence via a Western Loop at Reading to Basingstoke. The mixed-gauge would be confined to an Avoiding Line at Didcot and no additional rails would be laid through the station. To ensue that carriages of both gauges were brought close to the platforms at stations, the outside rail became the common one.

Thus, effectively the Wallingford Road station would become the first station on the Brunellian main line through which narrow-gauge tracks would pass. On 22 December 1856, the narrow-gauge rails between Oxford and Basingstoke - proposed by the Report of 1846 - and made compulsory by the Shrewsbury Amalgamation Act of 1 September 1854 to provide through communications between the railways north of Wolverhampton and the London & South Western Railway came into use.

The extra traffic brought about by the mixed-gauge and indeed, the popularity of the Great Western Railway generally, soon ensured that east of Didcot the original double track clearly would not be able to cope with the amount of traffic projected for the railway. The situation was complicated further by the many train movements from stations between Didcot and the metropolis, as many movements had to be conducted on the two running lines, which frequently led to through trains' routes being impeded.

Widening powers for the quadrupling of the line in the London District had been obtained from Parliament in 1873. The Wharncliffe Viaduct, although widened would have its original form and appearance preserved and various short sections of the widened line would be completed by 1877. The two additional lines reached Slough on 1 June 1879, eventually reaching Taplow at the east end of the Maidenhead bridge on 8 September 1884, where they stopped for nearly nine years! The quadrupling of the main line between Taplow and Didcot commenced in the summer of 1890 and this included the widening of the Maidenhead bridge in which Brunel's unique flat arches were preserved. Westwards from Maidenhead to Didcot as the quadrupling progressed, Brunel's original designs were duplicated as much as possible and various short sections were opened as goods loops from April 1892 onwards. However, the four lines from Didcot to Paddington would not be finally completely opened until 1899 when the new station at Reading was completed.

A 4.5-mile section of the now quadrupled line from Didcot stretched eastwards to a brand new station at Cholsey, which would also become the new junction station for the Wallingford branch. Following a Board of Trade inspection, the Great Western Railway advertised the opening of the new station in the 27 February 1892 issue of the *Reading Mercury* in the following terms:

FIGURE 84. The site of the Brunellian station complex at Moulsford (Wallingford Road), apart from the station building and goods shed which were demolished c1892 when the main line was quadrupled. The Brunel-designed railwaymens' accommodation is in the middle of the photograph, while in the foreground, the former Station Hotel and stable block still dominate the scene. *(Author's collection)*

'On Monday, 29 February, a new station for Cholsey & Moulsford, situated about ¾ mile west of the existing Moulsford station will be opened, and on and from that date the existing station at Moulsford will be closed'.

Thus, the fate of Brunel's station at Moulsford was sealed. The new running lines would be laid on the northern side of the existing double track and for this purpose it was necessary to demolish the main station building, platform, goods shed and the Wallingford branch bay. The exact date of the demolition of Brunel's station at Moulsford is not known.

APPENDIX TWO

THE BRIDGES OVER THE THAMES AT MOULSFORD AND GATEHAMPTON TODAY

The differences in the construction and appearance of Brunel's bridges over the Thames at Gatehampton and Moulsford has already been described in some detail. However, the differences were highlighted when the quadrupling of the main line between Didcot and Paddington became necessary during the 1890s. During the latter part of the 1800s, it became apparent that the original Brunellian double tracked main line from Didcot Junction to the London terminus could not cope with the traffic from both the west and the north and that quadrupling of the tracks from Didcot eastwards was a priority. As part of this process, both the Moulsford and Gatehampton bridges would have to be extended and following design work begun in 1890, the additions to the two bridges commenced the following year.

The contractor for both bridges was H. Lovatt under the overall responsibility of the Company's engineer W. Armstrong. At Moulsford, a completely separate bridge was constructed to the north of Brunel's original, while at Gatehampton the absence of Bath stone voussoirs allowed the foundations and superstructure of the new bridge to be integrated with those of the original viaduct. In the latter case, the structure was literally widened on one side.

The condition of all the bridges and other structures in the care of British Rail was monitored very carefully and the two original Brunellian bridges at Moulsford and Gatehampton became the subject of careful scrutiny in March 1976 during a major assessment of both viaducts by BR Western Region Assessment Section. Access to the interior vaults of the viaducts was by means of vertical manholes set in the 'six foot'. Access apertures were situated above each pier and over each abutment, making a total of five manholes for each bridge. Surveyors found that access was severely limited because of firstly, 1.4 metres of ballast and accumulated ash and secondly the manholes could only be accessed under occupation conditions due to 125-mph running over the viaducts.

Sunday occupation having been arranged, the survey commenced. The surveyors reported that at both viaduct sites, the new structures built in the 1890s were in good condition and did not require any remedial work. Regarding the original viaducts, the surveyors experienced initial problems caused by the narrow entrance manholes and later with the horizontal manholes inside the structure of each viaduct which allowed access through the interior spandrel walls. Few indications of any earlier repairs to the interior of either viaduct was detected. However, it did appear that originally the viaducts were constructed with access to the whole length of each structure, but this was not now possible due to the crown of each arch being bricked-up. The surveyors experienced extreme difficulty in moving about inside the structures due to lack of light and the narrowness of some of the vaults. The survey revealed to some extent, evidence of water seepage in all the vaults which had precipitated deterioration and leaching of the lime mortar, leading to the poor condition of many vaults with numbers of bricks being noted as fallen out of place.

The surveyors' report concluded that the design of the viaducts could not be faulted. The deterioration had been caused by the breakdown of the original waterproofing on the top surface of the structures - normally tar. Every arch of both viaducts had six spandrel walls (two outer and four inner). The outer and inner spandrels supported five 'jack' or secondary arches and it was these arches which carried the ballast and track. The jack arches consisted of 9-inch brickwork, which despite being repointed, failed again within three months.

At Paddington various solutions were considered, viz:

1. Interior grouting. Considered impracticable due to difficult access and uncertainty whether correct solution anyway.

2. Rebuilding from inside. This would be a very slow process with every possibility of mortar wash-out again.

3. Infilling of vaults with concrete. Considered likely to defeat Brunel's original intention of saving weight.

External solutions were also considered:

4. Pre-cast units placed over top of failing jack arches. This was ruled out after on-site investigations by means of trial holes revealed considerable differences in levels, widths, projections, tie-rods etc.

5. In situ concrete slab over jack arches. Due to the setting time of the concrete, this could entail the bridge being under occupation for 3-4 weeks. This was felt to be untenable as the viaduct need to be returned to the Operating Department in a much shorter space of time.

However, it was eventually concluded that Option 5 appeared the most viable, if the setting time of the concrete could be reduced.

A reinforced concrete slab was designed to span continuously over the intermediate spandrel walls, using the remains of the jack arches as permanent shuttering. The concrete setting time was eventually reduced to 18-hours, which entailed a process using vacuum dewatering mats to reduce the waiting time for the *in situ* concrete to set. In order not to spoil the vacuum, the open vaults beneath the new slab required a polyethylene membrane to be laid over the tops of the old jack arches before the concrete was poured. Thirty-six hour track possessions were found to be available and the new concrete slab was cast on a track basis, rather than a complete transverse bay pour in order to retain a service road.

The Moulsford viaduct was the first to be tackled and access to the viaduct would be from the site of the Down platform of the original Moulsford (Wallingford Road) station and immediately to the east of the main A329 road bridge across the railway. Earlier, an experiment had been conducted to ensure that the procedures were viable. A small area of land between the road access point and the viaduct was used for this test, with a small area of 'Readimix' concrete being layed and then dewatered using vacuum dewatering mats. Samples of the finished concrete were analysed and the setting time was proved as viable.

Possession of the viaduct at Moulsford having been obtained from the Operating Department, work began. Possession could be for a maximum of 36-hours and while one track was worked on, the other was used for access etc. The first attempt was doomed to failure. It had been intended that the concrete would be pumped from 'Readimix' lorries situated at the western end of the viaduct. This proved abortive, due to the concrete setting in the pipes connected to the pump set up on the viaduct itself. The problem was solved by boards being layed in the service track, allowing lorries to drive onto the viaduct itself to discharge their loads directly where the concrete was required. In order that the service road was not adversely affected by the operation, a new precast concrete stop end block was inserted before the pour commenced, thus ensuring that the ballast, track etc of the service road was held in place. The polyethylene membrane was first laid down, followed by steel reinforcing and then the concrete. No problems were experienced and the process was repeated with the other track.

A similar procedure was followed with the Gatehampton viaduct, although here access by the lorries would be over fields adjacent to the main road. Also the difference in the construction of the two bridges caused another problem. The

FIGURE 85. Brunel's viaduct at Gatehampton today. During the 1890s quadrupling of the main line between Didcot and Paddington, the original structure was doubled in width, the new arches being faithfully copied on the west side. *(Author's collection)*

Gatehampton viaduct had been literally widened when the line had been quadrupled and to ensure that the Relief lines were retained in a serviceable position, a precast concrete stop end unit had to be inserted before work on the original viaduct could commence. Ventilation to the original structures would have been beneficial to ensure that drying process inside the chambers was speeded up, but did not prove possible as ventilation could only be provided by leaving the access manhole covers open. Clearly this was a most dangerous process and the chambers were left to dry out naturally. New access arrangements were provided in the new *in situ* concrete slab and arrangements were made to monitor the drying out of the old vaults by regular return visits.

The vacuum dewatering of the freshly laid concrete slabs on the Moulsford and Gatehampton viaducts were almost certainly the first time the process had been used on a railway structure in the United Kingdom. The remedial work undertaken at Moulsford during 1978 and at Gatehampton during 1979 ensured that these viaducts would continue to carry loads and at speeds that even Brunel could not have foreseen. The cost of the repairs were: Moulsford £144,000, Gatehampton £124,000.

A few years before the viaducts at Moulsford and Gatehampton received the remedial work just described, they became the subject of local controversy following the installation of refuges on the Gatehampton viaduct. The concern was highlighted in a letter to *Country Life* on 7 August 1975, by the secretary of the River Thames Society who complained:

> '*Sir, At Maidenhead, Gatehampton and Moulsford, red-brick railway bridges span the Thames. Built by Brunel more than 130 years ago they have always been cherished by the public as examples of that rarity, an attractive railway bridge. The best known of the three, that at Maidenhead, was immortalised in Turner's painting 'Rain, Steam and Speed'. James Thorne, writng in 1849, described Moulsford Bridge as a considerable ornament to the river, of bold form and with very handsome proportions. Of how many modern structures can this be said?*
>
> '*It is sad to report that, in this European Architectural Heritage Year, two of the bridges have been damaged, not by accident or by vandals, but by the owners, British Rail. Gatehampton Bridge, on its upstream side, has had three holes hacked in the brick- work of the parapet and iron structures inserted, and an iron railing now runs along the length of the bridge .... At Moulsford only the holes have been made, but presumably the intention is to disfigure the structure as at Gatehampton. This Society hopes that the weight of public opinion will force British Rail to restore the bridges to their former appearance, and that they will thereafter be protected by preservation orders'.*

The controversy stemmed from the preparation by BR for the general introduction of HST sets, which began with the Western Region Timetables of 4 October 1976 and consideration for the men working on the tracks. From Paddington to Chippenham, high-speed running was authorised except for the restrictions through Reading and Swindon stations. In the middle of 1975, BR began work on the construction of the refuges on both the viaducts, despite the fact that the structures were already protected by Preservation Orders. The

FIGURE 86. Prior to the advent of High Speed Train operation, in March 1976, Brunel's original viaducts at Moulsford and Gatehampton were found to require substantial repairs due to the breakdown of the original waterproofing of the top surface of both bridges. Pictured above is the Moulsford bridge under repair on 16 May 1978, looking east (top) and looking west (bottom). Note the height of the ballast and manhole access to the structure's interior.

In the bottom picture the site of the original Brunellian station at Moulsford can be seen in the middle background, the erstwhile Station Hotel providing an easy landmark.

(D. E. Canning)

alterations had not been discussed with local councils and Cholsey Parish Council also protested about the disfigurations.

Both bridges were to have refuges constructed in the original parapets directly adjacent to the Up Fast line. The way the work was undertaken, created a cut-out effect on the parapet and seriously detracted from the structure's original appearance. Cholsey Parish Council protested direct to the Minister of Transport at the time - Richard Marsh - as well as to BR, requesting that masonry or concrete be used on the Moulsford viaduct instead of the metal frames already in place at Gatehampton. After a site meeting had taken place between members of the Parish Council and a BR representative, the Council's Chairman stated that:

> *'He understood that British Rail's chief engineer at Reading was not happy with the present work, and that it was now likely that two alternative plans would be submitted to the planning authority'.*

The watchfulness of the Council paid off and the viaduct at Moulsford was spared the indignity inflicted on the Gatehampton structure, brick with concrete copings being used instead of the unsightly iron. Today, the Gatehampton viaduct still carries - with dignity - this disfiguration, further emphasising the differences in these two bridges.

APPENDIX THREE

THE ROYAL CONNECTION

Queen Victoria spent a considerable amount of time at opposite ends of her kingdom, as having Royal residences on Deeside and on the Isle of Wight ensured that the Monarch spent part of her time travelling between the two locations.

The renowned 'break-of- gauge' was to become well known to Her Majesty who experienced some of the worst aspects of this arrangement! For instance, in the Autumn of 1849, Queen Victoria travelled south by the Midland Railway, eventually arriving at Gloucester. Here the infamous 'change' had to take place and even the Queen of England was not spared this inconvenience. However, she may have been placated somewhat by the knowledge that the Great Western Railway had - by now - built a new and more luxurious Royal saloon to replace the original of 1840.

Continuing the journey, the Great Western Railway would have taken the Queen south to join the broad-gauge Bristol-London main line at Didcot Junction. The Royal train would have passed the Great Western Railway station at Moulsford (by now renamed Wallingford Road) and travelled the 13 miles 49 chains to Basingstoke via Southcote Junction (just under two miles west from Reading station). At Basingstoke, the Queen would have to transfer to the narrow-gauge London & South Western Royal saloon, an old vehicle which she had used since 1844. It was not until 1856, when the mixing of gauge between Oxford and Basingstoke allowed the Monarch to travel right through from Aboyne on Deeside to Gosport - for the Isle of Wight - without changing her railway carriage. Of course, the Great Western Railway Royal Saloon could not be used on these occasions, but it did ensure that the Queen regularly passed through the railway station at Moulsford.

The Royal family's connection with railways in the Wallingford area would continue for many years, indeed right up to 1981. From an unknown date, Royal trains were stabled overnight on the former Great Western Railway Wallingford branchline. The last of these took place on Saturday 30 May 1981, one day before the official closure of the branchline by British Railways. On this occasion, the Royal train departed from the branch via BR Cholsey & Moulsford main line station in the early hours of the following morning, then travelling to Slough where the Royal Party - HRH the Prince of Wales - continued to Windsor by road.

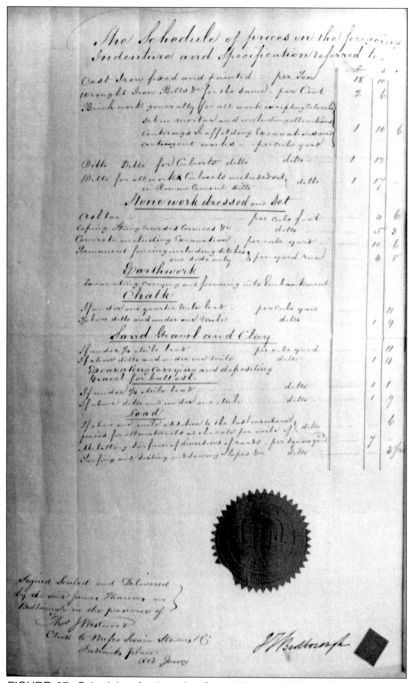

FIGURE 87. Schedule of prices for Great Western Railway Contract '4R', signed by the contractor James Thomas Bedborough. *(Author's collection)*

APPENDIX FOUR
CONTRACT R4

The original 'Indenture' - or sealed agreement - relating to Contract 'R4' was found almost by chance in the Plans Room at Paddington station by the author in 1984. Luckily, he photographed parts of the indenture and also with the aid of a pocket recording-machine, recorded for posterity the content of the document.

The contents of the Plans Room at Paddington were at that time under the diligent custodianship of Mr. L. Szczyrba, who had made a study of the Brunellian plans and who was also in the process of gradually rehabilitating some of the plans which were in a very brittle condition. Following the work initiated by Mr. Szczyrba, the plans were placed under the stewardship of Mr. Ian Nulty (Records Assistant), Regional Railways (South Wales & West) based at Western House, Swindon.

During a BR reorganisation, all plans were transferred to Swindon and many documents which were not considered essential to the modern railway scene were 'dispersed'.

'This Indenture made the 30th day of April in the year of Our Lord One-thousand Eight-Hundred and Thirty-Eight between the Great Western Railway Company established and incorporate by an Act of Parliament passed in the Fifth and Sixth years of the Reign of his late Majesty King William the Fourth entitled 'An Act for making a Railway from Bristol to Join the London and Birmingham Railway near London to be called the Great Western Railway with branches therefrom to the town of Bradford and Trowbridge in the County of Wilts. of the one part and James Thomas Bedborough of Windsor in the County of Berks. Excavator of the other part.

Whereas the said Great Western Railway Company have pursuant to the powers and authority to or invested in them by the above mentioned Act of Parliament and certain subsequent Acts of Parliament relating to the said Company or their railway determine that certain earthwork bridges culverts and other works shall be done made executed and completed according, to the Specifications hereunder written and the drawings or plans annexed to these presents And whereas the said specifications and drawings or plans have been prepared by or under the direction of Isambard Kingdom Brunel Esq. Principal Engineer appointed by the said Company for the purpose of designing and superintending the making of the said railway and the works connected therewith And Whereas the said J.T.B. have contracted with the said Company to execute the whole of the works described or mentioned in such Specification according to the said drawings or plans to the satisfaction of the said Company and of their principal engineer already appointed or hereafter to be appointed by the said Company and do execute and perform the whole of the works aforesaid and each and every part thereof within the period or respective periods hereinafter limited or referred to in that behalf with such powers in favour of the Company as are hereinafter reserved to them And whereas the said plans or drawings ten in number and severally numbered from 1-9 and marked Contract No. 4R have been signed by the said JTB and by the said IKB on behalf of the said Company and the same together with these presents are intended to be deposited with the London solicitors or Secretary for the time being of the said Company and copies of the said plans or drawings are intended to be deposited with the Assistant Engineer for the time being of the said Company resident at or near the site of the said intended works And whereas the said Company have agreed to advance to the said J.T.B. from time to time during the progress of the works so contracted to be executed by him as aforesaid sums of money by way of instalments upon account of and in part payment of the work then actually done and executed by the said J.T.B. (such execution to be certified by the said I.K.B. or the principal engineer of the said Company for the time being) and after the completion of the works so contracted to be executed by the said J.T.B. as aforesaid such completion also to be certified as hereinbefore mentioned the said J.T.B. is to receive and to be paid the remainder of the monies due to him upon this contract at the time and in manner hereinafter mentioned And whereas it has been agreed that the said J.T.B. shall secure the performance of his said contract according to the stipulations hereinafter contained by his bond or obligation in the penal sum of £4000 conditioned among other things for the payment to the said Company of the several penal sums in the said Specification mentioned in that behalf in the event of the said works or any of them or any part thereof not being completed according to the said specification within the period or respective periods in and by these presents and the said Specification limited and appointed for the completion of the whole of the said works or any part or parts thereof respectively but so that the payment of such penal sums shall not in any way relieve the said J.T.B. from the responsibility of any further payments to the said Company nor from any deductions from the money to be paid by the said Company to the said J.T.B. to which he may become liable by the terms of this contract and it hath been further agreed that the due performance of this present contract by the said J.T.B. shall be secured by the joint and several bond or obligation of John Ramsbottom of London Esq. and Thomas Jenner of Windsor in the County of Berks Gentleman Sureties for the said J.T.B. in the penal sum of Four-thousand Pounds Now this indenture witnesseth that for the more fully evidencing the intent and meaning of the said parties hereto and in consideration of the sum hereinafter agreed to be paid by the said Company in manner hereinafter mentioned and of such further sums as are also hereinafter agreed to be paid by the said Company for extra work as hereinafter also mentioned he the said J.T.B. doth hereby for himself his heirs executors and administrators covenant promise and agree to and with the said Great Western Railway Company and their successors in manner following this to say that he the said J.T.B. shall and will and substantially and in a good and lasting workmanlike manner do make execute and complete the earthwork bridges culverts fences and drains and all and every other of the works temporary or permanent specified mentioned and described in the said Specification hereinunder written in the order or course and in the manner specified or referred to in the same Specification according to the directions and instructions contained in the said Specification and drawings and such additional or other instructions and drawings if any shall or may from time to time be given or furnished by the Principal Engineer Assistant Resident Engineer for the time being of the said Company as hereinafter mentioned and shall and will duly execute perform and complete and provide as well all and singular the works and materials respectively described specified required and set forth in the aforesaid Specification or in the said drawings or therein respectively contained or referred to as also all and singular the works and materials thereby implied according to said Specification and the aforesaid drawings and also according to the general or particular instructions and such explanatory drawings as shall or may from time to time be provided by the said Company during the progress of the works hereby agreed to be done and shall and will abide and be bound by perform follow and fulfill all the stipulations requisitions and instructions in the said Specifications set forth or contained (except so far) if at all as the same may be at variance with these presents And further that the said works shall be commenced and that the whole of the same works and each and every part thereof shall be executed performed and fully completed within the time or respective times in the said Specification appointed or mentioned in that behalf And further that the said J.T.B. shall and will during the progress of the said works and for the space of one year to commence and be computed from the time when all the works hereby contracted for shall have been completed and delivered over to the said Company maintain and keep in good sound and perfect repair and condition including all accidents from whatever cause arising the said earthworks bridges culverts permanent fencing and draining and other works contracted to be done made and executed as aforesaid and also all the additional works that shall be done or required to be done according to this present contract or the said Specifications in by and with all and all manner of necessary reparations and amendments whatsoever and find and provide all the requisite materials and things for the doing thereof and in such good sound and perfect repair and condition shall and will leave the said earthwork bridges culverts and their works at the expiration of the year aforesaid And also that he the said J.T.B. shall and will do perform execute and complete all the said works with such materials as in the said Specification mentioned and in the most workmanlike manner to the satisfaction in all things of the said Company and their principal engineer already appointed or hereafter to be appointed and in all respects comply with and abide by the true intent and meaning of the said Specification drawings directions and instructions and of these presents And further that in case the said Company or their principal engineer or assistant resident engineer for the time being shall at any time or times be of opinion that a sufficient number of workmen are not employed by the said J.T.B. in the execution and completion of the works or any of the works hereby agreed to be done with reference to the completion thereof within the time or times in which the said several works are hereinbefore agreed to be done or that the said several works are not progressing with due diligence or despatch with reference to the completion thereof within such time or times then and in every such case it shall be lawful for the said Company by a written notice or notices signed by the Principal Engineer or assistant resident engineer for the time being of the said Company to be delivered to the said J.T.B. or to be left with him or his sureties or his foreman for the time being or at his or their or any or either of their usual place or places of abode to require that the said J.T.B. shall provide such additional number of workmen as the said Principal Engineer or assistant resident engineer for the time being may think necessary or reasonable to be kept or employed in the said works either permanently or for a limited period as by such written notice or notices shall be required And in case the said J.T.B. shall not within three days after any such notice or notices shall be so given or left as aforesaid provide the additional workmen thereby required and in all respects comply with such notice or notices then and in every such case it shall be lawful for the said Company or their agents to provide such additional workmen and to continue to employ them for such length of time and generally and in such manner as shall have been required in and by such notice or notices and at such weekly or other payments or wages as the said Company or their Principal Engineer or Assistant Resident Engineer for the time being may think proper which payments shall be made and deducted out of the monies which may then remain due to the said J.T.B. by virtue of these presents and that the said Company shall be at liberty to use the tools and materials provided for the construction or execution of any of the said works and also to provide such other tools and materials as may be requisite for proceeding with the said several works and that in case the balance then due to the said J.T.B. shall be insufficient to cover as well the said payments or wages as the expenses incurred for providing tools or materials as last aforesaid then that the said J.T.B. his heirs executors or administrators shall and will make good and pay to the said Company the deficiency on demand And further that the said J.T.B. shall during the progress of the said works hereby contracted for provide and keep one or more competent foreman or foremen to superintend the said works and to remain constantly during the hours of work upon or close at hand to the site of the said works and that if the said Principal Engineer or Assistant Resident Engineer for the time being of the Company shall at any time consider any such foreman or foremen as in anywise incompetent or as acting improperly it shall be lawful in every such case for the said Principal or Assistant Engineer for the time being to give a notice in writing to the said J.T.B. to remove or supercede such foreman or foremen and put another or others in his or their place or places And in case the said J.T.B. shall neglect to do so within one week after the delivery of such notice it shall be lawful for the said Company or their Principal Engineer for the time being to supercede such foreman or foremen and put another or others in his or their place on payment of such weekly payment or wages as the said Company may think proper which payment or wages shall be deducted out of the monies which may be due to the said J.T.B. for by virtue of these presents And further that the said J.T.B. shall not nor will in the execution of the said works hereby contracted for or otherwise injure or obstruct or interrupt the free use of a passage over any public or private road or path whether temporary or permanent beyond what may be unavoidable in the due execution of the said works and that if any such injury or obstruction or interruption shall be unavoidable then that the said J.T.B. shall and will be wholly responsible for all such injury or obstruction or interruption and save harmless and indemnify the said Company from all costs losses damages and expenses on account thereof And further that the said J.T.B. shall not nor will in the execution of the works hereby contracted for or otherwise enter upon or otherwise make use of any of the lands adjoining to the land or ground whereof possession shall be given by the said Company to the said J.T.B. for the purposes of this Contract without the consent of the said Company signified in writing under the hand of one of the Secretaries for the time being thereof or of the owners and occupiers of such adjoining lands being previously attained but shall (except with such consent) strictly confine his operating within the site of the said intended works And also that he the said J.T.B. shall and will make full compensation and satisfaction as required by the said first mentioned Act to all owners and occupiers of lands adjoining or near the site of the works to be done under this Contract which shall be taken temporarily used injured or occupied for any of the purposes hereinbefore mentioned or by the said Acts authorised for all damages to be by them sustained in or by the execution of the said works herein contracted for or by the neglect or ommission of the said J.T.B. to comply with the provisions of the said Acts in the performance of the same works and shall and will make full compensation and satisfaction to all other persons whatsoever who may be entitled to compensation for any loss or damage to be by them sustained in consequence of the execution of the aforesaid works or by or in consequence of the neglect or ommission of the said J.T.B. to comply with the provisions of the aforesaid Acts of Parliament or any of them and shall and will save defend keep harmless and indemnified the said Company and their successors and their lands and tenements goods and chattels in respect of all such damages And further that if at any time the said Company shall be called upon to pay and make good any such damages as aforesaid it shall be lawful for them to make such satisfaction and compensation as they shall think fit and to deduct the amount thereof together with any expenses incurred by them in and about the ascertaining the same from any monies which may be then due to the said J.T.B. under or by virtue of these presents or in case the balance then due to the said J.T.B. shall be insufficient to cover the same then that the said J.T.B. his heirs executors or administrators shall and will make good and pay the deficiency on demand And further that if the said J.T.B. shall be desirous of temporarily using or occupying any of the lands adjoining the site of the said works then and in such case he the said J.T.B. shall give ten days previous notice in writing to the London

Secretary for the time being of the said Company of such his desire stating the purpose or purposes for which he shall desire to use or occupy such lands And further that he the said J.T.B. will use and take all necessary or proper precautions against the destroying or injuring any work whatsoever upon or adjoining or near to the line of the said intended railway for the construction or performance of which any person or persons hath or have agreed or may agree with the said Company and that the said J.T.B. shall and will be answerable for all such destruction or injury if occasioned by his neglect or default and it shall be lawful for the said Company if they think proper to repair and make good the same at the expense of the said J.T.B. and to deduct and to retain the amount thereof out of any monies which may be then due to the said J.T.B. under this Contract And further that the said J.T.B. shall not unless with the consent of the said Company signified in writing under the hand of one of the Secretaries for the time being thereof make any subcontract or subcontracts for the execution of the works hereby contracted for or any part thereof except as to labour only or the supply of materials distinct from labour and then with the consent of the said Principal Engineer for the time nor unless with such consent as aforesaid of the said Company assign this contract or any part thereof And further that in case the said J.T.B. shall become insolvent or be declared bankrupt or shall not commence the said works or any part thereof at the time or respective times in the said Specification appointed or mentioned in that behalf or shall not prosecute the same or proceed in or towards the finishing and completion thereof with due diligence and to the satisfaction of the Principal Engineer for the time being of the said Company then and in every or any such case and either upon or at any time after the happening of the same it shall be lawful to and for the said Company if they shall think fit to take the execution of the said works out of the hands of the said J.T.B. and to employ any other persons or persons either by contract or measure and value or otherwise as the said Company shall think fit to proceed with the said works and to complete the same And further that the monies which previously shall have been pad to the said J.T.B. on account of any work or materials then already done or executed or provided by the said J.T.B. shall be considered as the full value and be taken by the said J.T.B. in full payment and satisfaction not only of and for the said work or materials in respect of which payment may have been made but likewise of and for any other work and materials which the said J.T.B. shall have then done or executed or provided although no such payments may have been previously made in respect thereof And further that all the balance and monies whatsoever which shall be then or thereafter would have been or become due or payable to the said James Thomas Bedborough under this present contract if this present clause had not been inserted together with all the engines machinery implements tools and materials then being upon or about the site of the said works shall upon the execution of the said works being taken or attempted to be taken out of the hands of the said J.T.B. as aforesaid become and be considered as the absolute property of the said Company to all intents and purposes whatsoever And further that in case such balance or monies engines machinery implements tools and materials so to become the property of the said Company shall not be sufficient for the purpose of finishing and completing the said works and keeping the same in repair for one year after the completion thereof and defraying all the costs charges and expenses incidental to or attending the same and which may be paid or incurred by the said Company then and in such case the said J.T.B. his heirs executors or administrators shall and will make good and pay to the said Company such deficiency on demand And further that all materials which may be brought and left on the site of any works to be done under this Contract by the said J.T.B. or by his order prior to the execution of the said works being taken out of his hands as aforesaid for the purpose of being used in or about the carrying on the said works shall from the time of their being so brought and left as aforesaid be considered as the property of and belonging to the said Company appropriated to special purposes of being used and employed in the said works and shall not on *any account or pretence whatsoever be taken away by the said J.T.B. his executors or administrators or any other person or persons whom so ever without the special licence and consent of the said Company but the said Company shall not be in any wise answerable or liable for any loss or damage which may happen to or in respect of the said materials either by the said materials being stolen or injured by weather or otherwise howsoever And further that in case any of the said materials so brought by the said J.T.B. shall be considered by the Principal Engineer or Assistant Resident Engineer for the time being of the said Company as unsound or unfit or of inferior quality or in any respect improper the said J.T.B. shall and will upon notice in writing to him or his foreman or foremen given by the said Company or their Principal Engineer or Assistant Resident Engineer immediately cause the same to be removed from off the ground and proceed with the said works with materials corresponding with the said Specifications to the satisfaction of the said Company and that in default of such removal within two days after the said notice in writing it shall and may be lawful to and for the said Company or their agents to cause the same to be removed to such place or places as they may think proper without being in any wise answerable or accountable for any loss or damage that shall or may happen to such materials so removed and to cause proper materials to be substituted for the same and to pay all expenses attending such removal and substitutions out of the monies which may then be due to the said J.T.B. by virtue of these presents And further that in case at any time during the progress of the said works or within twelve calendar months after the completion of the same it shall appear to the said Company or to their Principal Engineer or Assistant Resident Engineer for the time being that any part of the said works are unsoundly or improperly executed or not made of proper materials or not performed in the most workmanlike manner agreeable to the said Specification or, if any accident shall occur from frost or bad weather during the said period or from whatever cause such imperfection or accident shall arise and not withstanding any such certificate as hereinafter mentioned as to the due execution of any such works in every such case the said J.T.B. shall cause the same to be immediately taken down and executed properly to the satisfaction of the said Engineer or their Principal Engineer or Assistant Resident Engineer for the time being without any extra charge whatsoever and without any delay in the period fixed for executing the said works or any of them Provided always And it is hereby declared and agreed by and between the said parties hereto that all work in the said Specification described or referred to as Extra Work which the Principal Engineer or Assistant Resident Engineer for the time being of the said Company shall by any writing under his hand required to be executed shall be and the same is deemed and considered as included in the Covenants and Agreements hereinbefore contained on the part of the said J.T.B. so far as such covenants and agreements can be applied to such extra work and that such extra work shall be paid for by the said Company at the times after the rate and in manner hereinafter mentioned And further that if the said Company shall think proper at any time or times to make any alterations additions or omissions to or in the works herein contracted for they shall be at liberty to do so giving to the said J.T.B. written instructions for such alterations additions or omissions signed by two of the Directors of the said Company or by their Principal Engineer or Assistant Resident Engineer for the time being but the said J.T.B. shall not be considered as having authority for any alterations addition or ommission nor as entitled to make any claim for the value or in respect of such alterations or addition without such written instructions signed as aforesaid although such alteration or addition may have been actually executed by the said J.T.B. And further that no such alteration addition or ommission shall vacate this contract or affect the same beyond what may be the necessary consequence of any such alteration addition or ommission And further that the period by the said Specification limited or appointed for the completion of the said works or any part thereof shall not be altered or affected by reason of any such alteration addition or ommission as aforesaid unless and except so far as the said Principal Engineer for the time being shall by writing under his hand certify whether any and what extension of the period limited for the completion of the said works or any part thereof ought to be made or allowed in consequence of any such alteration addition or ommission And further that all such additional or altered work shall be ascertained and valued by measurement and evaluation in all respects according to or by comparison with the price of labour and articles respectively set forth in the Schedule of Prices hereinunder written or annexed to these presents or as near to such prices as may be and that the value thereof so ascertained shall be added to or deducted from the amount of this Contract as the case may be and the addition in value if any paid for in the manner and at the time or times hereinafter mentioned And it is further hereby agreed between and by the said parties that the said Principal Engineer or Assistant Resident Engineer shall not be bound to set out any of the works or to furnish copies of the said drawings in the possession of the Assistant Resident Engineer for the use of the said J.T.B. but he shall be at liberty at his own expense to take copies of the said drawings so as aforesaid deposited with the said Assistant Resident Engineer and that any deviations made in the said works from the original drawings or the said Specifications except what are ordered by the said Company their Principal or Assistant Resident Engineer in writing as aforesaid shall be altered and corrected by and at the expense of the said J.T.B. And it is further hereby declared and agreed that all buildings walls fences turf trees and other matters or things now under or upon the surface of the land to be occupied by the said works being the property of the said Company shall remain the property of the said Company and that the said J.T.B. shall remove such trees and the materials of such buildings walls and fences at his own expense to the nearest public road or to such other places within a reasonable distance from the works as shall be appointed by the said Principal or Assistant Resident Engineer for the purpose of doing as little damage thereto as may be And it is hereby further agreed by and between the said parties to these presents that the said J.T.B. shall generally do execute and provide not only all the works and materials respectively expressed declared and specified or referred to in the said Specification and drawings hereinbefore referred to but likewise all such works matters and materials as are necessarily implied or may be reasonably inferred in or from the said Specification and drawings respectively although the same may not happen to be therein expressly mentioned as to be done or provided by the said J.T.B. the true intent and meanings of these presents being that the works and materials hereby contracted to be done executed and provided shall include all that is requisite for the making doing and construction of the said earthworks bridges culverts and other works hereby contracted to be done as aforesaid And also that in the event of any dispute arising between the said J.T.B. and any Assistant Engineer or Inspector for the time being concerning any of the matters aforesaid the said J.T.B. his executors administrators and assigns shall and will abide by observe perform fulfil and keep in all things obey the decision in writing of the Principal Engineer for the time being of the said Company Provided always that in all cases in which there shall be or appear to be any variation between the agreement stipulations and provisions contained in these presents and in the said Specification the agreements stipulations and provisions contained in these presents shall be and be considered to be the agreement stipulations and provisions to be performed and executed by the said J.T.B. but in all cases matters and things not sufficiently provided for and regulated by these presents the agreements stipulations and provisions contained in the said Specification shall be and be considered as the agreement stipulations and provisions to be observed and performed and executed by the said J.T.B. Provided also And it is hereby declared and agreed by and between the said parties hereto when in the said Specification the word 'Engineer' occurs such word shall be read and construed as meaning such Principal Engineer or Assistant Resident Engineer for the time being as hereinbefore mentioned - unless such construction shall be inconsistent with the* context of the said Specification and except as to the certificates or certificate of the due execution of any works or any other matters which according to these presents ought to be done judged or decided by the said Principal Engineer for the time being only And further that when in the said Specification the word Contractor occurs the same shall be read and considered as meaning the said J.T.B. Provided also And it is hereby agreed and declared between and by the said parties hereto that if the said J.T.B. shall be prevented from or materially impeded or delayed in the proceeding with or completion of any of the works which under this Contract or to be performed and executed by the said J.T.B. by reason or inconsequence of any acts which may contrary to the true intent and meaning of these Presents and of the said Specification be done or omitted to be done by the said Company or any authorised engineer or agent on their behalf or any person or persons with whom the said Company have contracted or made contract for the execution of any works such prevention impediment or delay shall not vacate these Presents or otherwise affect the same except that in every case the Principal Engineer for the time being of the said Company shall determine whether any and if any what extension of time ought to be allowed for the execution and completion of all or any of the works hereby contracted for and whether any and (if any) what compensation or allowance ought to be paid or allowed to the said J.T.B. in respect of such prevention impediment or delay and in what manner such compensation or allowance ought to be paid or allowed and the determination of such Principal Engineer for the time being shall be binding and conclusive on all parties And this Indenture further witnesseth that in consideration of the premises and of the covenants hereinbefore contained on the part of the said J.T.B. his heirs executive and administrators to be performed the said Great Western Railway Company do hereby on behalf of themselves and their successors covenant and agree with the said J.T.B. his executors and administrators that they the said Company shall and will the sum of fifty-nine thousand five- hundred and seventy pounds of lawful money of Great Britain being the sum which has been agreed to be paid for the execution of the whole of the works hereby contracted for (exclusive of the work in the said Specification described as Extra Work) and for the providing the materials for the same at the times and in the manner following (that is to say) that the said Company shall and will at the expiration of fourteen days to commence and be computed from the day on which the said works hereby contracted to be done shall; have been commenced pay unto the said J.T.B. his executive his administrators or assigns four-fifths parts of the whole value of the work which shall have been then executed such value to be estimated by the Principal Engineer or Assistant Resident Engineer for the time being having regard to the prices specified in the said Schedule of Prices hereinunder written or hereunder annexed as also to the entire sum hereby agreed to be paid for the execution of the whole of the said Works (the execution of such works to be from time to time certified by the Principal Engineer as hereinafter mentioned) and so from time to time at the expiration of every succeeding fourteen days in the manner shall and will pay unto the said J.T.B. his executors administrators or assigns four-fifth part of the whole amount or value of the work which shall have been actually performed during the preceding days until the four-fifths part or twenty-percent to be retained from time to time by the said Company shall either alone or together with the sums to be retained out of the estimated value of any extra work which may be executed and certified from time to time as hereinafter mentioned amount to the sum of four thousands pounds and shall and will thence forward until the whole of the works hereby contracted be done shall be completed at the expiration of every succeeding fourteen days pay unto the said J.T.B. his executors administrators or assigns the full value of the work to be ,ascertained and certified as aforesaid which shall have been done in the preceding fourteen days and shall and will at the expiration of one calendar month after the whole of the works hereby contracted to be executed are completely finished to the satisfaction of the Principal Engineer of the said Company to be certified by him in manner hereinafter *mentioned pay unto the said J.T.B. his executors administrators or assigns the sum of two-thousand pounds being one equal half part of the monies so to be retained by the said Company as aforesaid without any interest thereon and shall and will at the expiration of one-month after the determination of the year during which the said earthworks bridges culverts and otherworks are hereinbefore contracted to be kept in repair by the said J.T.B. (the same having been certified by the Engineer in the same manner as the completion of the works) pay to the said J.T.B. his executors administrators or assigns the sum of two-thousand pounds being the balance of the money to be so retained by the said Company together with interest on such balance at the rate of four pounds percent to be computed from the day on which the whole of the said works shall have been completed as aforesaid And further that the said Company shall and will pay unto the said J.T.B. his executors administrators or assigns or in respect of the extra work hereinbefore contracted to be executed by him at and after the prices mentioned or referred to in the said Specification and set forth in the set Schedule of Prices according to the true intent and meaning of the same respectively the amount and value of such extra work the amount and value thereof to be from time to time certified by such Principal Engineer and to be paid and payable in the same manner and subject to the same deductions as above directed with respect to the said sum of Fifty-nine thousand Five-hundred and seventy pounds Provided nevertheless that the works hereby contracted to be executed or any part thereof shall not be deemed or considered as executed unless the shame shall have been executed within the time or respected times specified for that purpose by these Presents to the satisfaction of the said Principal Engineer for the time being and shall have been certified by him to have been so executed and that on notice being given by the said J.T.B. for that purpose the said Principal Engineer or the Assistant Resident Engineer for the time being shall without delay examine the works which from time to time shall be alleged to have been executed by the said J.T.B. persuant to this contract and then if the same shall be so completed to the satisfaction of such Principal Engineer he shall certify the same to the said Company and thereupon the said J.T.B. his executors administrators or assigns shall be entitled to receive from the said Company the amount of the payment then due in respect of the works so certified to have been executed subject to the retaining thereout of such sums as hereinbefore in that behalf mentioned Provided always that the said Principal Engineer or assistant Resident Engineer for the time being shall not be bound to estimate the value of any works which the said J.T.B. shall allege to have been executed without one week previous notice so to do on the part of the said J.T.B. And further that no default on the part of the said Company in payment of any of the monies hereby agreed to be paid by them nor any other breach of any other covenant or agreement on their part herein contained shall vacate these Presents or discharge the said J.T.B. from the observance and performance of the several covenants and agreements on his part herein contained And it is hereby further agreed that during the progress and until the completion of the works hereby contracted to be done and executed the decision of the said Principal Engineer with respect to the amount state and condition of the work actually executed and also in respect of any and every question that may arise concerning the construction of this present contract or the aforesaid drawings and specification or the nature of the material or the execution of the works hereby contracted for or any other matter or thing whatsoever relating to the same shall be final and without appeal But, if any difference of opinion should arise between the Company or their engineer and the said J.T.B. after the completion of the contract as to any matter of charge or account as between the said Company and the said J.T.B. such dispute shall be referred to and finally settled and concluded by the arbitration of the said engineer on the part of the said Company and an engineer appointed by the said J.T.B. on his part and in any case of their not being able to agree a third person shall be named in writing as arbitrator by such two engineers before they proceed upon the subject of the reference and the decision of such two arbitrators or* their umpire so nominated shall be final and binding on all parties In witness whereof the said Great Western Railway Company have hereunto caused their Common Seal to be affixed and the said J.T.B. hath, hereunder set his hand and sealed the day and year first above written

The specification to which the foregoing Indenture Refers

This Contract comprehends inclosing the ground to be used by the contractors the excavation and forming of all the earthworks by permanent fences and drains the diverting of roads and the construction of all bridges and other masonry hereafter specified and the supply of all labour materials tools implements and everything required for these and every other work necessary for the entire completion (excepting the ballasting and laying the permanent rails) of that portion of the railway extending from a proposed bridge across the Thames at Moulsford to a road near Vauxhall Farm in the Parish of Didcot a distance of about six miles and four chains according to the accompanying drawings and subject to all the terms and conditions of this specification together with such extra works as may be required by the engineer and as are hereinafter described and referred to and the maintaining the same in perfect repair for twelve months after the completion of the works.

The drawings referred to in the Specification are ten in number and are numbered from 1 to 9 and marked Contract 4R.

A general description and order of proceeding with works.

The land required for the permanent works and coloured red in the Plan drawing No. 1 will be procured by the Company and immediately upon the Contractor being enabled to attain possession of this land or of such part of it as the engineer may consider necessary at the time for the commencement of the works and a notice being given to the contractor to commence the said works as hereinafter mentioned he will be required immediately to enclose the same land with a temporary fence and drains in the manner hereinafter described and when and as often as such portion of the remainder of this land as the engineer may consider necessary at the time for the progress of the works is put into the possession of the contractor he will be required immediately to inclose the same as in the first instance.

The centre line of the railway as shown upon the plan will be marked on the ground as well as the boundary lines of the property to be inclosed but the contractor will not withstanding be held responsible for the perfect setting out of the line (although he may be assisted by the engineer) with such regular curves and fair lines and in such general directions as are shown in the drawings or which may be more particularly furnished hereafter by the engineer and the contractor is to find all the necessary flagpoles and stakes or pegs and all tools and labour required for the final setting out of the centre line the width and other marks considered necessary by the engineer.

All brickwork of arches culverts etc. to be proceeded with immediately on the commencement of the contract or as soon after as practicable in order that the longest possible time may be given for such work to stand after completion before the earthwork approaches it. This instruction will be strictly enforced.

Before commencing the excavations or the formation of the embankments a sufficient portion of the topsoil or turf where the turf is good for the purpose of the part to be excavated as well as that of the portion of the ground which will be covered by the embankment is to be laid aside and the best selected to soil and turf the slopes of the embankment and cuttings as hereinafter described.

In carrying any of the materials across or under any existing path or rod or any temporary or permanent deviation of such road every necessary precaution must be taken by the contractor to avoid injuring or improperly interfering with the use of the said path or road or deviation of the same and he will be responsible for any consequence which may result from any such injury or improper interference should any be caused in the execution of this Contract.

Before proceeding, with any parts of the works by which the existing drainage of the ground can be interfered with the streams drains or ditches must be properly and efficiently deviated or led into new drains or channels to be formed by the contractor so as effectually to secure and maintain the existing drainage of the adjoining lands in as good a state as they are now and thoroughly to drain any ground upon or through which any works are to be executed under the contract. The temporary fencing is to be replaced by the permanent fencing in the manner hereinafter described as early and as rapidly as the progress of the other works will permit

"Particular Description of Works Included in the Contract Independent of Extra Work

"Fencing

The temporary fencing will consist of split oak posts not less than six-feet six-inches in length and having at least fourteen- square-inches of cross section. These posts to be placed nine- feet apart and three-feet nine-inches above the surface of the ground - to be morticed to receive the ends of four horizontal oak or larch rails which are to be further supported by an intermediate small post of oak or larch firmly nailed to each rail - the fence must be firmly and substantially fixed and must be continue round the whole of the ground to be inclosed and maintained in repair with cross fencing at those parts where bridges are to be built and where passages must be left to communicate with the adjoining lands until such bridges be completed so as effectually to, exclude sheep nd other cattle and to protect the adjoining lands from trespass at all times joining the progress of the work and the whole or such portions of the permanent drains or such temporary drains shall be made and considered as part of the temporary fencing and may be required for the perfect drainage of the ground to be used in this contract for the purpose of maintaining the drainage of the remaining lands and which may be interfered with by the execution of this contract.

The Permanent fencing to be continued along the whole extent of the contract and on both sides of the railway excepting at the spaces occupied by the various bridges or cross drains and at those parts the fencing is to be returned round the foot of the slopes in the manner hereinafter described this fencing is to be formed as rapidly as the progress of the other works will permit, it consists of an oak post and rail fence placed along the extreme boundary of the Company's property with a ditch within this and a Quick hedge at the edge of the slopes of the form and dimensions and in a manner shown in drawing No. 3.

The posts are to be of split oak seven-feet three-inches in length and equal in sectional area to a scantling of five-inches by three-inches and a half at the least they are to be placed at a distance of nine-feet from centre to centre and to stand three-feet nine-inches above the surface of the ground - each post is to have four mortices completely through it for the reception of the ends of the rails and all these posts are to be as nearly of uniform size as possible.

The horizontal rails four in number between each pair of posts are to be of split oak or larch equal in sectional area to a scantling of three-inches-and-a-half by one-inch-and-a-half.

They are to be ten-feet in length and the ends to be scarfed so as to fill the mortices of the posts.

Halfway between the posts an oak or larch stay five-feet long having one-foot six-inches of the length in the ground three- inches wide and two inches thick is to be firmly nailed to each of the four horizontal rails with good ten-penny nails.

The posts and stays must be firmly fixed in the grounds the ends of the rails firmly driven into the mortices of the posts and a piece of new iron hoop one-inch-and-a-quarter wide and one-pound to three feet shall be nailed all around the top of every posts to prevent it splitting.

Such parts of the temporary fencing as can be made available shall be permitted to be used in the construction of the permanent fencing provided the materials be of the requisite strength *and quality and uninjured by previous use.*

A ditch is to be formed within this fence and is shown in the drawing No. 3.

The material excavated from the ditch shall be used to form a mound on the space between the edge of the ditch and the railway slope both sides of which must be neatly faced with turf the soil or sod at the bottom of this mound being first dug and turned up when the material excavated from the ditch shall be more in quantity than sufficient to form the mound the surplus must be conveyed to the nearest embankment.

The best portion of the negatable soil excavated from the ditch shall be placed in the middle of the mound of which a double row of good three year old Quicks two years transplanted shall be planted and not less than fifteen quicksets shall be contained in one linear yard. The planting of the quicks shall proceed as quickly as the progress of the earthworks and the nature of the season will admit of.

At the bottom of the embankment draining tiles must be laid through the quick mound at intervals of not more than twenty yards for the purpose of effectually bringing all the water draining from the slopes of the embankments into the fence ditches.

During the progress of the work and until the expiration of twelve months during which the contract is to be maintained the works the quicksets shall be cleared and weeded at least twice a year and all the quicksets which may not take root and grow must be pulled up and three year old living Quicksets similar to those before described planted in their place and all broken posts rails or stays replaced by new ones equal in quality to those originally used.

The cross section of the ditches drawing No. 3 before referred to is to be considered as giving the average width and depth of those ditches but the dimensions must be increased when the undulations of the ground may require so that the ditches may effectually lead the water to the natural water courses at present existing or to such others and to such culverts as may be made.

At the several spaces or intervals to be occupied by the bridges or the roads leading thereto the ditches will be continued without interruption the water being carried through culverts to be constructed under the contract for extra works except when specified and included in the contract but the post rails and Quick fence will be returned around the foot of the slopes of the embankments or otherwise continued until they are about against the wing walls of the bridges - in crossing culverts the ditches are to be made to communicate properly with the water courses of the culverts and the Quick hedge and mound is to be diverted a little from the straight line and carried over the top of the culvert upon the slope of the embankment.

"Earthwork

The earthwork included in this contract comprehends the entire formation of the embankments and cuttings within the limits of the contract according to the longitudinal section drawing No. 2 and the cross sections drawings Nos. 3 and 4 and according to the following general directions and which such contingent works as and hereinafter described.

The bottoms of the cuttings and the top surface of the embankments will be formed everywhere to a distance of one-foot below a line marked on the drawing and referred to 'as line of rails'. This line from the commencement at the east and rises four-feet-per-mile for the distance of sixty-four-chains and then rises three-feet-six-inches-per-mile to the west end of the contract.

The total contents of the embankments within these limits are estimated at 495,000 cubic yards.

These quantities are calculated from the longitudinal sections taken along the centre line and without taking into consideration any sloping of the ground in the cross sections or the additions or deductions to be made on account of bridges culverts or approaches.

These calculations are believed to be correct but the contractor must satisfy himself of the quantities required and the above is given merely as a guide to him in forming his first estimate of the general amount of the work to be performed.

"Embankments

The upper surface of the embankments to be of the width shown in the several sections as hereafter referred to and is to be reduced to one uniform level surface so as to receive the ballasting and permanent road the formation of which does not form part of this contract except as an extra work but the ballasting used by the contractor for the temporary rails and remaining upon the embankments and in the cuttings if of a sufficiently good quality may be taken for that purpose as hereafter described.

As the embankment proceeds and becomes consolidated the sides or slopes shall be carefully trimmed to an even surface with the required slopes as before described as shown in the Drawing No. 3 and the permanent fences completed - the faces of the slopes are to be neatly covered with turves of grass not less than eight inches in thickness with the green sward outwards and well be at and pressed into place and where the turf set aside is not considered by the engineer sufficiently good for the purpose the top soil or vegetable mould above referred to must be informally distributed over the slopes not less than eight-inches in thickness - all the lumps must be broken d own and the surface neatly trimmed. The slopes thus covered with soil are to be sown as quickly as the weather or season will permit with Rye grass and Clover seed mixed in equal quantities and not less than five- pounds of the mixed seed per acre is to sown and equally distributed upon them and every part which may appear to require it until the expiration of the term of the contract must immediately be sown or turfed afresh.

When the contract work is completed the contractor shall if required preserve the temporary rails for carrying on the work for the purpose of performing such extra work hereinafter specified as may be ordered by the engineer and if the further use of these rails should be required by the Company for any period not exceeding four weeks beyond the time required for the performance of the extra works the contractor will be bound to leave the rails as may be required, a fair compensation being made to him for the detention and for the use thereof such compensation being determined by the engineer.

In forming those parts of the embankments which are in contact with any bridges culverts or other masonry which may be constructed on this part of the work and in laying the temporary rails and carrying the materials over any of these bridges or culverts the contractor must proceed in such manner and take all such precautions as the engineer may direct to prevent injury to the masonry - but the contractor will nevertheless be responsible for any damage done thereto.

In filling between the wing walls and against the abutments of any such bridges the material which will consist of chalk must be carefully packed in blocks or lumps set aside and if necessary trimmed for the purpose and if the interstices filled and washed in with small gravel or sand which such can be obtained or small pieces of chalk in such manner as the engineer may direct and every precaution should be adopted to prevent subsequent shrinking or settlement.

The embankments No. 1, No. 2, and No. 3 Drawing No. 2 will be formed according to the cross section No. 1 Drawing No. 3 - the embankment No. 4 will be formed according to cross section No. 2.

All the dimensions given and the forms shown in the drawings No. 2 and 3 are those to which the cuttings and embankments must be ultimately formed and maintained after they have become consolidated and have been turfed or soiled - in forming the embankments full allowance should be made at once for the shrinking of the materials so that there may be no necessity for making any subsequent additions to bring to their proper forms and dimensions.

"Cuttings

The cuttings are supposed to consist principally of chalk, chalk marle and beds of soft fine stone and sand but the contractor must satisfy himself upon these points.

261

The cuttings are to be carried to the depth before stated of one-foot below the 'line of rails' and formed of the slopes shown in the cross-sections Drawings No. 3 - that is to say Cutting No. 1 Drawing No. 2 will be formed thirty-eight-feet wide at the line of rails and with slopes of one-to-one - Cuttings No. 2 and 3 Drawing No. 2 will be formed according to the cross-section No. 1 Drawing No. 3 and Cutting No. 4 according to the cross section No. 2 Drawing No. 3.

The slopes must be neatly and carefully trimmed and dressed to an even and regular surface either in one continuous slope or in benches as may be directed by the engineer.

The top soil or clay will be sloped back as shown in the Cross Section Drawing No. 3 to a depth depending on that of the soil or clay - should it exceed six-foot at any point the excess will be paid for as extra work.

The contractor is supposed to form his estimate from the contents of the embankments to be formed of the dimensions and slopes specified to which the cuttings are supposed to be adjusted but if the amount of the excavation formed according to the drawings and ordered by the engineer shall exceed that required by the embankments or if any alterations in any of these dimensions be ordered by the engineer a proportionate allowance will be made for the excess of excavation or for the altered quantity of excavation or of removal or of both which may thereby be required either in addition or diminution as the case may be.

No materials whatsoever obtained in the excavation shall be removed by the contractor otherwise than in the construction of the works or spoil banks before referred to without the sanction of the engineer.

"General Instructions

"Materials

All the bricks to be used throughout the work to be sound hard well burnt and well shaped Stocks of the very best quality - the best in point of colour and shape to be carefully selected for the exterior work and attention must be paid that those be of one uniform colour and general appearance - all corner bricks must be rubbed down to a good face and if a sufficient number of perfectly well shaped good coloured bricks for the face works cannot be selected from those, used bricks of a superior quality must be procured on purpose.

"Mortar

The mortar to consist of one proportion of lime dry and two-and- a-half of sand as the engineer may direct according to the part of the works where it may be used - the lime to be of the best quality, to be carefully screened and slacked and to be thoroughly mixed with the required proportions of sand and water in a pug-mill and every other precaution used to procure the best mortar.

The mortar must be mixed in the pug-mill with as small a quantity of water as may be sufficient to reduce it to the consistence required for building and no water shall be added to the mortar on any account after it has once passed through the pug-mill.

"Roman Cement

The cement is to be of the best quality - to be used fresh and to be well mixed with sand in such small quantities as may from time to time be required in the proportion of one of cement to one- and-a-half of sand as the engineer may direct according to the part of the work where it is to be used.

No water on any account to be added to the cement after it has been once mixed and no cement to be used or mixed with other cement after it had once began to set.

"Sand

The sand to be clean sharp river sand - free from any vegetable substance and well screened through a screen having not less than four meshes in the inch.

"Concrete

The concrete is to consist of five parts of clean gravel perfectly free from loam or clay with a proper proportion of small gravel and sand as well and one part of lime measured dry - the lime to be thoroughly mixed with gravel in a pug-mill.

"Stone

The stone is to be of the Bramley Fall or Bath Stone from the best quarries or other free stone of equal quality to these and approved of by the engineer, to be of the best quality of the particular sort approved, to be of good colour and free from stains, beds and other defects.

"Cast Iron

The cast ironwork to be clean well shaped castings of the quality best adapted to the particular purpose for which the part is intended, to be subjected by the contractor to such tests as the engineer may direct and no casting will allowed to be fixed or if fixed will be allowed to remain in place in which any plugging or other attempt to conceal any defects shall be discovered.

All the ironwork after it is fixed is to be well cleaned and painted with three coats of strong oil paint.

"Workmanship

"Brickwork

The bricks to be bedded sound without striking after they are bedded - the mortar to be used sufficiently thin in the interior of the work to enable the workmen to flush the joints up full and sound without grouting and no grouting whatsoever shall be used in any part of the work unless especially directed by the engineer - (the bricks in each course to be well bonded and the different courses to cross joint so as to make the most sound and perfect work and the joints throughout the work to be kept as thin as possible consistently with sound work and all exterior joints in the soffets of the arches or elsewhere to be well pointed with mortar prepared for the purpose - no balls to be used unless where it may be necessary for obtaining the required dimensions in the different courses.

The upper course of all brick cornices, plinths or offsets of any sort which are exposed to the weather to be set in Roman Cement - in building the wing walls or any other battering walls if materials are not at hand to fill in immediately and if from the state of the weather or any other cause the work shall be liable to droop or fall inwards at all and alter its form, good and sufficient shores must be provided and the walls thoroughly secured until the backing is made good and where the back work comes in contact with the natural bed of chalk as in the wing-walls or abutments of the bridges in cuttings the chalk is to be dressed to a regular sound surface and the brickwork built close and sound up to this surface with a thin joint of mortar between.

Over the arches of all the bridges a bed of concrete is to be laid and the surface brought up level with the crown of the arch or to such other levels as may be shown on the drawings.

Under all foundations where the engineer may consider it necessary a bed of concrete shall be formed of such thickness as he may direct - such concrete to be payed for (if not included in the specification or drawings of that particular case) according to the price of concrete in the Schedule - the materials obtained from any such excavations as well as from any other required in the execution of the contract to be thrown into the nearest embankment.

The thickness and strength of the wing-walls and other parts of the bridges nd culverts in this contract are calculated upon the assumption of the packing of the chalk and the filling-in being carefully formed in the manner before described and the contractor must be responsible therefore for any injury to the brickwork arising from the injury of such filling in or from the natural surface of the chalk in the excavation not being properly dressed and the work built soundly against it.

Circular mouldings of brickwork are shown in some of the drawings - if there should be any difficulty in obtaining such bricks and if the Company cannot provide them they will be dispensed with.

"Stonework

All coping stones to be at least two feet in length and to average not less than two-feet six-inches - to be cramped to each other by cast-iron dovetailed cramps one-inch-square at the smallest part and let in at least two inches to a dove-tailed hole formed in the centre of the end joint of each stone and the space around these filled in with Roman Cement through a channel left for that purpose.

Cornice stones or string courses to be of the same general length as the coping stones and a throating of half-an-inch to be cut on the underside of all the projections.

The exterior facing of all stonework to be fair tooled - the joints to be fine picked with a chisel draught of an inch-and-a- half all round.

"Centreing

All the centreings used for the different bridges or culverts must be of the most substantial description and must sustain the weight of the superincumbent brickwork without sensible flexure - no centreing must be struck or slackened at all without permission from the engineer but no permission to that effect will relieve the contractor from the entire responsibility of the sufficiency and proper state of the work and if any centre should be struck without such permission and if any settlement should result either from this or any other cause the contractor will in every case without exception be required to rebuild such portion of the work as may have been so damaged.

"General Instructions as to Formation of Bridges and Diversion of Roads

The situation of the different bridges and culverts are shown in the General Section Drawing No. 2.

Where these bridges are so placed as to interfere during their construction with the free use of the existing road a good and sufficient temporary road is to be formed and maintained on one side of it and to be kept properly inclosed by a temporary fencing and formed of a width proportioned to the dimensions and uses of the present road and in every other respect such as the Surveyors of the Highways or other persons interested in the road have a right to demand.

When the bridge is completed a new road is to be formed over or under it as the case may be and maintained until the surface is consolidated at the level marked 'road line' in the drawing.

In the case of roads carried over a bridge and constructed according to Drawing No. 4 any embankment which may be necessary for the approaches must have a gradual inclination of one-in- twenty unless otherwise specified and shall be at least twenty- one-feet wide at the tops and shall have slopes of one-and-a- half-to-one and good and sufficient permanent drains shall be carried along the foot of such slopes and connected with the drains of the railway and a post and rail fence and hedge without any drain carried along the top of the slope and the roads shall in every respect of quality and quantity of materials and workmanship be at least equal to the existing road.

Where the road is carried under the railway and any excavation is required to form such excavation unless specified otherwise shall form a gradual inclination of one-in-fifteen and the sides shall in every case be formed to a slope of one-and-a- quarter to one and as regards fences and drains and in every other respect formed and finished as the slopes of the railway cuttings unless where the fences of the existing road can be maintained.

The width at the bottom of such cuttings will be twenty-four feet including footpaths and the new surface of the road shall be properly installed and shall in every respect of quantity and quality of materials be at least equal to the existing road.

During the construction of the bridges and as regards proper and sufficient formation of the permanent and temporary road the contractor is to be responsible for all damage or compensation

to which he or the Company may be rendered liable by the improper execution of the work and if the temporary use of any land is required beyond that furnished by the Company the contractor must procure the same at his own cost.

"Bridges and Culverts included in the Contract

No. 1 - Bridge over railway for the turnpike road No. 86 Cholsey Drawing No. 4A

No. 2 - Bridge over the road 29A Cholsey road to be lowered three feet and the side drain on the north side of the railway deepened so as to drain it Drawing No. 5

No. 3 - Bridge over road 18 Cholsey road to be lowered three feet Drawing No. 5

No. 4 - Five feet culvert over No. 5 Cholsey Drawing No. 7

No. 5 - Five feet culvert in No. 44 South Moreton Drawing No. 7

No. 6 - Bridge over the road No. 39 the side drain on the south side of railway to be carried under the road by a barrel drain of not less than two-feet diameter and twenty-two feet long Drawing No. 6

No. 7 - A twelve feet archway over mill stream Drawing No. 9

No. 8 - Bridge over railway from road 19 South Moreton width between the parapets sixteen-feet Drawing No. 4

No. 9 - Bridge over railway from road 16 South Moreton width between the parapets sixteen-feet Drawing No. 4

No. 10 - Bridge over turnpike road No. 313 South Moreton to be lowered five-feet and diverted in the manner shown on the plan Drawing No. 1 - the inclination to be one-in-twenty side slopes one-and-a-half-to-one and the width thirty feet including footpath Drawing No. 8

No. 11 - Three foot culvert at boundaries of Didcot and East Hagborne Parishes

No. 12 - Bridge over road 24 Didcot road lowered two feet Drawing No. 5

"Culverts

The culverts to be constructed according to the drawings and general instructions regarding drainage, the length of the barrel being determined by the extent of the slope of the embankment, the back of the coping stone on the top of the culvert corresponding with the line of the slope as shown in the Drawing No. 15 and that depth of the culvert to be as shown in the Drawing No. 16 except to keep the bottom at least as low as the side drains or other drains communicating with the culvert.

"Periods of Commencement and Completion

The works shall be commenced within ten days after a notice to that effect signed by the Principal Engineer or one of the Secretaries to the Company shall have been given to the contractor or left at his last or usual place of abode and all the works between the proposed bridge at Moulsford and a point at two-hundreds-yards west of the said bridge for the turnpike road in the Parish of Cholsey and marked no. 86 in the general Plan Drawing No. 1 shall be entirely completed and ready for ballasting within ten months after service of the said notice under a penalty of fifty pounds every week after this time And the whole of the work comprehended in this contract as well as such extra work as may be required by the engineer and which may form part of or be connected with the completion of the contract work shall be completed within fourteen months after service of the said notice.

And should the whole of the work not be completed within this period then for each week after this period the contractor will pay to the Company a penalty increasing in the following ratio videlicit Fifty pounds for the first week and one hundred pounds for the second week making one-hundred-and-fifty pounds for the first two weeks and one hundred and fifty pounds for the third week making three hundred pounds for the three weeks and so on the penalty for each succeeding week increasing by fifty pounds but the payment of such penalty shall not in any way relieve the contractor from the responsibility of any or other further payments or from any penalties or deductions from the money to be paid to him to which he may have become liable by the terms of this contract but if any delay should occur in putting the contractor in possession of property actually required at the time for the immediate progress of the works a proportionate extension will be made by the Company in the time allowed for the completion of the works of this contract.

The contractor is to maintain all the permanent works constructed under this contract and to leave the same in perfect repair twelve calendar months after the completion of the work.

"Extra Work

The contractor shall if required increase the dimensions of the embankments or cuttings at such places as the engineer may direct for the purpose of forming sidings or branches or for increasing the slopes or for any other object, such carriage of materials or increased dimensions not in any way to affect his contract as regard to levelling the surface, trimming and soiling the slopes, fencing and any other of the contingent works but he will be paid for the additional excavation or the additional lead or both as the case may be of any of the materials actually required according to the measurement of the net content of the addition ordered and at the price stated in the Schedule of Prices for extra works according to the increased quantity or the average increase of distance which the materials required has to be carried.

The contractor shall also if required excavate any gravel or sand that may be found and which the Company may select from the general excavation for the purposes of ballast and carry the same and spread it or deposit it in regular heaps as such intervals nd places and in such quantities long the top of the embankment as the engineer may direct for which he will be paid accordingly to the net measurement when spread or heaped and that the average price of all distances stated in the Schedule.

The total quantity required will be probably four-and-a-half cubic yards to the yard forward of embankment

If the whole or any portion of the gravel or sand or other material used by the contractor for ballasting his temporary rails be considered by the engineer sufficiently good for the purposes of forming the permanent ballasting such portion of it may be above the required level shall be placed in such heaps and at such convenient places as the engineer may direct and shall be estimated and paid for as if brought there from the nearest cutting.

The actual quantities of all earthwork are to be calculated whenever practicable from the dimensions of the original cuttings formed - the dimensions when formed into embankments being used only to determine the proportion carried to different distances.

The contractor shall also build such other bridges and culverts and may be directed to be made by the engineer during the progress of the works and shall make the necessary roads over or under such bridges and inclose the same with fencing and shall make such other diversions of roads that may be required of which works shall be executed according to the same terms and conditions as regards the nature and quality of materials and modes of construction and periods of completion as are specified for the works included in the contract and all such extra works shall be estimated and paid for in the manner hereinafter described and according to the prices in the Schedule hereunto annexed.

If any extra work is required to be executed by the contractor not specifically provided for in the said Schedule the value of the same will be determined by the engineer as far as possible from the prices of the works most similar to.

"General Stipulations

The drawings are to be considered as giving the general forms and character of the works but all dimensions given in the Specification are to be taken in preference to dimensions written on the drawings and dimensions on the drawings are preferred to dimensions by scale.

The contractor is to provide copies of the drawings for his own use.

The contractor must make arrangements with the landlowners or tenants for any accommodation he may may require beyond those afforded by the lands actually provided by the Company.

The contractor must satisfy himself of the nature of the soil of the general forms of the surface of the ground, of the quantity of the materials required for forming the embankments and all other matters which can in any way influence his contract and no information upon any such matters derived from the drawings or specifications or from the engineer or his assistants will in any way relieve the contractor from all risk or from fulfilling all the terms of the contract and as there may be details or incidental works not particularly mentioned in the Specification the contract sum is to include all such items whether in the temporary or in the permanent works as may thus have been omitted which fairly can be considered an omission or which must evidently be required by the nature of the work included in the contract it being clearly understood that the contractor is to find all the labour materials scaffolding centreing tools and implements in the general sense of the word and to execute all the works requisite for the perfect completion of the bridges culverts fencings drainings cuttings and embankments in every respect ready to receive the ballasting and permanent rails according to the true intent and meaning of this Specification as well as such extra work above described or referred to as may be required by the engineer.

The whole of the works herein specified as well as the mode of execution are to be to the entire satisfaction of the engineer for the time and he is to have the power of altering enlarging or diminuting the quantity of work to be performed - deductions for diminished and additions for additional work being made "pro "rata according to the prices inserted in the Schedule hereunto annexed and the contractor is to comply with every order given by the engineer both as to the quantity of the work to be performed and the manner of doing the work and no other work than otherwise hereinbefore specified is to be undertaken unless by an express order from the engineer in writing for that purpose and should there hereafter appear to be any discrepancies between the Scale attached to the drawings and the written dimensions or between the drawings and the specifications or should there be any difference of opinion as to the mode of carrying on the works the quantities to be excavated and carried into the embankment as to the workmanship or anything touching the execution of the work or to the meaning of any clause matter or thing in this Specification or the drawings annexed to the same is to be decided by the said engineer and his decision shall be final and lasting.

If during the progress of the works or within twelve calendar months after its completion any imperfection should appear in any part of the work or any accident should occur whether from frost or bad weather or from whatever cause such imperfection or accident may rise and notwithstanding any certificates which may have been to enable the contractor to obtain payment for work supposed to have been properly completed it shall be immediately repaired and made good at the contractor's expense to the satisfaction of the engineer and should the contractor not comply with such orders as may be given to him from time to time by the engineer or not proceed with sufficient expedition in the performance of the works as directed it shall be in the power of the Company to take the work wholly or in part out of the contractor's hands or to employ any number of other or additional materials or workmen to complete the same and whatever extra expense thereby be incurred by the Company in completing the work in a proper manner and which proper expedition shall be defrayed by the contractor and if at any time the Company shall find it necessary to take the work entirely or ion part out of the hands of the contractor or put on additional workmen or to supply additional materials to expedite the work or to enforce its proper execution the company shall have full power to take possession of the whole or such part of the materials tools or other implements used by the contractor which the Company's engineer may consider requisite for carrying on the work And lastly the contractor must take upon himself the entire responsibility of the sufficiency of the centreing scaffolding coffer dams tools and generally of the means used for the fulfilment of his contract whether such means may or may not be approved of or recommended by the engineer of the Company and the Contractor must run all risks of accidents or damage whatsoever that may occur to the work from whatever cause they may arise until he should have fulfilled all the terms of his contract - all materials and work of every description excepting earthworks will be measured and estimated according to the net contents when completed and without any allowance for circular or other work not withstanding any custom to the contrary - earthwork whether it is practicable will be measured by the net contents of the excavations and not of the embankments.

No work to be considered complete unless performed within the time specified and to the satisfaction of the engineer and certified as such by him and the contract not to be considered fulfilled until the entire completion of the work and the expiration of the time during which the whole is to be completed.

"The Schedule of Prices

"The foregoing Indenture and the Specification Referred to

Cast Iron Fixed and Painted per ton 18s-10d.

Wrought Iron Bolts etc. for the same per cwt. £2-6s-0d.

Brickwork generally (for all work excepting culverts) set in mortar and including all erections centreings scaffoldings excavations and contingent works - £1-10s-6d.

Ditto Ditto for Culverts Ditto per cubic yard £1-12s-0d.

Ditto for all works culverts included set in Roman Cement per cubic yard £1-17s-0d.

Stonework Dressed and Set Ashlar per cubic foot 4s-6d. Coping, String Course Cornices etc. per cubic yard 5s-3d.

Concrete including Excavation per cubic yard 10s-6d.

Permanent Fencing including Ditches one side only per yard run 4s-8d.

"Earthwork

Excavating carrying and forming into Embankments Chalk if under one quarter mile lead per cubic foot yard 11d. If above ditto and under one mile per cubic yard 1s-4d.

Sand Gravel and Clay. If under quarter of a mile lead per cubic yard 11d. If above quarter mile and under one mile per cubic yard 1s-4d.

Excavating carrying and depositing gravel for ballast if under quarter of a mile lead per cubic yard 1s-1d. If above quarter mile and under one mile per cubic yard 1s-9d.

Lead. If above one mile addition to the last mentioned prices for all materials at the rate per mile per cubic yard 6d.

Metalling surface of diversions and of roads per square yard 7s

Turfing and Soiling slopes etc. per cubic yard 3½d.

Signed Sealed and Delivered by the said James Thomas Bedborough in the Presence of James J Westwood Clerk to Messrs. Swain Stevens & Co. Frederick's Place, Old Jewry

Signed
J. T. Bedborough

Common Seal of GWR Co.

dated

FIGURE 88. The final sheet of the Contract '4R', document signed by J. T. Bedborough
- the contractor - in the presence of a clerk from Swain Stevens & Co., the Great Western
Railway Company's solicitors. *(Author's collection)*

FIGURE 89. The Shrivenham station which opened on 17 December 1840. The construction details for this station were virtually identical to those of the Moulsford station, with flint again being used to full advantage, including being used for the supporting walls of the platforms. *(OPC/BR)*

GREAT WESTERN RAILWAY LANDMARKS 1833-1841

1833

21 January	First meeting of the Bristol Committee that was to launch the Great Western Railway.
7 March	Brunel appointed as engineer.
9 March	Brunel commences his survey.
30 July	Bristol Committee's first public meeting.
19 August	'Great Western Railway' title adopted at a joint meeting of the London and Bristol Committees in the City of London.

1834

25 July	First Great Western Railway Bill rejected by House of Lords.

1835

31 August	Great Western Railway Act received the Royal Assent.
29 October	Decision by Great Western Railway Board to adopt broad gauge.

1837

3 July	Act obtained for London Terminus at Paddington.
18 August	Gooch became Superintendent of Locomotive engines.

1838

15 January	Locomotive *North Star* steams for the first time.
4 June	Paddington (Old Station) to Maidenhead ('Dumb-bell' bridge) section opened.

1839

9 January	Brunel vindicated and the broad gauge reaffirmed after difficulties and criticism.
	Electric telegraph in operation as far as Hanwell by April
1 July	Maidenhead ('Dumb-bell' bridge) to Twyford section opened.

1840

30 March	Twyford to Reading section opened.
1 June	Reading to Steventon section opened.
20 July	Steventon to Faringdon Road (Challow) section opened.
15 August	The first official Great Western Railway Royal journey. Dowager Queen Adelaide travels from the Moulsford station to Slough.
21 August	Trial trip between Bristol and Bath.
31 August	Bristol (Old Terminus) to Bath section opened.

25 October	Great Western Railway's first recorded accident at Faringdon Road engine shed.
17 December	Faringdon Road to Hay Lane section opened.

The year was also notable for the opening of the first portion of the Taff Vale Railway and the adoption of disc and crossbar signals. A decision taken on 6 October led to the establishment of Swindon Locomotive Works.

1841

31 May	Wootton Bassett (Hay Lane) to Chippenham section opened.
30 June	Chippenham to Bath opened.
14 June	Opening of Bristol & Exeter Railway between Bristol and Bridgwater.
30 June	Great Western Railway line from Bristol to Paddington completed with the opening of the Chippenham-Bath section, including Box Tunnel.

The year also saw the opening of the Cheltenham & Western Union Railway from Swindon Junction to Cirencester on 31 May, with the Great Western Railway acquiring the enterprise on 1 July.

FIGURE 90. Brunel's Wharncliffe Viaduct at Hanwell, pictured after the completion of widening, the original design being faithfully copied and which opened to traffic in October 1877.   *(OPC/BR)*

FURTHER READING

1. Acworth, W. M. 'The Railways of England', John Murray 1900.
    Reprinted Ian Allan.
2. Adams, J. and Elkin, P. 'Isambard Kingdom Brunel', Jarrold, 1988.
3. Awdry, C. 'Brunel's Broad Gauge Railway', Oxford Publishing Co, 1992.
4. Bagwell, P. S. 'The Railwaymen', George Allen & Unwin Ltd., 1963.
5. Beckett, D. 'Brunel's Britain', David & Charles, 1980.
6. Booker, F. 'The Great Western Railway - A New History', David & Charles.
7. 'Bradshaw's Railway Guides', First published 19 November 1839,
    second edition 30 March 1840 (includes GWR).
8. Burton, A. 'The Canal Builders', Eyre Methuen, 1972.
9. Carter, F. C. 'The Railway Encyclopaedia', Harold Starke Ltd., 1963.
10. Clark R, 'The Charmouth Ichthyosaur',
    Bristol City Museum and Art Gallery, 1989.
11. Clarke, M. L. 'A History of Cholsey Church', 1982.
12. Clew, K. R. 'The Somersetshire Coal Canal and Railways', David & Charles.
13. Coleman, T. 'The Railway Navvies',
    Hutchinson Publishing Group Ltd., 1965.
14. Dewey, J. & S. 'Change at Cholsey', Pie Powder Press, 1986.
15. Ellis, H. 'Railway Carriages in the British Isles, From 1830 to 1914',
    George Allen & Unwin Ltd., 1965.
16. Hamilton Ellis, C. 'Royal Journey', British Transport Commission, 1960.
17. Hamilton Ellis, C. 'The Royal Trains', Routledge & Kegan Paul, 1975.
18. Haresnape, B. 'Railway Design Since 1830', Vol. 1 1830-1914,
    Ian Allan, 1968.
19. Karau, P. and Turner, C. 'The Wallingford Branch',
    Wild Swan Publications Ltd., 1982.
20. Kelly, P. J. 'Road Vehicles of the Great Western Railway',
    Oxford Publishing Co., 1973.
21. Langdon, R. 'The Life of Roger Langdon (told by himself),
    with additions by his Daughter Ellen', Elliot Stock, 1908.
22. Lingham, B. 'The Railway Comes to Didcot', Alan Sutton, 1992.
23. MacDermot, E. T. 'History of the Great Western Railway', Vol. 1,
    (Revised by C. R. Clinker 1964), Ian Allan Ltd., 1982.
24. Maggs, C. G. 'Bristol Railway Panorama', Millstream Books, 1990.
25. Measom, G. 'The Illustrated Guide to the Great Western Railway', 1852.
    Reprinted 1983 by Berkshire County Library.
26. Muir, R. 'The Stones of Britain', Michael Joseph Ltd., 1986.
27. Ottley, G. 'A Bibliography of British Railway History',
    Allen & Unwin Ltd., 1965.
28. Pendleton, J. 'Our Railway's, Vols. 1 & 2, Cassell & Company Ltd., 1896.

29. Pugsley, Sir Alfred. 'The Works of Isambard Kingdom Brunel', Cambridge University Press, 1976.
30. Rolt, L. T. C. 'The Making of a Railway', Alan Sutton Publishing Limited, 1990.
31. Rolt, L. T. C. 'Isambard Kingdom Brunel', Longmans, Green and Co., 1957.
32. Roney, Sir Cusack P. 'Rambles on Railways', Effinghmam Wilson, 1868.
33. Russell, K. L. 'GWR Company Servants', Wild Swan Publications, 1983.
34. Simmons, J. (Ed.). 'The Birth of the Great Western Railway, Extracts from the Diary and Correspondence of George Henry Gibbs', Adams & Dart, 1971.
35. Simmons, E. J. 'Memoirs of a Station Master', 1879. Reprinted 1974 by Adams & Dart.
36. Simmons, J. 'The Railway Travellers Handy Book', 1862. Reprinted 1971, Adams & Dart.
37. Slinn, J. O. 'Great Western Way', Historical Model Railway Society, 1978.
38. Steele, A. K. 'Great Western Broad Gauge Album', Oxford Publishing Co., 1972.
39. Vaughan, A. 'A Pictorial Record of Great Western Architecture', Oxford Publishing Co., 1977.
40. Vaughan, A. 'Isambard Kingdom Brunel', John Murray Ltd, 1991.
41. Williams, A. 'Brunel and After', Great Western Railway, 1925 (reprinted 1972).
42. Wilson, R. W. 'Sir Daniel Gooch - Memoirs & Diary', David & Charles, 1972.
43. Ziegler, P. 'King William IV', Collins, 1971.

FIGURE 91. Seal of the Great Western Railway Company.   *(OPC/BR)*

INDEX

Abingdon: 17, 22, 34, 35, 85, 137, 147, 202
    Branch: 5
    Milton Rectory: 85
Accidents: 60, 61, 62, 64, 86, 202, 222 223
Acts of Parliament
    'Act for the Payment of Constables for
    Keeping the Peace Near Public Works'
    (1 & 2 Vict. c.80) 1838: 55
    Enclosure Acts: 189, 190
    Municipal Corporations Act 1835: 4, 5
    Poor Law Amendment Act 1834: 4
    Reform Act 1832: 3, 5
    Truck Acts: 81
Allnatt, Richard H. M.D.
    (Archaeologist): 68, 69, 70, 180
Allnutt, Zachariah (Receiver and General
    Surveyor to the Thames Navigation): 21
Andrews, G. H.: 116
Andrews, William
    (Magistrates Clerk, Reading): 56
Arnould (Justice-of-the-Peace, Cholsey): 192

Basildon (Gatehampton)
    Bridge: 71, 102, 109, 119, 144, 202
    Brickyards: 166
    Estate: 166, 170
    House: 170
    Lower: xiv
    Park: 170
    Morrison, James M.P.: 170, 171
Bath: 5, 6, 8, 12, 13, 19, 20, 21, 29, 30, 34, 39, 51, 62,
    65, 66, 76, 77, 78, 102, 115, 117, 132, 135, 139,
    140, 141, 142, 160, 162, 165, 175, 211, 212, 221,
    223, 224, 235
    Skew bridge: 132
    Station: 224
    Opening to: 224
    Bath Stone: 81, 127, 148, 151, 161, 162, 163,
    165, 166, 167, 168, 170, 171, 181, 182, 186, 192,
    241, 264
'Battle of the Gauges': 237, 247
    Basingstoke: 237
    Gloucester: 237, 247
    Broad-Gauge: 130, 176, 199, 200, 201, 225, 228,
    231, 232, 235, 237, 238, 247
    Mixed-Gauge: 237, 238, 247
    Oxford-Basingstoke: 237, 247
    Reading-Paddington: 239
    Narrow-Gauge: 232, 235, 237, 238, 247
    Royal Commission: 237, 238
    Trials: 238
Baulking: 201
Beckett, Derrick: 29
Beloff, Lord Max: 189
Benson: 168, 204, 218
Berkshire Downs: 34, 59, 71, 72, 73, 169, 175, 180,
    194
Bill of 1834 (GWR): 17, 18, 19, 20
Bill of 1835 (GWR): 20, 21, 22, 23, 30, 34, 36, 39, 40
Birmingham: 7, 60, 238
Blewbury: 33, 34, 35, 38, 41, 43
    Manor Farm: 33

Blewburton Hill: 73
    Fort: 101
Borings: 30, 31, 36, 153
Boulger, Dr. Edward: 97
Bourne, John Cooke: 50, 67, 144, 166, 169, 176,
    177, 181, 215
Box: 211
    Tunnel: 62, 77, 142, 165, 235
Brent Valley: 48, 115, 117, 152, 164
Brickyards: 166
Bridges (Railway)
    Bath: 76, 132
    'Dumb-bell': 107, 110, 111, 113, 133, 177
    Gatehampton (Basildon): 21, 47, 48, 59, 60, 61,
    70, 71, 72, 81, 102, 103, 109, 115, 119, 131, 133,
    135, 143, 144, 145, 146, 147, 148, 150, 151, 155,
    156, 157, 158, 163, 164, 165, 166, 167, 169, 170,
    171, 195, 202, 241, 243, 244, 245
    Maidenhead: 48, 110, 130, 131, 132, 136, 147,
    155, 199, 239
    Moulsford: 37, 40, 41, 47, 48, 59, 60, 67, 71, 72,
    73, 102, 103, 109, 115, 119, 120, 131, 133, 135,
    143, 144, 146, 147, 150, 151, 152, 153, 154, 155,
    156, 157, 158, 163, 164, 165, 166, 167, 168, 169,
    170, 171, 195, 196, 212, 241, 243, 244, 245
    'Silly': 191, 192, 194
    Sonning: 50, 167
Bridge Rails: 198, 199
Bright, Robert: 212, 224
Bristol: 6, 7, 9, 10, 12, 15, 20, 21, 22, 23, 27, 39, 47,
    49, 66, 71, 78, 102, 115, 117, 134, 141, 142, 161,
    162, 176, 177, 189, 203, 211, 222, 224, 225, 247
    Clifton Suspension Bridge: 134
    Board of Directors (GWR): 10, 11, 29, 63, 78,
    139, 159, 161, 179
    Division (GWR): 47, 54, 59, 76, 108, 126, 163,
    197, 221
    Docks: 140
    & Gloucester Railway: 9, 27
    Guild Hall: 10, 13
    Institution for the Advancement
    of Science, Literature and the Arts: 67
    & London Railway: 7
    Merchant's Hall: 18
    Museum: ix, 65, 66, 67, 140, 141, 142
    Port of: 7
    Station (Temple Meads): xiv, 159, 160, 161, 197,
    224, 235
    Opening: 224
    Turnpike Trust: 6
    University: ix, 66, 100, 152
British Rail: 66, 241, 244, 246
'Britzka': 26
Brunel, Isambard Kingdom: xiv, xv, 9, 10, 12, 13,
    16, 20, 21, 26, 27, 28, 29, 30, 31, 35, 36, 37, 40,
    41, 42, 47, 48, 50, 54, 55, 61, 62, 64, 65, 66, 67,
    70, 71, 72, 73, 76, 77, 78, 80, 81, 86, 95, 96, 97,
    102, 103, 106, 109, 110, 111, 113, 114, 115, 117,
    119, 121, 122, 126, 131, 132, 133, 134, 135, 136,
    137, 138, 139, 140, 142, 143, 144, 146, 147, 148,
    149, 150, 151, 152, 154, 155, 156, 157, 158, 159,
    160, 161, 162, 163, 164, 165, 166, 168, 169, 170,

275

FIGURE 92. A water colour by an unidentified artist illustrates the scene as a Great Western Railway train pulls into a country station. However, the artist appears to have taken a few liberties! There is no record that Great Western Railway locomotives ever carried nameplates on the front of their boilers. Similarly, there is no record of a locomotive named *Red Deer*, however, a 2-2-2 locomotive - *Red Star* - with seven-feet driving wheels and built by R. Stephenson of Liverpool, was delivered to the Great Western Railway in August 1840. *(Elton Collection: Ironbridge Gorge Museum Trust)*